Modern Japanese Prints

1912–1989

Modern Japanese Prints

1912–1989
Woodblocks and Stencils

LAWRENCE SMITH

Published for the Trustees of the British Museum by

BRITISH MUSEUM PRESS

FRONT COVER Itō Shinsui (1898–1972): *Snowy Night*, 1923 (Cat. 36)
BACK COVER Maeda Tōshirō (1904–90): *'Round Moon Island' at Shirahama*,
1940 (Cat. 18)

© 1994 The Trustees of the British Museum
Published by British Museum Press
A division of British Museum Publications Ltd
46 Bloomsbury Street, London WC1B 3QQ

British Library Cataloguing in Publication Data
A catalogue record for this book is available from the British Library

ISBN 0 7141 1461 8

Designed by Roger Davies

Phototypeset in Monotype Photina
by Southern Positives and Negatives (SPAN)

Printed in Great Britain by Cambridge University Press, Cambridge

Contents

The Trustees of the British Museum
acknowledge with gratitude
generous assistance towards the
production of this book from
The Daiwa Anglo-Japanese Foundation

Acknowledgements

This catalogue is based on the holdings of the British Museum, considerably augmented since 1985 by the acquisitions of the collections of Robert Vergez and Gaston Petit, both of Tokyo. Both are thanked for the smoothness with which they allowed these important acquisitions to be made, and for the considerable information provided by the act of informed collecting itself and by their publications. My good friend Robert Vergez also provided very careful listings of his collection, which have proved of great use in the writing of this catalogue, and in addition read and commented on all the individual entries for the prints. Both men also gave to the British Museum significant parts of their reference libraries relevant to twentieth-century prints, which have included many rare and unobtainable catalogues. Scott Johnson of Kyoto, whose collection of Japanese illustrated books was also acquired by the British Museum, has provided much help and information through his listings, writings and correspondence.

Without the generous financial support of The Daiwa Foundation this catalogue could not have included colour plates of all the items, and would therefore have not been able to give a true impression of the field that the works in the collection deserve. We thank them warmly for once again coming to our aid.

I am indebted to all those scholars, Japanese and Western, who have written on twentieth-century prints, but especially to Oliver Statler, whose work opened Western eyes to the post-war achievement, and to Helen Merritt, whose two recent works *Modern Japanese Woodblock Prints: The Early Years* and *Guide to Modern Japanese Woodblock Prints 1900–1975* (with N. Yamada) have proved of immense help in writing this catalogue. The latter includes much material not available in Japanese-language publications. I most cordially thank her for the very hard work which clearly went into their writing, and which will ensure they are used for many years to come.

I have been indebted for certain items of information to the courteous staff of Yamada Shoten and of Yōseidō in Tokyo; to Mrs Sekino, widow of the artist Sekino Jun'ichirō; to Catherine Olver; to Rupert Faulkner of the Victoria and Albert Museum; and to my colleagues Victor Harris and Timothy Clark. Other colleagues have helped on various aspects: Mavis Pilbeam with bibliographical enquiries; Sally Morton, Dylan Jackson and David Penn on the care of the collections catalogued; and Kevin Lovelock, who took the photographs. Catherine Edwards has typed and retyped a complex manuscript with her customary accuracy and cheerfulness. Teresa Francis of British Museum Press has shown fortitude and patience in finally and successfully obtaining the text from me, and the editor Deborah Wakeling and the designer Roger Davies have worked with the detailed professionalism we have come to expect from them.

Finally I wish to thank my wife for her support and understanding during the domestic disruption the writing of this catalogue has necessarily caused.

LAWRENCE SMITH
Keeper of Japanese Antiquities
March 1994

'A very Japanese art'

The renewal of Japanese woodblock printing
1912–1989

The period and scope of this catalogue

The collections of Japanese prints in the British Museum are now adequate to cover all important trends, schools and individual artists of the twentieth century. The idea of showing everything that has happened in all techniques and formats is an attractive one, and was attempted in 1983 in *The Japanese Print since 1900*. It was possible to do that only because of the then limited range of the collections, but they are now too extensive to allow such a wide field.

The subject has therefore been restricted to that one technique of woodblock (now generically called *mokuhan*) which has always been rightly considered Japan's most important and characteristic graphic medium. A close study of the changes which have occurred in woodblock in Japan this century can provide a coherent survey of the way deeply traditional skills and styles have adapted to the double pressures of foreign influences and drastic political and social changes, and how a fundamental aesthetic constantly reasserts itself through those changes. It became clear during selection, however, that the equally old art of stencil was not only important in rather the same way but was also intimately linked through the Folk Art Movement with woodblock. The main stencil artists – Serizawa Keisuke, Mori Yoshitoshi, Watanabe Sadao – shared similar attitudes, aesthetics and subject-matter with woodblock artists such as Munakata Shikō or Kida Yasuhiko. To leave them out proved intellectually too difficult. It seemed reasonable, too, to include occasional prints by mainly woodblock artists in closely related relief techniques such as paperblock (Cat. 80) or linocut (Cat. 96). The extensive intaglio output of Sekino Jun'ichirō in his earlier career seemed, on the other hand, to bear little resemblance to his work in woodblock and has been omitted.

Beginning typically with the adventurous Onchi Kōshirō, woodblock began in the 1930s to be combined with other processes in the manner now called 'mixed media'. Initially the product of the restless Western search for originality, the idea began to gain ground in Japanese prints in the 1950s as it appealed to the native interest in contrasting textures. Woodblock, easily and neatly applied by hand with the *baren*, became a natural partner for other techniques, most notably and successfully in the prints of Tetsuya Noda (b.1940). But to pursue these lines of investigation would have again widened the theme too much for coherence, and would have placed too much emphasis on the more recent works. (Cat. 130 by Funasaka Yoshisuke is a work on the edge of his transition from woodblock to mixed media, and may in fact have a very subtle addition by the silk-screen process.)

The selection attempts to represent the main achievements of the Japanese woodblock print in the period covered, as far as the collections will allow. For a few significant artists there is no work important enough to include, for example, Komura Settai, and others have been omitted on the grounds that their works appeal to a side of Japanese sensibility which Westerners might find incomprehensibly obscure. This is admittedly applying Western judgement to Japanese art, but ultimately that is a proper function of the Western commentator when sufficiently well informed. It is also in itself part of that continuing interaction between Japanese and Western opinion and practice which is described in more detail below. Some good artists have had to be left out simply to avoid overcrowding with works of similar types and dates.

As far as the period covered is concerned, it seemed better to avoid the misleading neatness of beginning in the year 1900 and start the story in 1912, when the Emperor Meiji died and was replaced by the Emperor Taishō (Taishō era, 1912–26). To start the story in 1900 would mean that the fairly large output (1900–12) of the fast-dying *Ukiyo-e* school and its manner of production and selling would have to be examined, which is the end of a 250-year-old history rather than the prelude to a new age; that process would also involve constant reference to a more distinguished past. And although the first stirrings had occurred of the processes which would produce the two major new print movements of *Shin Hanga* and *Sōsaku Hanga*, it would be difficult to argue that before 1912 either of them had produced a single distinguished print. Remarkably few good print artists worked across the period before and after 1912, or if they did their styles differed in the later era, as did, for example, that of Hashiguchi Goyō. If ever there was a natural break in recorded Japanese artistic history, it was the year 1912 – in fact, more so even than 1945.

Historically, too, 1912 was a watershed. The death of the Meiji Emperor after a long and eventful reign also seemed to conclude Japan's successful and rapid rise from an isolated feudal state to a Western-style industrial and colonial power. The Meiji era had begun in 1868 with the end of the centuries-long feudal rule of the Tokugawa Shoguns and the moving of the capital to Edo, now renamed Tokyo. In 1912 the city had become the capital of a prosperous, mechanised country which had already annexed Taiwan (1895), defeated Russia in the war of 1904–5, and annexed Korea (1910), as well as gaining a significant foothold in China, alongside Germany, France and Britain. Prosperity, a sense of confidence in the future, and an apparently firm alliance with Britain, then the world's most powerful colonialist power, plus the beginning of a new reign, all set the stage for a period of mixed euphoria, hedonism and apprehension which characterises the Taishō era. The stage was also set for major developments in the arts, and these did not take long to arrive, affecting first of all traditional-style painting and the woodblock print. It will be argued below that 1989, the end of the Shōwa era which succeeded Taishō, is another natural point at which to conclude this history.

The crucial role played by the West

In 1956, almost exactly halfway through the period covered by this catalogue, the artist Kitaoka Fumio (b.1918) is quoted by Oliver Statler (1) as saying 'I like prints, too, because when they are made the Japanese way, with *baren* and handmade paper, they are a very Japanese art, and it's good to feel at home in one's medium'. Many of the contradictions inherent in the art of the Japanese woodblock this century are contained in that statement and its context.

There is no reason to doubt that Kitaoka was or is whole-hearted in his search for a Japanese art; indeed, that has frequently been the stated objective of remarkably many Japanese artists this century, all concerned about their acute sense of coming from a culture different from others, but all working in an international artistic world. It is quite true that the majority of woodblock prints produced in the years 1912–89 were made on *washi* (Japanese handmade paper) and were printed by hand with the rubbing-pad called the *baren*, also unique to Japan. Yet almost everything else about Kitaoka's career has been connected with foreign countries. His statement quoted above is an explanation of why he had given up Western-style painting, in which he had been trained; yet the style of his mature landscapes is closely modelled on oil-painting, and their technique consciously seeks to imitate some of its effects (Cat. 109). For that reason he has been popular in the West, and in the 1960s and 70s his prints were vigorously sold to foreigners through the clearly illustrated catalogues, written in English, of the Red Lantern Shop, Kyoto.

A parallel can be found earlier in our period in the activities of Yoshida Hiroshi (1876–1950, Cat.47–8) whose techniques were developed to express in woodblock some of the effects of the *plein-air* water-colour style he had first fully encountered in the USA as early as 1899. He too became very popular in the West and vigorously promoted his work through English-language catalogues, particularly those of the two exhibitions at the Toledo Museum of Art in 1930 and 1936 (Blair (1) and (2)). His son, Yoshida Tōshi, continues to sell reprints of these works marketed through well-illustrated catalogues, again in English.

Kitaoka's foreign connections have been much wider than that, however, and his experiences are typical of many other Japanese artists of the century in one or other respect. In 1945 he was sent to Japanese-occupied Manchuria to the North-east Asia Culture Development Society, where Japanese art was being fostered as a political weapon. (Yoshida Hiroshi, by then quite old, was also sent as a war artist to Manchuria.) His return mainly on foot through China brought him into contact with proletarian art based on earlier European Expressionist models, which had already been a major influence on a whole school of earlier woodblock artists led by Onchi Kōshirō (Cat.27–30, 76–80, biography). Back in post-war Japan Kitaoka was one of many whose careers were made by contact with Oliver Statler and publicity in his book *Modern Japanese Prints: An Art Reborn*. Virtually every artist in it increased in prosperity as a result of its advocacy. Ironically it was in that book, directed entirely at Westerners and profoundly driven by Western tastes, that Kitaoka made his statement of Japaneseness. In fact by the time it was published he was already on a period of study at the Ecole des Beaux-Arts, Paris (1955–6), which served only to make his style and subject-matter more Japanese. Similar reactions occurred after periods abroad to print artists as major as Munakata Shikō (biography) and Mori Yoshitoshi (biography).

Exhibitions which could be seen by Westerners, as in Toledo (1930 and 1936) and Paris (Musée des Arts Décoratifs, 1934), played from early on a crucial role in the self-image of twentieth-century Japanese print artists as well as making them known abroad. Toledo in 1930 was the first of any importance and publicised the *Shin Hanga* movement (see below). Yoshida was the pioneer in all of this, having several times very successfully shown his paintings in the USA from 1899 onwards. Paris did a similar job for *Sōsaku Hanga* ('Creative Prints'). After 1937, because of the Manchurian Incident (the *de facto* take-over of Manchuria by Japan) which brought Japan into direct international conflict there were almost no more foreign exhibitions until 1951. It is no accident that this period represents a slump of artistic excellence in the Japanese print between the two 'golden ages' of 1915–40 and 1950–75. Foreign exhibitions had become an artery of life-blood for the printmakers and were to become so again from the first São Paolo Art Biennale in 1951, when Saitō Kiyoshi (biography) with the etcher Komai Tetsurō (1920–76) won first prizes in the Japanese section in preference to painters. This, characteristically, caused much excitement in Japanese art circles, simply because foreign judges had made a strong statement which seemed to contradict the native view that prints were of little importance.

This event led within six years to the establishment of the first Tokyo Print Biennale, the first large international print exhibition in Japan to include both foreigners and Japanese, in a city where an international audience could now also be expected to attend. Kitaoka was the leading light in this idea; significantly, he had just returned from Paris. As described by Helen Merritt it fell into the hands of modern-minded critics who regarded the prints of the *Sōsaku Hanga* movement as already old-fashioned. In fact they had just reached their apogee, but there were already intellectuals looking over their shoulders at a new wave of Western ideas which they felt should be quickly adopted. Kitaoka had to argue passionately for the inclusion of 'creative prints' as representatives of a true Japanese tradition, where only twelve years earlier they had been thought of as essentially Western; but his instinct was at heart correct. The very fact that prints were in woodblock on Japanese paper, the very fact that forms and colours had to be simplified to accommodate the technique resulted in a fundamentally Japanese art form. Kitaoka, like Yoshida before him, eventually gave up his first career of painting and became effectively a print artist only.

Kitaoka and Yoshida came from completely different schools of printmaking, which were for long in conscious opposition to each other. Yet both were educated in Western-style painting, and their careers were shaped from beginning to end by foreign influences. Broadening their example out to the whole field of woodblock printmaking, and indeed to any other technique of printmaking in the period under discussion, it is possible to make the general statement that almost every individual was affected by foreign criticism and publicity, foreign influence, foreign exhibition and, increasingly, foreign markets. Up to 1936 travel abroad by printmakers became ever commoner. Since 1955 not only has travel in the West become almost *de rigueur*, but also artists have tended to spend longer periods of study in Western art colleges, universities and print centres (for example, Hagiwara Hideo, Kawachi Seikō, Watanabe Sadao); to become teachers in such places (Saitō Kiyoshi, Kurosaki Akira, Mizufune Rokushū, Munakata Shikō, Sekino Jun'ichirō); or even to find themselves living permanently in the West (Matsubara Naoko, Amano Kunihiro, and most surprisingly of all Hiratsuka Un'ichi, the grand old man of twentieth-century Japanese prints). Conversely, throughout this period Western artists have gone to Japan to learn woodblock-printing techniques from Japanese teachers such as the staff of the publisher Watanabe Shōzaburō, and the artists Yoshida Tōshi and Tokuriki Tomikichirō.

There are broadly speaking three distinct periods of mature activity in the Japanese pictorial woodblock print. The first is the mid- and late Edo periods (c.1660 to the end of the policy of Isolation in 1853); the second is the period from 1853 to the end of the Meiji era in 1912; and the last the period of this catalogue, 1912–89. For reasons which will be explained at the end of this Introduction 1989 seems likely to be seen by future art historians as the beginning of a new era.

The first period is that of *Ukiyo-e*, that great school of art based on the life of pleasure of the great cities, to which the much older skills of woodblock printing were harnessed to produce what most Westerners still think of as simply 'Japanese prints'. *Ukiyo-e* prints are products of a period of political isolation (1639–1853) which allowed the emergence of a truly native style, and that ultimately is their greatest strength. Overt Western influence was occasionally seen in the 'perspective prints' which first appeared in the mid-eighteenth century, notably in the hands of Okumura Masanobu (1686–1764) and in rather superficial experiments in light and shade effects in the prints of, for example, Katsushika Hokusai (1760–1849) and Utagawa Kuniyoshi (1797–1861). Very much stronger Chinese influences were found in other schools of art, particularly *Nanga* and *Maruyama-Shijō*, whose works also appeared in woodblock-printed form but usually in books or de-luxe prints called *surimono*. The Isolation ensured that these, like Westernising *Ukiyo-e*, were done in a very native manner, with little likelihood of either criticism by informed foreigners or comparison with the genuine article; it also ensured that work was done almost without exception for the internal Japanese market. It is that which separates the first period so drastically from later ones.

The second period is characterised in every way by its mixture of cultures. From the ending of the Isolation, Western subject-matter and Western styles began to pour into and disrupt Japanese art. From the 1860s to the 1880s rapid expansion occurred of foreign processes – etching and engraving, lithography, wood-engraving – which quickly took over much of book illustration and of the developing newspaper industry, and which were all naturally better suited to the expression of the Western artistic convention of light and shade. With strong government support Western drawing and painting techniques were learned, first from imported teachers such as Antonio Fontanesi (1818–82) and then from native Japanese artists, such as Kuroda Seiki (1866–1924), who began to study, for the first time since the fifteenth century, in foreign countries. Kuroda went to Paris as early as 1884. In spite of all these apparently relentless trends *Ukiyo-e* prints and books continued to appear, as did *Nanga* and *Maruyama-Shijō* works, and these remained directed at native audiences. Woodblock prints remained an important source of information and propaganda on internal politics and Japan's new foreign wars with China (1894–5) and Russia (1904–5). Nevertheless, Western influence on style was now unavoidable and is part of the make-up of all the most important woodblock-print artists of the era, including Kobayashi Kiyochika (1847–1915), Taisō Yoshitoshi (1839–92), sometimes regarded as the last true *Ukiyo-e* artist, and Kawanabe Kyōsai (1831–89). However strong Western influence was on them they were nevertheless working to sell to their countrymen. But in the same period Westerners were buying the older *Ukiyo-e* prints to take back home, and this fact was to have profound consequences in the rise of the *Shin Hanga* movement early in the twentieth century.

It will be seen, then, that what eventually distinguishes the modern Japanese woodblock print, especially after 1912, is a major turning towards not only foreign styles but also foreign markets and foreign criticism. Japanese commentators have now accepted this view. For example, number 73 of the influential and long-running magazine *Hanga Geijutsu* ('Print Art') published in 1993 was devoted to 'One Hundred Years of the Woodblock Print', in which the beginning of the modern era is identified as experiments by Kobayashi Kiyochika in the 1870s to combine traditional woodblock techniques with the convincing expression of light and shade. These successful attempts at landscape and townscape showed that a synthesis was possible, but they were not directed at the outside world at all as were the later, more smoothly integrated productions of Kawase Hasui (biography and Cat. 38–9, 49) and Itō Shinsui (biography, Cat. 33–7).

The sense of belonging to an international artistic world now seems ineradicably fixed in the minds of Japanese print artists, whatever technique they use. In 1912, when this catalogue begins, the founder of the *Sōsaku Hanga* movement, Yamamoto Kanae (biography, Cat. 1–2), went to France to study. In 1989, where it ends, Tsuruya Kōkei (biography, Cat. 139–40) was selling a significant proportion of each of his small editions to Western collectors, dealers and museums. When his early prints on the native Kabuki theatre failed at first to impress many of his countrymen, his instinct was to send examples to Western museums, perhaps unconsciously aware that in the twentieth century recognition for Japanese printmakers has usually come first from abroad. His instinct proved right.

Woodblock printing 1912–89: one technique with many variations

During the period *c.*1660–1853 the only processes for pictorial printing, apart from a few short-lived and localised experiments in engraving, were woodblock and stencil, the latter comparatively rare but persistent. Woodblock prints were so commonly accepted that they simply had the name *han*, meaning either 'print' or 'impression' or 'block'. If further distinctions needed to be made, it was done by describing their subject, as in *shunga* (erotic designs) or *nishiki-e* ('brocade', or highly coloured pictures). Stencils, which existed mainly for textiles, were called *kappa-ban* to distinguish them (*-ban* is *han* used as a suffix). Designs in these two media were often closely related through artist or publisher and have remained so in the twentieth century; that is one reason for including some stencil prints in this catalogue.

Woodblock, therefore, was overwhelmingly the dominant medium of this long period, and was used for every sort of artistic style, from simple black-line book illustration to 'brocade pictures' requiring as many as twenty or more colour blocks, to the subtlest reproductions of an individual painter's brushwork. All of these prints, as sheets or in book form, were done by the same co-operative system, which was first properly described by T. Volker in *Ukiyo-e Quartet* (Brill, Leiden, 1949) and has often been repeated since. Under this system a publisher or *hanmoto* ('print-master') was instigator, financial backer, co-ordinator and seller. He employed, or paid item by item, artists to make designs which would be turned into prints. These usually consisted of ink sketches with annotations about the colours required; better-recorded twentieth-century practice shows that the artist too must have often worked closely with the block cutter and the printer to ensure the result was what was envisaged, although the publisher would also take a guiding role and probably have the final decision. The cutter and the printer might be separate craftsmen or the same person.

This process used blocks made usually in this period from the wood of the mountain cherry, cut with the grain and not across it as in Western-style wood-engraving. Because of this, elegant patterns from the grain transferred to the paper when flat areas of relief were printed from fresh blocks. These patterns were much appreciated and came to be expected on a good, new print, a tradition which continued even into those twentieth-century schools which were opposed to the old collective system and did not use cherry-wood at all. For example, the works of Kawachi Seikō (Cat. 135–8), huge though they are and printed by him working alone from veneer-faced boards, continue to make effective use of grain patterns. Naturally the *Shin Hanga* artists of the period 1915–40, who worked in the old way with publishers and craftsmen, also made much use of grain.

Woodblock is traditionally a relief process, that is to say the cutter removes the areas of the block which will not be used for printing, leaving the rest standing in relief. In the seventeenth and early eighteenth centuries that usually meant simple black line, similar to that used in the printing of texts, which were done in exactly the same way. As colour blocks were in time added, they did not replace line but were used to fill the line in. This was the fundamental style of printing for the *Ukiyo-e* school, and it was carried on in the

Shin Hanga movement; Hasui, Shinsui, Shunsen, Kanpō, Shirō, Ishiwata and Yoshida Hiroshi all used line and colour in this manner, as Tsuruya Kōkei does still, though not in cherry-wood.

The size of prints was limited by the size of blocks which could be obtained from the cherry tree, and that too remained a tradition even among twentieth-century printmakers of other schools. Onchi in the 1930s was the first to realise that the format could be expanded with different woods and veneers (Cat. 27–9). But wood was not the only factor in limiting size: another was the traditional method of taking an impression, which instead of a press as used in the West consisted only of a small hand-held pad called a *baren*. Once the block had been inked or loaded with colour by brush, the paper was placed on it and rubbed from behind by the printer's *baren*. The whorling patterns left by this vigorous circular pressure came also to be admired, and were continued this century both by artists working the co-operative system and those working alone. It is easy to see that a lone artist performing this exhausting task will tend either to resist making larger prints, or alternatively produce them in smaller editions. Takahashi Rikio (biography, Cat. 114–15), Iwami Reika (biography, Cat. 112) and Kawachi are examples of such post-war artists for whom the demand for or artistic drive towards much larger prints has necessitated a limited production. The co-operative *hanmoto* system, allowing a number of printers to work together, was able to produce much larger output. Although the concept of a limited edition did not exist in Japan until the Taishō era (1912–26), it is known that the old system, in a sufficiently large workshop, could produce 200 prints in a day before the blocks became too wet to use.

It should not be imagined from the above that the traditional method consisted only of outline with flat colour. By the late eighteenth century the technique called *bokashi* was beginning to be used, whereby the colour or ink applied to larger, flatter areas of a cut block could be gradated from strong to light tones by the careful use of a blocking rice-paste in combination with the pigment. This imitated the effects of a painter's brush, which could be unevenly loaded in a similar way with colour to produce a stroke shifting from strong to light tones. Although this was not in itself developed to represent light and shade, but rather the finesse of brushwork of the artist, or in *Ukiyo-e* more often the delicate skills of the printer, nevertheless the technique did allow artists of the *Shin Hanga* movement such as Hashiguchi Goyō (Cat. 31–2), Shinsui (Cat. 33–7) and Hasui (Cat. 38–9, 49) to introduce some of the effects of Western-style light and shade into their prints. This was done very unobtrusively, as, for example, in Goyō's *Woman Making Up* (Cat. 31) where the delicately gradated *bokashi* on the subject's cheek adds an almost unnoticeable modernity to what is at heart a very

Ukiyo-e image. *Bokashi* was not entirely limited to *Shin Hanga* and makes a very smoothly crafted reappearance in the post-war works of Kurosaki Akira (Cat. 131–2, biography), notwithstanding their Surrealist subject-matter. Kurosaki is able to do this, because alone among modernist printmakers he works with a permanent assistant who cuts the blocks and takes the impressions, while the artist himself acts as his own *hanmoto* almost in the old manner. It is to be doubted that an artist working on his own could carry out this demanding technique and still have time to do much else.

In total reaction to the system described above the artists of the *Sōsaku Hanga* movement, led by Yamamoto Kanae, sought quite different results from woodblock, driven partly by a new idealism and partly by their own poverty, for without the *hanmoto* they could not rely on either financial support, supplies and tools, or sales. Their basic motivation was a desire to use the print as a means of artistic self-expression rather than to submit sketches which would be turned into a quite different, polished end-product as directed by the *hanmoto*. Yamamoto had realised in his early career as a wood-engraver, the process which had been the usual means of book illustration in mid-nineteenth-century Europe, that this was, while still a relief process, in effect the reverse of the old *Ukiyo-e* technique. In the latter, straight-sided chisels were used to produce a sharp, clean edge to both the line and also to the blocks of colour, which were required to fit exactly inside the outlines (see, for example, *Visiting Kiyomizu Temple* by Miki Suizan, Cat. 40). The individual blocks needed to produce a full-colour print would rarely have much wood left in relief, and the rest would be deeply gouged out. In black and white wood-engraving, by contrast, the area left in relief was the major part, which would be inked. Small areas or lines of white would be left in the paper as a result of carving with round-ended tools. Yamamoto saw that these could reproduce the exact line of the artist's hand if he carved it himself, as well as being able to realise the effects of light and shade, and developed the idea of transferring this technique to the larger and more beautiful cherry-wood blocks of traditional Japanese woodblock.

In fact, intricate light and shade never proved important among *Sōsaku Hanga* printmakers or any other woodblock artists of the period 1912–89, because it was quickly realised in the early 1920s that lithograph and metal-plate intaglio techniques were much better suited to that sort of subject-matter. Other artists were to take up those techniques, but the curved chisel (*komasuki*) was kept by them and quickly developed into the 'brush' of the carver. The *komasuki* had been used by Japanese woodblock carvers since the end of the nineteenth century, but only for removing big areas of wood quickly. Its varied, soft, individual line allowed each artist to express himself directly on to the block, without intervention of carver or printer, or at least that was the ideal. This type of line can be seen in a number of prints in this catalogue, especially Cat. 5–21. Its greatest development was to occur later in the prints of Munakata Shikō, whose speed with chisel on wood became legendary, and who rarely worked from sketches even if he had prepared them. In his extraordinary hands the woodblock and chisel became almost literally as quick and expressive as brush and ink on paper, and took the medium to its furthest remove from the old *Ukiyo-e* methods (Cat. 59–65, biography).

It will be noticed from the pre-war prints of the *Sōsaku Hanga* movement that many of them did not in fact use line at all. Kanae's *French Pastoral in Spring* of 1913 (Cat. 1) is constructed substantially of blocks of wash, either carelessly juxtaposed or sometimes loosely overlapping with minimal use of line. The texture of the wood is very lightly reproduced, and the water-based colours are not strongly rubbed into the paper. This roughly grainy effect, so far removed from the dense flat colours of *Ukiyo-e* and its successor *Shin Hanga*, was modelled on woodblocks of the short-lived European woodblock revival of *c*.1880–1910. Their lightly grained pastel images were the result of a combination of the textures of lithograph and, ironically enough, the flat areas of colour learned from *Ukiyo-e*. This loose but lucid style was learned partly in Europe by Yamamoto, who went to France in 1912, Minami Kunzō (1883–1950), in England and France in 1910–12, and Ishii Hakutei, in France from 1910. Their favourite models were Gauguin, Münch and Henri Rivière; the first two remained highly influential on Japanese printmakers until well into the 1960s. Few, if any, of these Japanese artists realised that light printing, clear pastel colours and blocks used without outline had all flourished in Kyoto and Osaka in the late eighteenth and early nineteenth centuries in books reproducing the paintings of artists of the *Nanga* school. These artists, for example, Kamamura Bunpō (1779–1821) who was particularly well-served by book illustration, consciously emulated the deliberate rough, seemingly amateur brushwork of the Chinese scholar-painters. Early *Sōsaku Hanga* artists, notably Onchi, took a very similar attitude to their graphic art.

It was Onchi Kōshirō (biography, Cat. 27–30, 76–80) who developed the technical and artistic possibilities of woodblock from the limited emancipation described above into a hitherto unimagined range: in this exploration he had the frequent help of the adventurous but practical Hiratsuka Un'ichi (biography). Onchi regarded the woodblock print as a work of art in its own right, each design with its own artistic logic, and therefore experimented freely with technique, materials and size. His *Mannequin in the Studio* of 1936 (Cat. 27) is one of the largest Japanese woodblocks produced in Japan up to that date and was followed by others still larger, now done on cheaper, rougher woods, often in very small editions within which the colours might vary con-

siderably. The almost careless bravura with which Onchi ran off abstract compositions such as *Poème No. 7* (Cat. 77), more especially after 1945, suggests a woodblock technique very close to the act of painting itself. He also led his younger contemporaries for the first time away from pure woodblock into combinations of it with photographs, as in his pioneering book *Hikō Kannō* (1934); into printing parts of the composition with natural objects such as shells, stones or driftwood; into the use of metal foils and embossing; and into complete substitutions of wood by paperblocks (Cat. 80). All of these innovations were to be severally taken up after 1945 by artists associated with him, including Iwami Reika (Cat. 112), Maki Haku (Cat. 107–8), Sekino Jun'ichirō (Cat. 98–9), Takahashi Rikio (Cat. 114–15), Yamaguchi Gen (Cat. 100–2) and Yoshida Masaji (Cat. 103–6).

If Onchi of the Creative Print Movement was a liberator in woodblock technique, then Munakata of the Folk Art Movement (*Mingei Undō*) was thoroughly liberated. As mentioned earlier, he took the act of cutting block as close to painting as it could become, but by 1938 was beginning to take this even further and apply simple colours by hand, as in his *Kannon* series. On the advice of Yanagi Sōetsu (1889–1961), the great theoretician of the movement, he switched to much thinner paper than that customary for woodblock prints and applied the colours from behind, first extensively used in his series *Shōkeishō* in 1945 (Cat. 63). As each print was hand-coloured, each was slightly different. The old reproductive attitude of *Ukiyo-e* had been totally turned on its head.

Munakata's other great technical innovation was to extend his compositions to the biggest woodblock prints yet made in Japan from single blocks. These were the set *Ten Great Followers of Shaka* of 1939 (Cat. 61) which was over a metre high, produced after a search for suitably large *katsura* boards. With two additions one set of these was attached to a pair of six-fold folding screens, an idea which has subsequently been adopted by Kawachi (Cat. 135–8) and Kida Yasuhiko (biography). Munakata after 1945 extended his scale to compositions such as *Flower Hunting* (1954) consisting of many separately printed sheets mounted as one very big picture (1.32 m × 1.58 m).

Until the end of the Pacific War and of the Occupation in 1952 woodblock techniques followed lines based on schools, groups and association, and their common practices. After that, and especially after the *de facto* ending of the concept of schools of print artists after the Tokyo International Print Biennale of 1957, printmakers began to innovate much more widely in isolation from each other and often under direct Western influence. That influence could take the form either of example, or of the new need to produce a style and a technique individual enough to raise a following in the West, where the most profitable market still lay. The details of these new techniques were luckily recorded by the Canadian artist Father Gaston Petit, who settled in Tokyo in the late 1950s and who got to know many printmakers who came to his studio. As a printmaker himself who could use all the four main techniques of woodblock, intaglio, silk screen and lithograph, Petit was well equipped to study the special techniques of his contemporaries in Japan and publish them in his books *44 Modern Japanese Print Artists* (1973) and *Evolving Techniques in Japanese Woodblock Prints* (with A. Arboleda, 1977). His work, together with the technical information which has appeared since 1973 in the quarterly magazine *Hanga Geijutsu* on specific artists, has provided a solid basis for the assessment of the variations in woodblock technique which proliferated after the Pacific War. For the more conservative artists there is also very useful information on the woods, papers and printing stages used in the prints published by Oliver Statler in *Modern Japanese Prints: An Art Reborn* (1956).

Kitaoka Fumio, quoted earlier, says that the essence of the Japanese woodblock is *washi* (handmade Japanese paper) and the *baren* (printing-pad). He is also quoted by Statler as preferring wood cut with the grain, that is, vertically up the trunk of the tree, which was the way it had invariably been done before wood-engraving was introduced from the West (Statler (1), p. 153). Kitaoka does not mention, and perhaps did not realise, that in only one generation a considerable revolution had taken place in the woods actually used. The *Sōsaku Hanga* pioneers like Yamamoto Kanae and Ishii Hakutei had at first continued to use cherry-wood (*sakura*), as the *Shin Hanga* artists and publishers also insisted on doing in the name of preserving their traditions as intact as possible. But from the 1920s onwards the artists of the Creative Print Movement began to move away from this expensive material which was also very limiting in size and required long training to carve well. Its close texture and medium hardness allowed it to be used for fine lines, but that was of little interest to artists who sought a more spontaneous style. At first they used *katsura (Cercidiphyllum japonicum)* and *hō-no-ki (Magnolia obovata)*, traditional softer substitutes for cherry-wood which were easier to carve and were equally resistant to warping when dampened in the process of printing. These were important considerations for the semi-skilled artists of this school. *Katsura* at least had the added advantage of producing larger blocks or boards, and by around 1930 had become the usual material for the classic *Sōsaku Hanga* artists such as Hiratsuka, Un'ichi, Maekawa Senpan (biography) and Munakata.

Those who could afford or obtain it continued to use *katsura* after the Pacific War, but the shortages caused by the conflict soon led to the use of plywood veneer, usually faced with *shina*, the Japanese lime (*Tilia japonica*). This became after 1945 increasingly the normal wood for prints, because it is easy to carve, cheap and possible to make very big. The largest post-war prints in this catalogue are all done with *shina*-faced blocks, even that by Yoshida Tōshi (Cat. 51) who in his more old-fashioned work is still supervising reprinting from cherry. A further advantage of *shina* for more recent artists has been its relatively light grain, which can be brought out if the artist wishes (Kawachi Seikō, Takahashi Rikio) but offers no hindrance to a smoother, denser surface, if required (Amano Kazumi, Akira Kurosaki, Azechi Umetarō). Foreign woods such as *rawan (Shoren negrosensis)*, a mahogany from the Philippines, also began to be used by the 1960s as Japan's fine native timbers came under increasing demand for high-quality architectural use.

If the woods used underwent a revolution in the generation 1930–50, the *baren* pad for taking a hand-rubbed impression from a block did not, although variations on it have been developed by Kurosaki Akira and Yuki Rei (not included in this catalogue), and nor did the use of *washi*, for which there is no serious substitute for woodblock printing. The native papers – principally from the plants called *kōzo*, *mitsumata* and *ganpi* – can be made in a large range of thicknesses, sizes and qualities, but almost all will elegantly accept the impression of the block and allow the ink or pigments to sink slowly into them so that the final product feels softly integrated. The strength of the long-fibred varieties will also allow a translucent quality which was used most effectively by Munakata in his later prints hand-coloured from behind. The absorbency of *washi* was also harnessed by Hagiwara from the 1950s (Cat. 110–11) who pre-printed his paper from the reverse side with dense colours forced into the paper, providing a base on which to enrich the colours later printed on the usual side. The absorbency of *washi* was exploited by certain artists to achieve dense luminous effects not unlike those of traditional brush- and ink-painting (Kōsaka Gajin, Cat. 116) or even oil-painting (Yamaguchi Susumu, Cat. 86).

After 1945 the now accepted artists of the *Sōsaku Hanga* movement felt free to extend the techniques of woodblock, a tendency which accelerated in the decade 1960–70. Apart from the changes mentioned above, these included novel ways of preparing the block itself and of achieving good registration, and uses of new types of pigment. The most obvious addition to block preparation has been the use of intaglio as well as the more usual relief process, in other words scratching or gouging into the wood so that the indentations will take the pigment and transfer on to the paper when it is forced on to the block under high pressure. This often needs a press, rather than hand-rubbing, as in the works of Maki Haku (Cat. 107–8) or Morozumi Osamu (Cat. 133). Some artists began to build up their block surfaces with other materials such as sand, concrete, or crumpled paper to achieve highly textured effects (Maki, Tajima

Hiroyuki, Cat. 127–8). Blind-printing (*gauffrage*), using an unpigmented block, a technique often used in pre-modern prints, was employed to give a three-dimensional solidity to prints on thick paper (Amano Kazumi, Cat. 125, Amano Kunihiro, Cat. 126). Sasajima Kihei (Cat. 66) developed a unique system of using blind-printing (done in a press) to produce heavily raised designs in the paper to which he could apply ink by hand. This was a device to save effort. Mabuchi Tōru (Cat. 119) laboriously built up his blocks with tiny pieces of wood to realise a mosaic-like printed result. With the desire for greater smoothness of finish which began to be fashionable among younger artists from around 1960, problems of very fine registration of colour blocks became a new preoccupation. Masaji Yoshida, for example, invented a method of cutting all the different colour blocks from one board and fitting them together like a jigsaw puzzle in a frame; each piece was arranged so that it could be raised above the others for printing.

The artistic style of later *Sōsaku Hanga* remained generally light in tone following the tradition of the movement, but from around 1960 the shift to more contemporary styles of abstraction led printmakers to seek denser and smoother pigments which would more resemble the fast-growing rival technique of silk-screen printing. One answer to this was to use oil-based pigments, never before used in the woodblock print. These had to be processed very carefully so that most of the oil was removed in order to prevent excessive staining of the paper. Among those who followed this or similar techniques were Amano Kazumi, Amano Kunihiro, Fukita Fumiaki (Cat. 113), Hoshi Jōichi (Cat. 122–4), Kurosaki Akira (Cat. 131–2) and Kusaka Kenji (Cat. 129). Mizufune Rokushū (Cat. 120–1) achieved similarly dense effects by mixing ordinary water-colours with *gofun* and printing them over one pre-printed colour to give depth. In spite of these innovations all of these printmakers continued to use Japanese handmade paper.

Movements in Japanese woodblock prints, 1912–89: a brief survey

It has been usual to look at the prints of the period 1912–42 (after which most artistic production was severely curtailed until 1946) as fundamentally a tale of two movements. One, known as *Shin Hanga* ('New Prints') was a conscious attempt to renew the almost dead *Ukiyo-e* tradition, which had produced all of Japan's most admired sheet-prints in the period *c.* 1660–1910, by finding new artists who could work with the old co-operative system. This school is indeed sometimes called neo-*Ukiyo-e*, and was in terms of creativity over by 1960. The other, known as *Sōsaku Hanga* ('Creative Prints'), was conversely a conscious attempt to escape from the legacy of *Ukiyo-e* and encourage makers of prints to be part of an international community peopled mainly by supposedly independent Western artists. Creative print artists aimed to work in modern, that is, Western styles, and to conduct all the processes of making a print themselves. They survived the Pacific War with difficulty but then came into their own under new foreign patronage. After 1957 their sense of cohesion broke up, and from around 1960 onwards there has effectively been a large group of individual artists going their various ways.

Like all simplifications there is much solid truth in the above account, and the way it is written depends on the preference of the writer for *Shina Hanga* (Blair, Paechter and Stephens) or *Sōsaku Hanga* (Statler, Michener and Merritt, who for all her fairness clearly feels much greater liking for creative prints). The reader is referred especially to the books of Merritt, Statler (1) and Stephens for detailed accounts of the differences between these schools and their development. The reminiscences of the main actors themselves (for example, the energetic publisher Watanabe Shōzaburō on the one hand and the inspirational artist and leader Onchi Kōshirō on the other) are still more polarised.

But difficulties of adopting this relatively simple view are in practice many. Firstly, at least three of the major *Shin Hanga* artists, Yoshida Hiroshi, Hashiguchi Goyō and Natori Shunsen (Cat. 43), were trained and active Western-style artists. Secondly, a number of the early creative print artists were themselves trying to revitalise the *Ukiyo-e* tradition, including Ishii Hakutei, Sakamoto Hanjirō and even Yamamoto Kanae, their leader. Thirdly, this bipolar view takes little account of what might be considered the even more important role of the *Mingei Undō* (Folk Art Movement) which developed not long after the other two and ultimately had a more lasting influence on the history of woodblock prints, as well as producing its greatest artist, Munakata Shikō (Cat. 59–65), and profoundly affecting Hiratsuka Un'ichi (Cat. 7, 23–4, 81–2) and Maekawa Senpan (Cat. 14, 83–5), two of the most important *Sōsaku Hanga* printmakers.

For this brief survey all three are considered as aspects of one phenomenon – the wish to escape from the ghost of *Ukiyo-e* past and from the emptiness of industrial society present. Seen in this light even the woodblock artists of the period since 1960 may seem to follow a similar star, though not always arriving quite where they intended. This is not to deny the facts of the 'official histories' of the two main movements, as largely written by themselves, but to put them in a wider Japanese artistic and cultural context.

Japan's rapid modernisation and Westernisation since 1968 had all but killed many old arts and crafts in less than a generation. By the decade 1880–90 steps were already being taken to revive some of them through official schools of art, including traditional formats of painting and ivory, wood and metal sculpture. Other crafts, such as ceramics, lacquer, decorative metalwork and *cloisonné*, revived themselves by adapting to export markets. Woodblock prints were not affected so quickly, for they remained in production up to around 1910 for all sorts of internal domestic purposes, old and new, including pictorial journalism, the recording of Kabuki plays and actors, *surimono*, facsimiles of historical paintings, and *kuchi-e*, which were fold-out woodblock-printed frontispieces to novels otherwise printed and bound in Western style. There was also an inexorable outflow of pre-1868 *Ukiyo-e* prints, then considered by most Japanese as old-fashioned and even crude, to Western collectors. Most good examples had left Japan by 1900.

By 1905 the relentless advance of photography, photo-chemical printing and other imported processes such as lithography, wood-engraving and etching was finally bringing the once great woodblock-printing industry to its knees. Changes in Japanese society and education had also seriously damaged the traditional lines of artists who had once learned through apprenticeship to a master, some of whom had worked mainly as providers of designs for prints. One of the last of these, Kaburagi Kiyokata (1878–1973), while continuing to do some work for woodblock *kuchi-e*, was teaching only painting, and in fact by 1905 was converting from a late *Ukiyo-e* style to the new *Nihonga* manner.

Had it not been for the prestige of pre-1868 *Ukiyo-e* prints in the West, where they were still considered the best and most characteristic of all Japanese arts, the old woodblock tradition might indeed have died, particularly since the Japanese art establishment represented by the Monbushō (Ministry of Education) considered prints as simply reproductive and actively opposed promoting them. But Japanese artists who now went to the West – Yoshida Hiroshi and Tsuda Seifu (1880–1978), for example – had by 1905 already taken note of the immense prestige there of *Ukiyo-e*. So had the publisher Watanabe Shōzaburo (b.1885), who was partly a dealer in old *Ukiyo-e* prints and who from 1907 began selling new works, mainly small landscape and bird-and-flower prints, commissioned from minor artists; most of his customers were foreigners. On finding what a demand there was for old *Ukiyo-e* prints he also began to organise fine reprints under the old collaborative system, which he began to see as a great cultural asset about to be lost. For these idealistic reasons and also with a view to good business in the West he determined to find good young artists who would produce new designs for him to print under the old methods.

The first of these was Goyō (1915), who had already become intensely interested in *Ukiyo-e* in spite of his Western-style training in *Yōga*, but he soon went his own way as a self-appointed *hanmoto* (Cat. 31–2). Another was Yoshida Hiroshi, who after the 1923 earthquake also went his own way and set up his own workshop (Cat. 47–8). These defections indicate just why *Shin Hanga* in the end failed as a long-term

revival; good artists of the twentieth century were simply no longer willing to work permanently for an autocratic publisher. It is not surprising that three of Watanabe's best artists were all very young pupils of Kiyokata when he approached them. Of them Kasamatsu Shirō eventually after the Pacific War went independent too; Itō Shinsui worked mainly as a celebrated painter as he got older, leaving Watanabe to turn some of his paintings into reproductive prints; only Kawase Hasui spent the greater part of his career producing numerous designs of townscape and landscape, mostly for the one publisher Watanabe to turn directly into prints. In this sense Hasui was the last *Ukiyo-e* print artist.

Shin Hanga flourished most in the years 1920–40, and other publishers such as Satō Shōtarō in Kyoto and Nakajima Seikadō in Tokyo (and Osaka) joined this new wave of commercial opportunity. Nakajima in his portfolio cover for Kitano Tsunetomi's *Kuruwa no Shunshū* (Cat. 55) records a desire, which goes beyond the ambition to preserve the old skills, actually to recreate *Ukiyo-e* as a record of the current *demi-monde*. This ambition, too, was doomed to failure, because a different sort of Bohemian *demi-monde* now existed, typical of the Taishō era. Its leading protagonist was Take-hisa Yumeji, a quite distinct artist and writer who in a sense created his own world of emotional fantasy and recorded it in an extremely wide variety of up-to-date formats (biography, Cat. 52–4).

While *Shin Hanga* for a generation artificially revived *Ukiyo-e* prints, the artists of the *Sōsaku Hanga* movement tried to update woodblock printing as the vehicle for a representative modern art in its own right, based on the Western styles in which they were almost all trained. A loose and miscellaneous grouping of artists led first by Yamamoto Kanae (biography) and Ishii Hakutei (biography), they achieved some coherence by the formation of the Japanese Creative Print Association in 1918. (It was re-established in 1931 as the Japanese Print Association, which is still active and now covers all styles and techniques.) This was dominated by woodblock printers, but did include artists who used other techniques such as etching and lithograph. Yamamoto's ideal was that every artist should make his own designs, cut his own blocks and take his own impressions. In practice not all could perform all of these tasks or find time to, as they all, including even Onchi Kōshirō, their *de facto* leader after 1918, had to do other work to earn a living. In fact they helped each other a great deal and in a sense formed one great co-operative venture. Up to 1945 they sold little in Japan, even less abroad, and might have been considered then a commercial failure, if a limited artistic success.

Creative print artists were from the beginning haunted by the ghost of *Ukiyo-e*. They wished to produce fresh, new work, but the foreign buyers were interested only in the old *Ukiyo-e* style and found the modern prints derivative – which in part they were; yet they never lost sight of the aspiration to preserve woodblock printing in a new, more vigorous form and to be accepted as a natural progression from the prints of the past. Perhaps the most striking confirmation of this can be found in the two prefaces to Hiratsuka's series 'Tokyo After the Earthquake' (1924, not in this catalogue), a set of bleak yet subtly skilful prints in an apparently rough, Expressionist style. The authors of these prefaces, Yamamoto Kanae himself and the lithographer Oda Kazuma (1882–1956), both relate these works to the *Ukiyo-e* tradition as if they demonstrably belong to it. Yamamoto states that they combine reality with the skills of carving and printing in an atmosphere of co-operation which he thoroughly applauds.

With the occupation of Japan from 1945 to 1952 by the Allies led by the USA *Shin Hanga* fell quickly out of favour, but the *Sōsaku Hanga* artists began to be appreciated by resident Americans who now had the time to get to know them. From this process came Oliver Statler's book *Modern Japanese Prints* (1956). Its subtitle *An Art Reborn* was international recognition that *Sōsaku Hanga* had indeed succeeded in replacing *Ukiyo-e*. It had also, ironically enough, replaced *Shin Hanga* as the representative school of modern Japanese prints, whose main sales were to the West; they have continued to be directed to the West as *Sōsaku Hanga* has dissolved into a wider community of Japanese printmakers in every technique and style now internationally practised, but its legacy remains in the very concept of a print artist who does only that work. By 1989 there were many of them, as well as Professors of Printmaking at Tokyo University of Fine Arts and Music and Tama Art University, a tremendous step from Hiratsuka Un'ichi's first informal extracurricular classes in 1935, which the *Sōsaku Hanga* movement had long campaigned to establish.

It was claimed earlier that both groups were trying not only to lay the ghost of *Ukiyo-e* prints and to succeed them but also to escape from the drabness and hardness of the industrialised and increasingly militaristic country they actually lived in by creating an internalised world of beauty into which they could retreat. It will be noticed that none of the prints in this catalogue is in the satirical or social sense controversial, and artists like Maekawa Senpan (Cat. 14, 83–5) or Hirafuku Hyakusui (Cat. 5) who earned their living as cartoonists had no apparent difficulty in separating that side of their work from their 'serious' prints. Fine though many of the artists were and are, this slightly escapist attitude, which tends to idealise the beautiful and exclude the ugly or disturbing, remains among woodblock artists to the present day.

The importance of the folk art movement, which was formally declared by Yanagi Sōetsu and a group of supporters in 1926, was that it was able to adapt this turning away from the worst aspects of modern society into something far more positive. It was a celebration of the crafts and culture of the ordinary people of Japan, especially of the country regions with their numerous distinctive traditions. It drew no boundaries between different art and craft forms as long as they had their origins in the life of the people and their traditional techniques and designs. Its greatest strength was that it was able to apply one aesthetic to many different crafts and arts – textiles, ceramics, lacquer and prints, for example – with the result that the makers could fertilise and inspire each other. It also identified a strong base of inspiration in folk religion and lore, regional dance and dramatic forms, and the local festivals which abound in Japan. The joy and energy which can be felt in the prints of Munakata, Sasajima, Mori or Serizawa have given a stronger heartbeat to Japanese printmaking in the twentieth century and profoundly influenced artists strictly outside its boundaries such as Maekawa Senpan, Hiratsuka Un'ichi and Azechi Umetarō.

1989: the end of an era?

When it becomes necessary for art historians to stop calling the years since 1868 simply 'The Modern Period', and to begin to agree on meaningful divisions, 1989 may well be one of the dates seen as a significant break not only for political reasons but also as a convenient way of defining the end of a cultural era. In January that year the Emperor Shōwa, known in his lifetime as Hirohito, died in the sixty-fourth year of his reign, the last serious political link with Japan's pre-war years. This event enabled Japan at last to begin to acknowledge more openly its troubled past and come to terms with it. In the field of prints, as of other arts, it is already beginning to be easier to find out what really happened to many of the artists during the Pacific War, and perhaps for their as yet unacknowledged patriotic or propaganda work to come to light.

Almost immediately in 1989 a lessening of overt respect for authority began to be noticed, including for the first time open discussions in newspapers of the Imperial Family itself. In the field of conceptual art, then gaining popularity among younger artists in Japan, a move towards direct criticism of society, politics and institutions could be discerned. This was a major change in a society which had for long seen satire as the province of the cartoonist, not the artist, and the possibility of prints at last becoming capable of satire and free critical social comment is at least there. The prints in this catalogue are representative of their period in having virtually no such content.

In 1990 came the unexpected bursting of the economic bubble which had seen Japan become the world's richest country in the 1980s, the end of a period of apparently relentless increase in prosperity which had in truth begun almost immediately the war ended. For printmakers, as for other artists, the high prices and demand almost guaranteed within Japan itself during the previous two decades came abruptly to an end. It may be that the era of the self-supporting print artist, so recently established, also came to an end at that point, except for older and already very prestigious personalities such as Saitō Kiyoshi, Azechi Umetarō or Tokuriki Tomikichirō, all of them in any case in their eighties or nineties. In 1993, too, the party which had ruled Japan since 1952 fell from power and was replaced by a coalition. To any Japanese born since the Pacific War this has been an event of great significance and further evidence that the old stability has suddenly weakened. The effects on the arts of such changes are difficult to predict but they will certainly occur, as they invariably do in those circumstances. One such effect may already have shown in the quickening disintegration of the national *Nihonga* style of painting which has with a few exceptions run out of inspiration. It is possible that the modern print movement, which like *Nihonga* is a contemporary amalgamation of a number of once-opposed schools, as described in this catalogue, has, too, run out of energy. Certainly visits to the recent annual exhibitions of the Japanese Print Association have given the impression of superlative technique with little new artistic inspiration, a trend which can also be seen in *Nihonga*.

At the time of writing Japan's long stability and prosperity have clearly favoured the development and coming to maturity of crafts – pottery, lacquer, paper-making, glass, textiles, for example – which have required peace and a guaranteed and appreciative market to nurture the patient apprenticeships needed to bring them to the heights of excellence demanded in that most exacting of countries. Although a few younger woodblock artists have emerged of stature, they are individualists. Until a new Watanabe Shōzaburō or Yamamoto Kanae or Yanagi Sōetsu emerges to take a lead, the situation for woodblock prints at the end of the twentieth century begins to look strangely similar to that at the end of the nineteenth century, with a great reservoir of skill waiting to be put to new use.

Author's note

All works catalogued are on paper and all are from the collections of the British Museum. Vertical measurements are given before horizontal and unless otherwise stated are the dimensions of the whole sheet, not the image. This differs from Gaston Petit's practice of measuring only the image; hence discrepancies will appear where the same item is recorded by us both. Japanese names are given with the surname first in native style. Literature is quoted after the catalogue entry only when the specific copy of the print listed has been previously published. Other prints by the relevant artist from the British Museum collection are quoted in the literature section at the end of each biography. All inscriptions on prints, including their reverses, have been transliterated or translated; occasionally where readings have proved intractable, that fact is stated (this applies mostly to seals). For convenience a convention has been adopted that transliterations into Roman from a Japanese original are in *italic*; transliterations from original annotations in Roman are not. Both types frequently occur together in the annotations on post-1945 prints, and care has been taken to follow the convention exactly. These conventions also apply to transcriptions from seals; although they are nearly always in Japanese script, a few are not, and the distinction has been maintained.

Artists' Biographies

AKAMATSU Rinsaku (1878–1953)

Cat. 26

Akamatsu was born in Tsuyama City in Okayama Prefecture and studied Western-style painting under Yamauchi Gusen at the Tokyo School of Fine Arts. He began his career as an illustrator with the Osaka *Asahi Shinbun* newspaper, where he knew the other artists contributing to *Hanshin Meisho Zue* (Cat. 4) and became a close associate of its publisher Kanao Tanejirō (professional name Bunendō). His designs for the covers of the portfolios for this series (nos 1, 2 and 6) are also in the British Museum's collections. He taught at several art schools in the city and became an influential figure in its artistic life, acting as secretary of the Osaka Art Association. He was best known as a cartoonist and recorder of everyday life in newspapers. The British Museum collection also includes a portfolio of prints of nudes from his drawings, published by Bunendō in 1940.

Literature: Mitchell; Johnson; Maria Shobō; Merritt and Yamada, p. 8.

AMANO Kazumi (b.1927)

Cat. 125

Born two years before Amano Kunihiro (q.v.), also in northern Honshu (Takaoka, Tōyama Prefecture) and also working in abstract woodblock prints, the two Amanos seem destined to be frequently confused. Kazumi graduated in 1945 in furniture design at the Prefectural School of Crafts in his home town. He met Munakata in 1950 (he was still in Tōyama at the time) and took up woodblock prints, studying with the master for a time. He began exhibiting at the Japanese Print Association in 1953, moved to Tokyo in 1955 and won a series of prizes at Lugano (1964), the Tokyo International Print Biennale (1966) and Cracow (1968). He went to the USA first in 1968 to teach and made many subsequent visits. In 1975 he finally moved to New York with his family. His work resembled Munakata's at first but became increasingly smooth and elegant, before moving to the experimental, exploring the positive and negatives inherent in photographic screens, though always in woodblock technique; and after his move to New York, becoming more and more conceptual, inspired often by Teilhard de Chardin's theories in *Le Phénomène Humaine* (1955).

Literature: Gendai Hanga, p. 37; Petit, 1, pp. 48–9; Merritt and Yamada, p. 9; Baskett.

AMANO Kunihiro (b.1929)

Cat. 126

He was born in Hirosaki, Aomori Prefecture, in northern Honshu, but his family moved to Tokyo early in his life. He was largely self-taught, though he did attend classes for three years at Musashino University of Art in an unofficial capacity in the post-war years. He first exhibited with the Japanese Print Association in 1955 and began a long and active international career at the Tokyo International Print Biennale in 1957 and Ljubljana in 1963. He has avoided figural subects, but his works are based in the real world, and he has drawn much inspiration from fishing and the sea (see Petit). He is typical of the first post-war generation of *Sōsaku Hanga* artists in his emphasis on clarity of form and printing, and has achieved a consistent elegance through a very individual palette of oil pigments which he developed during the 1960s. Many of his later works have used patterns reminiscent of the Japanese *obi* (sash worn with the kimono). His most extensive series have been 'Distant Memory', 'Dark Change' and 'Imagination'.

Another print by Amano in the British Museum collection (*Waking Dream II*) is illustrated in colour in Smith (1), no. 133.

Literature: Hasegawa, p. 38; Amano; Petit, 1, pp. 56–7; Merritt and Yamada, p. 9.

ASADA Benji

(also known as Benji-O, 1899–1984)

Cat. 15

Asada was an adopted name; his original family name was Nakanishi. He was born in Kameoka, near Kyoto, and received his artistic education at the Kyoto City School of Fine Arts and Crafts (Kyōto Shiritsu Bijutsu Kōgei Gakkō) and the Kyoto City Specialist School of Painting (Kyōto Shiritsu Kaiga Senmon Daigaku) from which he graduated in 1924. In 1921 he first exhibited at the Teiten (Imperial Exhibition). He got to know the leaders of the *Sōsaku Hanga* movement and published in the magazine *Han* ('Prints', 1928–9), together with his fellow Kyoto artist Tokuriki Tomikichirō (q.v.). At the same period he began to study native-style painting under the Kyoto artist Nishimura Goun (1887–1938). He was a co-founder in 1929 of the Kyoto Creative Print Society with Tokuriki, Asano Takeji (b.1900) and others. With these two he designed the series 'Creative Prints of the Twelve Months in new Kyoto' (1930), a Kyoto answer to the Tokyo-dominated *Sōsaku Hanga* world. He became a member of the Japanese Print Society in 1932 and participated in 'One Hundred New Views of Japan' (Cat. 15). After 1945 he worked only as a painter in the *Nihonga* style, much influenced by the work of Yamaguchi Kayō (1899–1984), a fellow-pupil of Goun's and specialising in 'bird-and-flower' (*kachō*) subjects.

Literature: Merritt and Yamada, pp. 10–11; Maria Shobō, pp. 14–15; Kawakita (3), pp. 11–12.

AZECHI Umetarō (b.1902)

Cat. 87–9

Still alive at the time of writing, Azechi is the most senior surviving member of the *Sōsaku Hanga* movement after Hiratsuka and is still working. He was born in Futana village, Ehime Prefecture, on the island of Shikoku, the son of a poor farmer who was an amateur carver and also carved woodblocks for the local festival. Because of extreme poverty in the area he worked as a merchant seaman and then as a newsboy in Tokyo from 1920, where he took a correspondence course in art. After a brief return home after the 1923 earthquake, he returned to Tokyo in 1925 and joined a Government printing office the following year, where he began to experiment with etching from lead plates. Encouraged by Hiratsuka, whose name he had heard, to take up woodblock printing, he was accepted for the Creative Print Association exhibition in 1924 and from then on worked as a freelance on prints, book illustrations, newspaper illustrations, bookplates and numerous other graphic tasks, including taking the prints for Maekawa Senpan and Onchi Kōshirō, both of whom heavily influenced his pre-war work. His early work was typical of the *Sōsaku Hanga* movement, especially in monochrome, but a dignified and densely pigmented landscape style slowly developed, reaching early maturity in the series *Iyo Fūkei* (ten prints, 1936). The travel needed to sketch for this series awoke his love of the mountains of Japan, which he began to explore passionately on frequent climbing visits. Increasingly involved with the community of *Sōsaku Hanga* artists, he contributed to 'One Hundred New Views of Japan' in 1939 and 1941. His distinctive style of starkly drawn mountains in reverberant but sombre colours came to full maturity in his series *Yama* in 1940 and continued up to the late 1960s. He continued to work through the Pacific War and was sent to Manchuria in 1943–4. From the 1950s he developed a series of 'Mountain People' prints which have continued to the present, along with prolific writing of articles and books on the mountains, with his own illustrations, beginning with *Yama no Medama* in 1957. Like others of his generation, he benefited from American interest in his work after 1945, being promoted by Statler in *Modern Japanese Prints: An Art Reborn* (1956) and selected for Michener's *The Modern Japanese Print. An Appreciation* (1962). 'Snowman' from this portfolio is reproduced in colour in Smith (1), no.91a. His work gained from the increased scale demanded of prints in the 1950s and 60s, which saw him in his prime.

Literature: Petit, II, pp.72–3; Merritt and Yamada, pp.13–14; Merritt, pp.234–5 and *passim*; *Azechi Umetarō Zen Hanga-shū* (with a good life history up to 1979 but no bibliography); Azechi; Statler (1), pp.136–41; Michener, pp.40–2.

DŌMOTO Inshō (1891–1975)

Cat. 57

Dōmoto designed only a few prints but is remembered as an innovative *Nihonga* painter in the Kyoto tradition. He was born in Kyoto. His two brothers were the Nō drama researcher Dōmoto Kansei and the lacquer artist Dōmoto Shikken. He graduated in 1910 from the Kyoto City School of Fine Arts and Crafts (Kyōto Shiritsu Bijutsu Kōgei Gakkō). He initially did design work for Mitsukoshi Department Store and for the silk textile firm Tatsumura Heizō. He then entered the Kyoto City Specialist School of Painting (Kyōto Shiritsu Kaiga Senmon Gakkō), finally graduating after research studies in 1924. Meanwhile he was actively painting and became a pupil of the *Nihonga* artist Nishiyama Suishō (1879–1958) but also began to show Western influences. He taught at his old universities in the years 1930–41. In 1944 he became an Imperial Academician (*Teishitsu Gigeiin*). After the Pacific War he took up painting in oils, abstract styles, sculpture and other crafts, developing into a man of many skills. In 1961 he received the Order of Merit (*Kunshō*). In later years he continued to execute wall-paintings (*fusuma-e*, and so on) in temples (for example, Saihōji), a practice he had begun in 1924, and even in the Church of St Mary in Osaka. In 1966 a museum devoted to his work was opened in Kyōto (Dōmoto Inshō Bijutsukan). His prints included Cat. 57, *Eight Views of Kyoto* (1928) and *Inshō's Collection of Buddhist Paintings* (1941).

Literature: Kawakita (3), p.239; Merritt and Yamada, p.16.

FUJIMORI Shizuo (1891–1943)

Cat. 10

Fujimori is another of those short-lived activists of the pre-Pacific War who participated in the Creative Print Association and contributed to many of the *dōjin* (coterie) magazines while supporting himself by other jobs. Others were his co-artists on 'One Hundred New Views of Tokyo' – Henmi Takashi (Cat. 8), Fukawaza Sakuichi (Cat. 16) and Suwa Kanenori (Cat. 9). He was born in Kurume (Fukuoka Prefecture) and from 1910 attended the Hakuba-kai (Western Painting Institute) where he got to know Tanaka Kyōkichi, and from 1911 the Western Painting Section of Tokyo School of Fine Arts. From 1913 he began to make prints under the influence of Tanaka and was a founder of the art and poetry magazine *Tsukuhae* with him and Onchi Kōshirō (q.v.). He helped organise the memorial exhibition to Tanaka in 1915; all of this occurred before his graduation from Tokyo in 1916, after which he taught at middle schools in Taiwan and his native Fukuoka. In Taiwan he met Yamaguchi Gen (Cat. 100–2) and gave him lessons in woodblock carving. He was a founder member of the Creative Print Association in 1918, when he returned to Tokyo, and of its successor, the Nihon Hanga Kyōkai, in 1931. He contributed thirteen prints to 'One Hundred New Views of Tokyo' (1929–32), distinguished by an Expressionistic style increasingly softened by a gentle Romanticism; and designed his own series *Dai Tōkyō Jūnikei* ('Twelve Views of Great Tokyo') in 1934. From 1936 he began to produce woodblock illustrations for serials in the Fukuoka *Asahi Shinbun* newspaper and returned to live in Iizuka in 1940, dying in 1943, the year after the sudden death of his elder son. Fujimori's landscape and figurative styles were heavily influenced by Expressionism, and contributed notably to the bleak atmosphere of 'One Hundred New Views of Tokyo' and the Expressionistic tendencies of *Tsukuhae*. According to Onchi (2), he lost the thumb of his right hand in his youth, which may account for the simplicity of his engraving style.

Literature: Merritt, pp.179–81; Merritt and Yamada, pp.18–19; Kamon, Tozaka and Asahi, pp.83–5, and reproductions there of all his contributions to 'One Hundred New Views of Tokyo'; Katō, II, p.274; Fujii, *passim*; Onchi (2), p.23; *Hanga Geijutsu*, 37, pp.138–47.

FUKAZAWA Sakuichi (1896–1947)

Cat. 16

Fukazawa was born in Niigata Prefecture, but his parents moved soon after to Tokyo, where he attended Tokyo Central School of Commerce and Industry. From around 1918 he began to learn woodblock printing with the help of Suwa Kanenori (q.v.) and began exhibiting at the Sōsaku Hanga Kyōkai (Creative Print Association) in 1922 and contributing to coterie magazines, especially *Minato* and its successor *Kaze*. He was a founding member of the Japan Print Association in 1931. He became an associate on the magazine *Han* with Hiratsuka (q.v.), Azechi (q.v.) and Munakata (q.v.). He contributed thirteen prints to 'One Hundred New Views of Tokyo' and at the same time to *Hanga CLUB* magazine, which featured the same group of artists. From 1936 he began to design woodblock-printed covers for books bound in Western style. He continued to produce prints throughout the Pacific War and briefly after it. His style is rather abbreviated and lonely, and his cutting and printing technique, according to Onchi, unusually soft, shallow and smooth.

Literature: Merritt and Yamada, p.21; Kamon, Tozaka and Asahi, pp.80–2, and where his prints for 'One Hundred New Views of Tokyo' are reproduced in colour; Katō, II, p.277, and pls 106–9; Onchi (2), p.24.

FUKITA Fumiaki (b.1926)

Cat. 113

Fukita was head of the Printmaking Department at Tama Art University for many years from 1968, succeeding the etcher Komai Tetsurō (1920–76), and the first full Professor in the subject in Japan. His influence has consequently been considerable, especially on Kawachi Seikō (q.v.), who has inherited much of his inventiveness in cutting and printing of woodblocks, and on Morozumi (q.v.). Fukita was born in Tokushima Prefecture (Island of Shikoku) and graduated from a teachers' college there (a route followed by many other print artists early in their careers). He then studied oil-painting for one year at the Tokyo University of Fine Arts. In 1957 he became associated with the Japanese Print Association and won a prize in their exhibition that year, as well as with the Modern Art Society. He developed new woodblock techniques using both its relief and engraving aspects. His prints were done mostly with *rawan*, a hard wood imported from the Philippines. Since the 1960s his subjects have been based on stars and galaxies, with a strong tendency to effects resembling firework displays.

Literature: Gendai Hanga, p. 74; Fukita (1); Merritt and Yamada, p. 21; Petit, 1, pp. 88–9; Hasegawa, pp. 192–3.

FUNASAKA Yoshisuke (b.1939)

Cat. 130

Funasaka was born in Gifu Prefecture, the son of the painter Funasaka Masayoshi, and graduated in 1962 from the Oil Painting Department of Tama Art University, Tokyo. He took up printmaking in the mid-1960s and won a prize at the Tokyo International Print Biennale in 1970. He studied in the USA and London in 1976–7 with a Japanese Government Bunkachō (Agency for Cultural Affairs) Fellowship and has exhibited extensively in international biennales, including the British one at Bradford five times (1970, 1972, 1974, 1975, 1979). Funasaka is a prolific printmaker who has experimented technically with a wide range of effects but whose works maintain a quiet and dignified abstraction even when using motifs such as holes – sometimes literal – from cigarette burns, and the shape of the lemon, which he used a great deal from 1957 until the mid-1970s. He has exhibited regularly with the College Women's Association of Japan print show, Tokyo, since 1979. In 1984 he was selected for their touring exhibition (Smith (2), no. 7). His early works were made from linoleum blocks, but he progressed to woodblock, silk screen and often complicated mixed-media techniques which have been well described by Petit. In the late 1970s he also produced works which were partly paper collage and partly painted.

Literature: Gendai Hanga, p. 76; Petit, 1, pp. 104–5; Petit and Arboleda, pp. 127–31.

HAGIWARA Hideo (b.1913)

Cat. 110–11

Hagiwara was born in Kōfu City, Yamanashi Prefecture. From 1921 he was educated in Japanese schools in Korea and Manchuria, where his father held various police jobs. He returned to Japan alone in 1929 to continue his education in Tokyo and first learned oil-painting in 1930, having a work accepted at the Hakujitsu-kai (a society of former expatriate artists) as early as 1932. That year he entered the Bunka Gakuin, Fine Art Section, and in 1933 the Oil Painting Section of the Tokyo School of Fine Arts, from which he graduated in 1938. While still there, he attended Hiratsuka Un'ichi's extracurricular woodblock printing course, and as a result joined the Takamizawa Woodblock Print Company in 1938 as a quality controller, where he learned much about *Ukiyo-e* print techniques. He was conscripted in 1943 into the army, where his health was so badly affected that he was bedridden for three years from 1945. He had lost his house, atelier and most of his early works in the May 1945 Tokyo air raids, but while sick took up the study of creative woodblock printing. In 1950 he built his own atelier and in 1951 had his first one-man exhibition of oil-paintings. His first one-man exhibition of prints was in 1956 at the Yōseidō Gallery, Tokyo, and the same year a print was accepted for the Japanese Print Association annual exhibition, where he has exhibited almost every year since. In 1958 he began to produce the abstract prints which made his international reputation; from that year he began also to exhibit abroad, including the paintings which he had never entirely abandoned. His 'Stone Flower' series was shown in part at the second International Tokyo Print Biennale in 1960 and brought him much recognition. This was enhanced by the 'Man in Armour' series (1962–4). In 1967 he taught briefly as an invited Professor at the University of Oregon; in 1977 he became a lecturer at the Tokyo University of Fine Arts and Music. In 1979 he became Chairman of the Japanese Print Association, a position he has held ever since.

Hagiwara has been a constant innovator both in technique and style. He developed the system of printing from the back of the paper, scratching into the blocks like etching, composing the blocks from cut-up pieces, and was able in his 'Clown' and 'Theatre' series to simulate lithographic effects in pure woodblock. He has ventured occasionally into figurative subjects, for example, 'Greek Mythology' (1965) and landscape ('Thirty-Six Views of Fuji', 1981), and shown an aliveness to foreign influences without ever being deflected for long by them from the serious abstract prints which he has continued to produce, their tones becoming more sombre as he has grown older. He is now identifiable as the dominant figure in Japanese woodblock printing since Munakata's death in 1975.

Literature: Robertson (includes a detailed account of Hagiwara's technique); Merritt and Yamada, p. 25; Merritt, pp. 256–7; Petit, 1, pp. 112–13; Hagiwara (with good bibliography up to 1982).

HASHIGUCHI Goyō (1880–1921)

Cat. 31–2

Goyō is usually known under this art name, a tradition carried from *Ukiyo-e* into *Shin Hanga*, but he in fact worked mainly as a Western-style painter, illustrator and book designer and should more properly be known as Hashiguchi. Born in Kagoshima, in the south of Kyushu, the son of a minor traditionalist painter, he became interested in Kanō-school painting in his youth and in 1899 went to Kyoto to study with Hashimoto Gahō (1835–1908). However, he was persuaded to take up Western painting by the influential Kuroda Seiki (1866–1924) who came from the same district as Goyō, and went to Tokyo to study at the Hakuba-kai (Western Painting Institute) and then at the Tokyo School of Art, where he graduated in 1905. His elder brother, the Western-style painter Hashiguchi Yasuo, introduced him to the novelist Natsume Sōseki (1867–1916), and as a result Goyō designed the first edition of his most famous novel *Wagahai wa neko de aru* ('I am a cat', 1905). He subsequently designed around seventy titles. His paintings were exhibited in 1907 at the Tokyo Industrial Exhibition and at the Ministry of Education Bunten exhibition, but failing to be selected subsequently he gradually gave up oils. In 1911 he became interested in *Ukiyo-e* prints after winning a poster competition with a study of a beautiful woman, and began to publish articles and studies on early artists of that school. As a consequence of these activities he met the publisher Watanabe Shōzaburō, for whom he designed a print ('Bath', 1915) which was virtually the first of the *Shin Hanga* movement, but wishing to have complete control over all the processes, he published his subsequent prints himself. In 1916–17 he supervised the twelve-volume *Ukiyo-e Fūzoku Yamoto Nishikie* ('Japanese Brocade Prints in Ukiyo-e Genre Style') containing hundreds of woodblock reduced-size facsimiles of the works of early masters. His handful of superbly produced prints of beautiful women have some of the stately sexuality of his model Kitagawa Utamaro (1754–1806). A small group of print designs unfinished at his early death were later published by his family.

Other prints by Goyō in the British Museum collection are illustrated in Smith (1), nos 25–9; Smith, Harris and Clark, no. 232.

Literature: Katō, 1, nos 91–104, and pp. 273–4; Kawakita (3), p. 274; Merritt, pp. 69–75 and *passim*; Stephens, pp. 127–31; Paechter, pp. 19–26; Blair (1); Nihon Ukiyo-e Kyōkai; Yoshida, Susugu; Hashiguchi; Ono (5).

HASHIMOTO Okiie (1899–1993)

Cat. 25

Hashimoto was born in Tottori Prefecture and graduated in 1924 as an art teacher from the Tokyo School of Fine Arts. He worked as a school-teacher from 1924 until 1955 and produced art in his spare time. After that he retired from teaching and began a full-time career as an artist. As a young man he pursued oil-painting but took up prints in 1936 as a result of attending Hiratsuka Un'ichi's short course in woodblock printing in Tokyo. He remained a close friend of Hiratsuka's from then on and participated in his various activities, such as the Yoyogi-ha group and the wartime print collection *Kitsutsuki Hangashū* (1943). He first exhibited at the Japanese Print Association show in 1937. He contributed to the last Ichimoku-kai collection in 1950 and from that time began to be better known, especially after appearing in Statler's *Modern Japanese Prints: An Art Reborn* (1956). Much of his work before and after the Pacific War was devoted to Japanese castles and gardens, including the series *Kojō Jūkei* ('Ten Views of Old Castles', 1946), but he also produced floral and figure subjects in his later career.

Literature: Kanagawa Prefectural Museum of Modern Art (2); Merritt and Yamada, p. 30; Merritt, pp. 250–1; Hashimoto.

HENMI Takashi (1895–1944)

Cat. 8

This artist was typical of the good amateurs who produced much of the work of the *Sōsaku Hanga* movement up to 1945. Their talents were brought out by the relative ease of the medium as used by the movement and the encouragement generously provided by its major figures, especially Onchi and Hiratsuka. Henmi was born in Wakayama and was inspired to make prints by the example of Tanaka Kyōkichi (1892–1915), a poet and artist from the same city, who collaborated with Onchi on the poetry and art magazine *Tsukuhae* (1914–15). Henmi was himself an active poet, and was involved in the design and publication of modern poetry books. He decided to make his living as an accountant in Tokyo so as to pursue prints and poetry in his spare time. In 1916–17 he spent a year in Shanghai with his company's branch office. A member of the Sōsaku Hanga Kyōkai from 1919, he contributed to the movement's magazines and series. Four of his prints were shown in the Paris exhibition of 1934 organised by Hasegawa Kiyoshi. He is best known for his thirteen contributions to 'One Hundred New Views of Tokyo', marked like much of his work by a gently atmospheric style, with generally lonely figures in townscapes. The early deaths of Tanaka and his close friend the poet Ōte Takuji (1887–1934) left his work with a pronounced melancholy, and he spent much of the rest of his life publishing the latter's literary remains.

Literature: Merritt, pp. 222–4 and *passim*; Merritt and Yamada, pp. 32–3; Onchi (2); Kamon, Tozaka and Asahi, pp. 86–9, give detailed information on Henmi's life and reproduce all thirteen of his prints in 'One Hundred New Views of Tokyo'.

HIRAFUKU Hyakusui (1877–1933)

Cat. 5

The son of Hirafuku Suian (1844–90), a painter in the old Chinese (*Nanga*) style, Hyakusui studied painting with the Shijō-school artist Kawabata Gyokushō (1842–1913) from 1894 and at the Tokyo School of Fine Arts from 1897 to 1899, where he became a painter in the new *Nihonga* style. In 1900 he formed with other artists the Musei-kai, a society devoted to greater naturalism in *Nihonga*. Again in 1916 he joined with Kaburagi Kiyokata (1878–1972) in forming a similar society called Kinrei-sha. He was a designer of prints for *Hosun*. Having also studied Western-style sketching at the Taiheiyō-Gakai (Pacific Painting Association) in Tokyo, he was able to make his living as a cartoonist and illustrator for newspapers and books, a calling he shared with his contemporary Kiyokata. From 1914 he became increasingly celebrated as a painter in a wide range of formats and styles within the *Nihonga* movement. His work in sheet-prints is relatively limited apart from his contribution to *Nihon Fukei Hanga* (Cat. 5), but his early illustrated book *Fuji Isshu* ('A Tour of Fuji') of 1907 is now much admired. He was also a notable poet in the *waka* form.

Literature: Tazawa, p. 102; Smith (4); Miyagawa, p. 105; Maria Shobō; Merritt and Yamada, p. 33.

HIRATSUKA Un'ichi (b.1895)

Cat. 7, 23–4, 81–2

Hiratsuka, still alive at the time of writing (February 1994), qualifies in every respect as the grand old man of the *Sōsaku Hanga* movement. He was born in Shimane Prefecture, the son of a shrine carpenter, but, having met Ishii Hakutei (q.v.) in his home town of Matsue in 1913, went to Tokyo in 1915 to study Western painting with Okada Saburōsuke (1869–1939). Ishii advised him to learn block-carving, in which he already had acquired a keen interest. This he did during 1915 with Igami Bonkotsu, the craftsman who had already done much work with the creative print artists (Cat. 3). His thorough training with Igami made him the 'hands' of *Sōsaku Hanga* thereafter. He showed his first prints in 1916 at the Nika-kai exhibition; in the late 1920s, inspired by early Buddhist woodblocks, he was producing work in his characteristic black and white technique (Cat. 7). His series of twelve prints 'Tokyo After the Earthquake'

(1925) was, however, in colours, and established his reputation. Until 1935 he taught practical woodblock printing around Japan and inspired Munakata (Cat. 59–65) to use black and white. In 1939 he exhibited his personal collection of old Buddhist prints at Yanagi Sōetsu's Mingeikan (Museum of Folk Art). From 1935 until 1944 he taught woodblock printing as an extra course at the Tokyo School of Fine Arts, the first time the subject had been permitted there, and inspired many young artists as a result, including Kitaoka Fumio (q.v.). In this period he came to know and influence almost every important print artist of his day. After the Pacific War, when he worked briefly in Beijing, he continued to collaborate closely with Onchi Kōshirō (q.v.) and in 1948 began his own school in Tokyo. From 1962 he has lived with his daughter in Washington, DC, continuing to produce large prints in black and white. He is also admired as a poet, and has designed illustrated editions of his poems.

Literature: Merritt and Yamada, pp. 34–5; Merritt, ch. 9, and *passim*; Statler (1), ch. 4, and *passim*; Kawakita (4); Michener, pp. 16–19; Sekino (1), pp. 147–53; Onchi (2), p. 16; Hiratsuka (1) and (2). Other prints by Hiratsuka in the British Museum collection are published in Smith, Harris and Clark, no. 235 (in colour); Carey, p. 43 (in colour).

HOSHI Jōichi (1913–79)

Cat. 122–4

Hoshi was born in Niigata Prefecture in the north of Honshu. He went with his family to Taiwan (then part of the Japanese empire) and graduated from a teachers' college there in 1932. In 1946 he was repatriated and began to take up printmaking as a result of working in a printing-shop, starting with silk screen, in which technique he won a prize at the Japanese Print Association as early as 1949, becoming a member in 1952. He turned to woodblock, studying at the course at Musashino University of Arts and graduating in 1956. From 1959 he began to exhibit at the Tokyo International Print Biennale with abstract works related to the dominant *Sōsaku Hanga* style of the time. He also taught calligraphy during this period. From 1967 he began to exhibit in the West, and from 1964 his subjects gradually changed to stars and constellations done in a heavily Expressionistic style, exploring in an ever more individual manner the possibilities of woodblock. His 'Constellation' series (1964–7) eventually reached forty-two prints. In the late 1960s he discovered his final and definitive theme of trees, reverting to a detailed naturalism of dazzling technical complexity, allied to the use of gold and silver and brilliant colours. The tree prints finally amounted to 163 sheets, nearly half of his entire graphic output. In 1977 he went on a sketching tour to Mongolia, which literally widened the horizons of his prints. Since his death his reputation has risen rapidly both in Japan and the West.

Literature: Hoshi; Petit, I, pp. 128–9. Other prints by Hoshi in the British Museum's collection are illustrated in Smith (I), nos 95 and 96; Smith, Harris and Clark, no. 247.

INAGAKI Tomoo (1902–80)

Cat. 97

Inagaki is best known for his many prints of cats which gained him a wide following in the West, but the first of these was not produced until 1951 after nearly thirty years as a typical artist of the Creative Print Movement. He was obliged to make his living until that time by teaching and various sorts of commercial design work such as *ex libris* plates and posters. He was born in Tokyo and graduated from the Okura Commercial High School in 1923; in the same year he began associating with Onchi Kōshirō and Kiratsuka Un'ichi in the group producing the magazine *Shi to Hanga* ('Poetry and Prints), to which he first contributed in 1924, the same year that he began exhibiting at the Creative Print Association. From 1935 he taught commercial art at the Kyōhoku Commercial High School, resigning in 1951 to become a teacher at the Japan Advertising Art School. He began to be widely known in the West through Statler's *Modern Japanese Prints: An Art Reborn* (1956), although he had participated widely in the travelling exhibitions to Europe and USA before World War II, and from then on was represented frequently in international exhibitions. His earlier works included many floral and still-life subjects, as well as landscapes and townscapes.

Literature: Statler (I), pp. 164–5; Merritt and Yamada, p. 41; Inagaki (English Supplement, 1985); Hasegawa, p. 48.

ISHII Hakutei (1882–1958)

Cat. 3

Born in Tokyo, Ishii was the son of the traditional-style painter Ishii Teiko (1848–97), with whom he studied early in his life. Through him he got to know Yamamoto Kanae (Cat. 1–2). This early training gave him a sympathy with native Japanese styles, which modified his later Westernising work.

Ishii's brother, Ishii Tsuruzō (1887–1973), was also a painter and printmaker, as well as a now respected sculptor. Hakutei became interested in Western-style art, which he took up following his father's death, and soon became very competent in both oils and water-colour, specialising in Japanese landscape. He was an activist in groups of Western-style artists and was co-founder of the magazine *Heitan* (1905–6). In 1905 he published Yamamoto Kanae's *Fisherman* as the first 'creative print' in the magazine *Myōjō*. From 1907 to 1910 he was co-founder and chief editor of the magazine *Hosun*, where many of his paintings were published in reproduction and where his ideas on the development of Japanese art were freely expressed. He went to Europe in 1910. On his return in 1912 he continued his prints series 'Twelve Views of Tokyo' (Cat. 3) and from 1917 contributed three sets to 'Prints of Japanese Landscape' (see Cat. 5 and 6). The fact that he did not participate in the founding of the Japanese Creative Print Association in 1918 suggests his interest had returned firmly to painting, where it remained. He went again to Europe in 1923–5. During his life he founded or joined many societies for the advancement of Western-style art, and wrote much on European and Japanese artists and aesthetics. He is today highly regarded in Japan as an oil-painter and water-colourist. Ishii was a communicator, encourager and prolific author, and his influence on printmaking, like that of Yamamoto, was out of proportion to the small body of prints he produced early in his career.

Literature: Merritt, ch. 6; Katō, I, pls 15–30 (includes on pls 25–7 three prints from 'Prints of Japanese Landscape' not acknowledged as such); Ono (I); Merritt and Yamada, p. 43; Oka, p. 5.

ISHIKAWA Toraji (1875–1964)

Cat. 56

Ishikawa was born in Kōchi on the island of Shikoku. In 1891 he moved to Tokyo to study Western-style painting under Koyama Shōtarō (1837–1916) at his private school called Fudōsha. He was a founder-member in 1902 of the Taiheiyō-Gakai (Pacific Painting Association), which also included Yoshida Hiroshi (q.v.). Like many of that circle he travelled as a young man in the USA and Europe (1902–4). In 1904 he became an instructor at the evening institute of the Taiheiyō-Gakai and held an exhibition of his water-colours in the USA. During the Taishō era he travelled also in Korea, Taiwan and China; some of his impressions of Taiwan are found in the prints he contributed to the book *Shin Nihon Kenbutsu* ('Views of New Japan') published in 1918, for which he produced twenty-one designs, and to the advertising portfolio of four prints by four artists for this book published by Kanao Tanejirō in 1917. He became a regular exhibitor at the Bunten and Teiten government-sponsored exhibitions, and principal of the Taiheiyō-Gakai in 1943, but resigned in 1947 to found his own Shigen-kai Society. After the Pacific War he was active in Tokyo art education. His early works are mostly of women, the later ones mostly landscapes in an Impressionist style with bright light. His output of prints was small, consisting of a few landscapes developed from paintings and the celebrated 'Ten Nudes' which were designed especially for woodblock printing.

Literature: Katō, III, p. 265; and pls 54–61, including five of the 'Ten Nudes' series; Kawakita (3), p. 31; Merritt and Yamada, pp. 44,

228. Another print by Ishikawa from the British Museum collections (*Leisure Hours*) is reproduced in Smith (I). no. 67.

ISHIWATA Kōitsu (1897–1987)

Cat. 45

Kōitsu is listed in some sources under his given name of Ishiwata Shōichirō. His family name is sometimes given as Ishiwatari. To add further possible confusion there is a different artist, not represented in this catalogue, named Tsuchiya Kōitsu (1870–1949), who also made woodblock prints for Watanabe. Ishiwata Kōitsu was born in Shiba, Tokyo, and learned the techniques of textile design and *Nihonga*-style painting from his brother-in-law Igusa Senshin. In 1917 he was introduced to Kawase Hasui (q.v.) and became fascinated by woodblock printing. After the 1923 Kantō earthquake he joined the design department of Nozawaya, a Yokohama department store, where he was very successful. The city provided the subject-matter for many of his prints, which he took up as a full-time occupation in 1930. He published first with Watanabe, but his subtle, dark and low-key subjects seem not to have been successful with Western customers, and around 1935 he switched to working with Katō Junji. According to the latter, he began also to use stencil from 1943. Apart from his Yokohama prints, he did series on toys and on hot-spring resorts.

Literature: Merritt, pp. 65–6; Merritt and Yamada, p. 45; Katō, III, p. 273, and good colour reproductions on pls 234–8. Another print by Kōitsu in the British Museum collections (*At Katsushika Sankaku*) is reproduced in Smith (I), no. 75.

ITŌ Shinsui (1898–1972)

Cat. 33–7

Born in the Fukagawa area of Tokyo, Shinsui had to start work with the Tokyo Printing Company in 1910 because of his family's poverty. In 1911 he had already developed an interest in art and studied the *Nihonga* style as well as continuing his education in the evenings, and was posted to the Company's drawing section. The *Nihonga* artist Yuki Somei (1875–1957) introduced him to the neo-*Ukiyo-e* painter Kaburagi Kiyokata (1879–1973) who accepted him as a pupil. From this time he earned a living as an illustrator, which he continued to do through much of his career, though it became inessential as he grew in fame. Shinsui's technical precociousness was shown by his winning prizes in 1912 at the exhibition of the Tatsumi Gakai (South-west Painting Society, Tokyo), in 1914 at the first Inten (Japan Art Institute Exhibition), and in 1915 at the annual Bunten (Ministry of Education Exhibition). This skill was accompanied by a remarkable emotional precocity combined with forceful elegance of design which attracted the attention of Watanabe Shōzaburō in 1916 when he saw the artist's painting *Before the Mirror*. With Kiyokata's consent he persuaded the young artist to begin to design works for him to produce as woodblocks, of which a version of *Before the Mirror* was the first in July 1916.

From that time until Watanabe's death in 1962 Watanabe and Shinsui collaborated on over sixty landscape prints and about 100 others, mostly of beautiful women. Shinsui occasionally worked for other publishers even before 1962. His series 'Eight Views of Lake Biwa' set standards for the landscape print which were taken up by Yoshida Hiroshi (q.v.) and by another Kiyokata pupil, Hasui (q.v.). Once Hasui had specialised in landscape, Shinsui confined himself more to *bijinga* in prints, and increasingly in paintings, which always occupied most of his time, especially after 1927, when he founded his own academy of painting, the Shinsui Gakujuku (Shinsui Academy); this was moved in 1930 and renamed Rōhō Gakujuku (Academy of the Clear Peak) and attracted many pupils, engendering another generation of *Nihonga* artists specialising in *bijinga*. An activist in art circles and government art institutions, Shinsui founded several societies, including the Seisei-kai in 1932 devoted to realism in portraiture, and the Seikin-kai in 1940, with Yamakawa Shūhō (1898–1944), which had similar aims. His many portraits of women in up-to-date Westernised fashions and hair-styles in the 1950s and 60s bear witness to his determination to keep *Nihonga* modernised. Meanwhile, like many other *Shin Hanga* artists, he had been vigorously publicised in the West by Watanabe, especially at the two Toledo Exhibitions (1930 and 1936), and as a result has tended ever since to be regarded outside Japan as primarily a print artist.

From 1937 Shinsui began to take a new interest in landscape prints (*Ōshima Jūnikei*, 'Twelve Views of Ōshima'). A visit to China in 1939 further stimulated this trend. He published three *Nanyō Suketchi* ('Sketches from the South') in 1943 after visiting the war zone as a Japanese Navy official war artist.

Shinsui was evacuated to Nagano Prefecture later in the Pacific War, which resulted in the 1948 series *Shinano Jūkei* ('Ten Views of Shinano'). After this he designed only a handful of prints: one of them (*Tresses*, 1953) was published by the Japanese Government when designating his skills as a print artist an 'Intangible Cultural Asset'. In 1958 he became a member of the Japanese Academy of Arts. His paintings include folding screens and albums as well as hanging scrolls, and he was equally at home on paper or silk, and in female subjects drawn from high or bourgeois life, the traditional dance forms, geishas, or the theatre. Today he and Uemura Shōen (1875–1949) are recognised as the two greatest *bijinga* artists of the *Nihonga* movement. Other prints by Shinsui in the collection of the British Museum

are illustrated in Smith (1), nos 30–41B, and Smith, Harris and Clark, no. 231.

Literature: Merritt and Yamada, p. 47, and list of his prints pp. 228–32; Merritt, pp. 47–54; Kozaki, p. 105; Stephens, pp. 180–94; Blair (1) and (2); Yamanashi Prefectural Museum of Art (with complete list of his prints); Hosono; Hamada and Hosono; Kawakita (3), p. 37.

IWAMI Reika (b.1927)
Cat. 112

Iwami was not a direct pupil of Onchi but she ranks as the last of his true *Sōsaku Hanga* line, having been taught by his close associates, Shinagawa Takumi (q.v.) and Sekino Jun'ichirō (q.v.). From Onchi's example she inherited skill in cool abstraction, as well as the printing from driftwood which has become an essential part of her later work and an interest in embossed effects. Her neatness of technique and preference for black and white, sometimes with gold and silver foil, take her far from the cerebral, romantic and unpredictable work of the early Creative Print Movement into a perfection and occasionally a sentimentality which is more closely related to contemporary *Nihonga* painting. She was born in Tokyo and first studied doll-making, as well as prints at the Sunday course of the Bunka Gakuin (Culture Institute) and subsequently at other workshops. She first exhibited in 1953 with the Japanese Print Association, from 1957 to 1964 at the Tokyo International Print Biennale, from 1957 every year at the College Women's Association of Japan print show in Tokyo, and in 1979 at the British International Print Biennale, Bradford. All of these made her known in the West, where she became popular because of her easily understood abstractions based on water, sky, rock and driftwood forms. Her name was finally made by being included in Michener's *The Modern Japanese Print. An Appreciation* (1962) with 'Winter Composition No. 2'. In 1957 she was one of the founders of a group of women printmakers, the Joryū Hanga Kyōkai. Since 1964 she has worked only as a printmaker, producing relatively few designs in small editions, since the embossing and *baren* printing in her often large compositions require much physical effort, difficult for the very small woman she is.

Literature: Michener, pp. 44–6; Merritt and Yamada, p. 48. Other prints by Iwami in the collections of the British Museum are reproduced in Smith (1), nos 102–3, and Smith (2), no. 14.

KANAMORI Yoshio (b.1922)
Cat. 67

Kanamori was born in Tōyama Prefecture, where Munakata came to live to avoid the Tokyo bombing in spring 1945. This gave him the opportunity to study woodblock printing directly with a practising master. Previously he

had read about woodblock techniques in *Hanga o tsukuru hito e* ('To People who Want to Make Woodblock Prints', 1922) by Nagase Yoshio. He studied at the Tokyo School of Fine Arts, but did not graduate. He first exhibited with the Kokuga-kai exhibition in 1950, and in the same year helped Munakata found the local print magazine *Etchū Hanga*. He was also a founder-member with the master in 1952 of the Nihon Hanga-in (Japanese Print Institute). In 1958 he was exhibited jointly with Munakata in a touring show in the USA. His work is dominated by the austere mountainous landscape of his native Tōyama, but increasingly intruded on by fancifully treated elements such as birds, flowers, feathers and butterflies which display a familiarly Japanese sentimentality.

Literature: Merritt and Yamada, p. 53; Blakemore, pp. 66–7; Kawakita (1), p. 180 and pl. 89.

KASAMATSU Shirō (b.1898)
Cat. 46

Shirō was born in Asakusa, Tokyo, and became a pupil of Kaburagi Kiyokata in 1911 at an even younger age than his fellow Tokyoites Shinsui and Hasui. He studied painting in the *Nihonga* manner and took up landscape. It was this side of his work which attracted the attention of the publisher Watanabe Shōzaburō, who commissioned his first print from him in 1919. Thereafter he worked regularly for Watanabe until after the Pacific War. His lyrical townscapes in particular made his work popular with Westerners, and his *Shinobazu Pond* has been extensively reprinted by the firm of Watanabe since it first appeared in 1932 (reproduced in Smith (1), no. 77). In the 1950s he became attracted by the ideals of the *Sōsaku Hanga* movement and began to produce his own prints, usually on a larger scale and with a looser construction than those done for Watanabe. His prints are relatively few and include the series *Tōkyō Kinkō Hakkei no Uchi* ('Eight Views Around Tokyo', 1939). He also worked in the 1950s for Unsōdō of Kyoto. Since the war he also developed his own distinctive style of ink-painting.

Literature: Fujikake, p. 88; Stephens, pp. 196–7; Merritt and Yamada, pp. 54–5; Katō, III, nos 25–7. Other prints by Shirō in the British Museum collection are reproduced in Smith (1), nos 79, 80, 82.

KAWACHI Seikō (b.1948)
Cat. 135–8

Kawachi was born in Uenohara in Yamanashi Prefecture. He graduated in 1973 from the Oil Painting Department of Tama Art University, but had already begun to experiment with prints as a result of the influence of the lively printmaking department there. He won the newcomer's prize at the Japanese Print Association Exhibition in 1970. From graduation up to 1985 he taught at his old university, at which time he went on a Monbushō (Ministry of Education) Scholarship to Columbia University, New York, Graduate School, followed by travel in Europe in 1986. In 1976 he had won the Grand Prix at the Japanese Print Association Exhibition and from then on worked mainly in woodblock, having experimented until then with silk screen, lithograph and even collages. His mature style has been semi-abstract, almost always on dark backgrounds, with constant reference to mechanical stress. He has periodically tried other forms of subject-matter but always so far returned to his basic themes. He has developed a potent combination of straightforward woodblock ('anastatic' to use his word) with engraved blocks ('intaglio'). Some of his compositions have been very large and in series of sheets. Until around 1982/3 he used the name Kawachi Shigeyuki.

Literature: Seikō Kawachi – the Graphic Work, 1968–87; Seikō Kawachi – Graphic Works, 1988–91. Other prints by Kawachi in the British Museum's collection are reproduced in Smith (1), nos 126–7, Smith (2), no. 19, and Smith, Harris and Clark, no. 249.

KAWANISHI Hide (1894–1965)
Cat. 20–1

Kawanishi was born in the city of Kobe, where he lived all his life and which was the main subject of his work, especially its cosmopolitan life as an international port. He taught himself woodblock printing after seeing a print by Yamamoto Kanae and worked in a post office rather than the family business so he could spend more time on his art. He worked from the beginning in a very colourful style with flat, simplified shapes which has its origin in the Art Deco poster style of the 1920s. He exhibited from 1923 with the Sōsaku Hanga Kyōkai (Creative Print Association). He was a prolific artist, producing some 1,000 sheets, including a number of series. Among the most important of these were *Shōwa Bijin Fūzoku Jūnitai* ('Twelve Popular Beauties of the Shōwa Era', 1929), *Kōbe Jūnikagetsu Fūkei* ('Views of Kobe in the Twelve Months', 1931), *Kōbe Hyakkei* ('One Hundred Views of Kōbe', 1933–5) and *Shin Kōbe Hyakkei* ('One Hundred New Views of Kōbe', 1953). He also produced a number of printed albums and books. In spite of his individuality Kawanishi remained closely associated with the *Sōsaku Hanga* movement and contributed to several of its magazines, to 'One Hundred New Views of Japan', to the first three collections of the Ichimoku-kai (1944, 1946, 1947) and to the post-war portfolios *Nihon Minzoku Zufu* and *Nihon Jozoku-sen* (both 1946). His son Kawanishi Yūzaburō (b.1923) works much in his father's style but with more international subjects.

Literature: Onchi (2), pp. 17; Merritt, pp. 230–2; Merritt and Yamada, p. 61; Kanagawa Prefectural Museum of Modern Art (2); Statler (1), pp. 114–18; Sekino (1), pp. 125–32; *Kawakami Sumio Zenshū*; Kawakami.

KAWASE Hasui (1883–1957)
Cat. 38–9, 49

Hasui was born as Kawase Bunjirō in Tokyo. His father ran a silk-braid business and his mother was the sister of the comic writer Kanagaki Rōbun (1829–1884) whose connections with Kabuki theatre were deep (see Clark, nos 33, 78, 79, 93); Hasui always retained theatre connections and designed actor portraits for the magazine *Engei Shashinchō* in the 1920s and stage sets later in his life. Because of delicate health, which affected him all his life, he spent much time as a boy in the hot-spring resort of Shiobara (Cat.49) where his aunt lived; his love of the Japanese landscape, and especially of scenes of snow, rain and mist, was born in those years. He received help in studying painting in 1897 from Aoyanagi Bokusen and in 1902 from Araki Kan'yū but was not able to take up art full time until 1908, when his father's business was transferred to a relative. In 1907 he began studying Western-style art, especially landscape, at the Hakuba-kai (White Horse Society) and took guidance from Okada Saburōsuke (1869–1939); subsequently in 1910 he became a pupil of Kaburagi Kiyokata who gave him the art name Hasui, though the greatest influence on his style and palette was the *Nihonga* painter Imamura Shikō (1880–1916). At this time he earned his living through designing *sashi-e*, magazine illustrations, posters and patterns for sashes. Through Kiyokata he became known to Watanabe Shōzaburō, who published his first landscape prints in 1918–19. These in turn were first inspired by 'Eight Views of Ōmi' by his fellow-pupil Shinsui, which had aroused Hasui's interest in single-sheet prints (Cat. 33 and 34). From then on Hasui worked very extensively as a designer of landscape prints for Watanabe, and from almost the beginning inspired the carvers and printers to produce newer and subtler efforts, especially in the expression of snow. These are evident in his series *Tōkyō Jūni-dai* ('Twelve Tokyo Subjects', 1919–21). After the 1923 earthquake, when he lost his house and his sketchbooks, he was financed by Watanabe to go on a sketching trip to produce more series, and also worked occasionally for other publishers to eke out his income. He was strongly represented in both the Toledo exhibitions (Blair (1) and (2)). During the Pacific War he spent much time back in Shiobara. After the war he was used by the Government to represent a gentler side of Japan in tourist publications, and in 1953 his *Zōjōji in Snow* was commissioned as an 'Intangible Cultural Asset' to represent the co-operative skills of the traditional print method. During his career he produced over 600 landscape prints, including seventeen series, covering most areas of Japan, which he constantly travelled. After a period of eclipse following his death, he has now become recognised as Japan's best print landscapist since Hiroshige.

Literature: Merritt and Yamada, p. 47, and listings of all his known prints; Narazaki; Yamanashi Prefectural Museum of Art; Merritt, pp. 54–6; Paechter, pp. 45–80; Kawakita (3); Stephens, pp. 139–52.

KIDA Yasuhiko (b.1944)
Cat. 75

Kida was born in Kyoto, which has usually been his home and the inspiration of much of his work. He graduated in 1967 from the Design Department of Kyoto National University of Education and mastered in 1970 from Kyoto City University of Arts. The same year he began exhibiting and organised *The Festivals of the Prefectures* at the Osaka Expo. From 1975 he has worked as a freelance print artist in Kyoto. His work was strongly influenced as a young man by Munakata, but he never received instruction from him. As a result Kida has tended to work in monochrome or simple colours, and sometimes on a large scale – for example, on sets of prints which can be mounted as folding screens. His themes have been largely restricted to Japanese folk festivals, temples and shrines, and the events associated with them.

Literature: Kida; Seibu Art Forum. Another print by Kida in the collection of the British Museum (*Nebuta Festival I*) is reproduced in Smith (2), no. 23.

KITANO Tsunetomi (1880–1947)
Cat. 55

Tsunetomi ended his life well known as a painter in the *Nihonga* style, but his original training was in the business of woodblock printing. Born in Kanazawa, he went to Osaka in 1892 and was apprenticed to Nishida Suketarō, who was a preparer of *hanshita-e*, the final drawings used when cutting the blocks for woodblock prints. He also studied *Nanga*-style painting, sculpture and woodblock carving under various teachers before joining the carving section of the *Hokkoku Shinpō* newspaper in 1897, where he was able to study newspaper illustrations; but he soon returned to Osaka to study painting under Inano Toshitsune, a minor artist who was in a line from the *Ukiyo-e* school. From him he adopted the 'Tsune' element in his art name, and absorbed a style of painting beautiful women which was a transition between *Ukiyo-e* and *Nihonga*. Inano made him work as a woodblock cutter. He published the first of his illustrations for serialised novels in an Osaka journal. While earning his living in this way, he continued to paint and first exhibited in the government-sponsored Bunten show in 1910. In 1912 he helped set up the Taishō Art Society devoted to the encouragement of child artists and in 1915 the

Osaka Art Society, at which he became a regular exhibitor. In 1917 he was elected to the Japan Art Institute, and thereafter remained a regular exhibitor at offical exhibitions. In 1934 he was invited to contribute wall-paintings to the Shōtoku Memorial Painting Hall in the Meiji Shrine, Tokyo.

Tsunetomi's subject-matter was usually beautiful women from the world of entertainment and fashion in the Osaka area, and his work is important as a record of that way of life. Many of his paintings are rescued from the common sentimentality of the period by a gritty edginess which is not unlike the early prints of Itō Shinsui (q.v.). He designed few sheet-prints, and all of them seem to have been adapted from earlier paintings. His best-known print is *Sagimusume* ('Heron Maiden'), published in 1925. Tsunetomi was an important figure in Osaka art circles, teaching many pupils, including the painter and print designer Shima Seien (1892–1970).

Literature: Baba; Stephens, pp. 132–3; Kawakita (3), p. 120; Maria Shobō, pp. 212. Another print by Tsunetomi from the British Museum collections (*Before the Mirror*) is reproduced in Smith, Clark and Harris, no. 236.

KITAOKA Fumio (b.1918)
Cat. 109

Born in Tokyo in 1918, Kitaoka studied from 1936 to 1941 with Fujishima Takeji (1867–1943) in the Western oil-painting course at Tokyo School of Fine Arts, but in his third and fourth years also learned woodblock printing in the classes given by Hiratsuka (q.v.). In 1945 he was sent to Manchuria to work with the Japanese government's North-east Asia Culture Development Society, returning after the surrender with his wife and daughter through Communist-dominated territory. Here he learned about contemporary social-realist Chinese prints in monochrome, and on his return to Japan published a portfolio *Sōkokue no tabi* ('Repatriation', 1947) influenced by them (a set is in the British Museum collection). He virtually gave up painting when he began to sell prints to the occupying forces; this came about from his attending the weekly Ichimoku-kai meetings organised by Onchi (q.v.), which then included Americans. He studied wood-engraving at the Ecole Nationale des Beaux-Arts, Paris, in 1955–6, and taught in the USA in 1964–5.

Since the 1960s Kitaoka has settled down to working in larger formats on gentle, evocative Japanese landscape.

Literature: Merritt and Yamada, p. 16; Merritt, pp. 253–5, and ch. 12; Statler (1), pp. 152–3; *Kitaoka Fumio Mokuhanga Sakukin-shū*. Kitaoka's print *Pond in Autumn: Moss Garden* in the British Museum's collection is reproduced in colour in Smith (1), no. 108.

KOIZUMI Kishio (1893–1945)
Cat. 13

Koizumi was born in Shizuoka, the son of a specialist in calligraphy who commissioned woodblock-printed manuals; he learned the craft from his father's block-carver Horigoe Kan'ichi. In common with many *Sōsaku Hanga* artists he studied Western-style water-colour, in his case under Ishii Hakutei (q.v.) and Maruyama Banka (1867–1942), at the Nihon Suisaiga-kai (Japan Watercolour Institute) in Tokyo. The three founders of the Institute (Ishii Hakutei, Tobari Kōgan and Nakagawa Hiromitsu) were all woodblock printmakers also, and Koizumi was naturally led along that path, especially by Tobari Kōgan, whom he knew as a colleague in carving blocks for newspaper illustration. He was an early member of the Creative Print Association from 1919 and an activist in it and its successors. Like Tobari he was a practical carver of blocks and like him wrote a practical manual much used by other artists, *Mokuhanga no horikata to surikata* ('The method of carving and printing woodblock prints', 1924). He is best known for his series *Shōwa Dai Tōkyō Hyakkei Zue* ('One Hundred Views of Great Tokyo in the Shōwa Era') which he produced himself between 1928 and 1940. Although artistically interesting only in parts, the series is a detailed and nostalgic survey of pre-war Tokyo, including a poignant view of Frank Lloyd Wright's old Imperial Hotel (no. 83; a copy of this is in the British Museum's collection). Koizumi was influential on the *Sōsaku Hanga* movement through his manual and through carving and printing for other artists. He was forced to leave Tokyo by the Pacific War, and died in Saitama in 1945 before he could return.

Literature: Merritt and Yamada, p. 74 (and listing of *Shōwa Dai Tōkyō Hyakkei Zue* on pp. 249–52); Merritt, pp. 224–5; Katō, II, nos 67–72, reproduces six of his prints; biography on p. 276.

KŌSAKA Gajin (1877–1953)
Cat. 116

Kōsaka, like some other twentieth-century Japanese artists, changed direction late in life, emotionally released perhaps by the end of the Pacific War, and achieved a certain recognition, at least outside Japan itself. In the 1960 Chicago Exhibition (Statler (2)) he was reproduced prominently on the flyleaf of the catalogue. This reputation was achieved entirely on the basis of his monochrome prints done in a style partly Expressionistic and partly related to Japanese ink-painting and calligraphy.

Born in Kyoto, Kōsaka learned native-style painting from Kōno Bairei (1844–95) and Yamamoto Shunkyō (1871–1933). He moved to Tokyo in 1907 and studied Western-style painting at the Hakuba-kai and Taiheiyō-Gakai academies. In 1922 he began to exhibit

woodblocks at Creative Print Association shows. These were close to the normal style of the movement. In 1931 he became an adviser to the Ministry of Education on art teaching in schools. All his blocks and stock of prints were destroyed in the May 1945 air raids on Tokyo. Evacuating to Sendai in northern Honshu, he began to work in his successful late style which was appreciated by foreign connoisseurs. He had one-man exhibitions in Los Angeles (1950) and Paris (1952).

Literature: Merritt, pp. 248–50; Merritt and Yamada, p. 77; Smith, Harris and Clark, no. 241; Jenkins, pp. 70–1; Statler (2); Fujikake (1957), pp. 174–5.

KURIYAMA Shigeru (b.1912)
Cat. 17

Kuriyama changed his family name to Matsunaga in 1937 and worked mostly under that name, but in 1982 he had reverted to Kuriyama. He was born in Shizuoka where he worked as a teacher and as early as 1929 was a co-founder of Dōdosha, a local *Sōsaku Hanga* group. He began exhibiting with the Japanese Print Association from 1931 and came into contact with Onchi and Hiratsuka. He was a founder of the Shizuoka creative print magazine *Yukari* (1931–5) and of another magazine, *Kasuri*, devoted both to prints and to traditional dyeing techniques (1934–6). He became actively involved in the Folk Art Movement. He was in Manchuria and China from 1939 and was not repatriated until 1948. His works since his return have been based on folk art motifs and he has also used paper blocks.

Literature: Merritt and Yamada, p. 80.

KUROSAKI Akira (b.1937)
Cat. 131–2

Kurosaki's work became justly admired internationally in the later 1960s and 70s for his darkly reverberant colours, smooth technique and for his imaginative and disturbing semi-Surrealistic images. His prints since around 1980 have become darker and more purely abstract, with occasional forays into the semi-representational which have been generally considered less successful. His reputation was built especially on his earlier series 'The Holy Night', 'Allegory', 'Les Ténèbres Vermeilles', 'Closed Room' and 'Lost Paradise'. He is technically unusual in that he has combined the attitudes of a modern independent artist with a reversion to the traditional use of a skilled craftsman who co-operates with him on the cutting of blocks and on most of the printing. This has allowed him to lead an actively international career while maintaining a good flow of original work.

Kurosaki was born in Japanese-occupied Manchuria. In his youth he was interested in *Ukiyo-e* prints. He graduated in 1962 from the

Kyoto College of Crafts and Textiles and lectured from 1963 to 1969 in the Department of Architecture, Kinki University. From 1970 to 1981 he was Associate Professor at his original College. From 1973 to 1974 he studied in the West under a scholarship from the Japanese Government (Agency for Cultural Affairs), and in 1978 was a guest lecturer at Washington University, Seattle. Since that time he has travelled widely and frequently taken Visiting Lecturer and Professor posts in the West. He has exhibited and travelled extensively in the West, where the concentrated power and originality of his work have been much admired. He now teaches at Kyoto Seika University College of Fine Arts in the Department of Printmaking in the city where he has been based since his student days. He has written much on the history of printmaking seen from both the technical and the international point of view, and has had many pupils in the woodblock technique. He is particularly interested in the history of paper-making.

Literature: Kurosaki; Petit, 1, pp. 194–5; Shirota. Another print by Kurosaki in the British Museum collection (*Between Moments 1*) is reproduced in Smith (2), no. 30.

KUSAKA Kenji (b.1936)

Cat. 129

Kusaka was born in the country in Tsuyama in Okayama Prefecture. He studied woodblock printing for five years with Nagare Kōji (b.1905), a member of the Nihon Hanga-in (Japanese Print Institute), who taught in Okayama. He moved to Tokyo and by 1964 was producing the first of his continuing series called simply 'Work', which began with some reference to identifiable objects but quickly became larger, simpler in colour, more abstract and full of movement. Some later works are titled, especially those concerned with his favourite concept of the horizon. In his smooth technique and confident abstraction he resembles others of the first post-war generation of woodblock artists such as Kurosaki, Amano Kazumi and Amano Kunihiro.

Literature: Gendai Hanga, p. 56; Merritt and Yamada, p. 83; Petit, 1, pp. 202–3; Hasegawa, pp. 86–7; *Kusaka Kenji Mokuhanga Sakuhin-shū.*

MABUCHI Tōru (b.1920)

Cat. 119

Mabuchi was born in Tokyo, the son of Mabuchi Rokutarō, a wood-engraver and later commercial artist who was a pioneer in the airbrush technique. Unusually for those days he encouraged his son to be an artist and taught him early about woodblock techniques. He attended the design course at the Tokyo University of Fine Arts but kept up work in prints and attended Hiratsuka's course there. He graduated in 1941 and spent the Pacific War in the Imperial Guard in Tokyo. After the

war he took over his father's business, which gave him the security to develop his intricate print technique. He became a member of the Japanese Print Association in 1954, and was publicised by inclusion in Statler's *Modern Japanese Prints: An Art Reborn* (1956). By this time he had developed a unique way of printing which is close to Pointillisme. He cuts up very thin wood into small pieces which he then glues to his block in a mosaic-like pattern. A large number of these may go to make one print. His production is therefore rather small. His early themes were landscape but now are mainly still life and the prehistoric *haniwa* pottery figures of Japan. He often writes his given name as Thoru in Roman.

Literature: Statler (1); Merritt and Yamada, p. 82.

MAEDA Masao (1904–74)

Cat. 22

Maeda was born in Hakodate, island of Hokkaido, and met Hiratsuka there in 1923. He moved to Tokyo in 1925 and joined the private Kawabata Painting School, moving on to study Western-style painting more thoroughly with Umehara Ryūzaburō (1888–1986), who knew Hiratsuka. At first he painted in oils, but by associating with Hiratsuka in the so-called Yoyogi Group and in the Kokuga-kai (National Painting Association) he learned woodblock techniques and began to make and exhibit prints in the 1930s. In 1940 he turned exclusively to prints. He was a member of Onchi's Ichimoku-kai (First Thursday Society). He contributed to 'One Hundred New Views of Japan' (1940), the two *Kitsutsuki Hanga-shū* collections (1942–3) and nos 3–6 of the *Ichimoku-shū* collections (1947–50), as well as *Tōkyō Kaikō Zue* (1945) and *Nihon Minzoku Zufu* (1946). He was publicised by Statler in *Modern Japanese Prints: An Art Reborn* (1956) where his date of birth is given as 1906. A typical *Sōsaku Hanga* group artist in many ways, Maeda nevertheless showed untypically the influence of *Nihonga* native-style painting. He also produced fine mountain scenes a little in the vein of Azechi (q.v.)

Literature: Sekino (3); Statler (1), pp. 131–3; Merritt and Yamada, pp. 82–3; Katō, 11, nos 175–84 and p. 280.

MAEDA Tōshirō (1904–90)

Cat. 18, 96

Maeda was born in Akashi City, Hyōgo Prefecture, and attended Kobe High School of Trade and Industry, where in 1924 he first formed a group to study oil-painting. According to Onchi (2), he worked only in linocut, but in fact he also worked in woodblock from the beginning of his print career, learning directly from Hiratsuka's book *Hanga no Gihō* during his time in the Imperial Army. While working as a commercial artist he participated in a number

of print groups in the Osaka area. He first exhibited with the Shunyō-kai in 1929 and became a member of the Japanese Print Association in 1932. In that year he first began to experiment with photographic transfers on to prints. He contributed to 'One Hundred New Views of Japan' in 1940 (Cat. 18) and spent most of the Pacific War in China with the North-east Asia Culture Development Society. After the war he worked in more abstract styles influenced partly by Cubism, using mainly linocuts with oil pigments which produced a characteristic palette and surface, and frequently exhibited in international exhibitions.

Literature: Merritt and Yamada, p. 87; Onchi (2), p. 12; Kanagawa Prefectural Museum of Modern Art (2); Maeda.

MAEKAWA Senpan (1888–1960)

Cat. 14, 83–5

Maekawa was one of the great personalities of twentieth-century Japanese prints, a man of notable independence, and a political radical, yet a staunch traditionalist and supporter of Japanese folk life and customs. In his career history he was rather typical, nevertheless, of his generation in the *Sōsaku Hanga* movement, working as a cartoonist and illustrator up to the Pacific War and participating in a succession of societies, exhibitions and coterie magazines. After the War he benefited from the new-found American enthusiasm for the movement's prints and by 1953 was able to devote himself entirely to them in generally larger formats.

Maekawa was born in Kyoto, the younger brother of a minor print-artist, Asaga Manjirō (1885–1965). He studied at the Kansai Bijutsuin from 1905, at first with Asai Chū (1856–1907), and moved to Tokyo in 1911 where he began his long career as a cartoonist on the magazine *Tokyo Puck*. In Tokyo he was inspired by Minami Kunzō (1883–1950) to take up self-carved woodblock printing, which he taught himself over a long period. He exhibited in the first Sōsaku Hanga Kyōkai exhibition in 1919 and was an active member of the Japanese Print Association from 1931 to 1960. He participated in many major group series, such as 'One Hundred New Views of Tokyo' (twelve prints) and 'One Hundred New Views of Japan', for part of which he was in charge of printing; and after the Pacific War in the three nostalgic portfolios (on Tokyo, folk customs and Japanese women) published by Fūgaku Shuppansha. His own major collections were the portfolio *Karuizawa* from *Nihon Fūkei Hanga* (1939), the five albums of *Yokusen fu* ('Hot Springs', 1944–59) and an extended series of small woodblock books called *Kanchū Kanbon* ('Leisure Time Leisure Books', 1945–60). He exhibited first abroad at the São Paolo Biennale in 1953. He achieved Western recognition through inclusion in Statler's *Modern Japanese Prints: An Art Reborn* (1956) and Michener's portfolio *The Modern Japanese Print. An Appreciation* (1962).

Literature: Merritt, pp. 218–22 and *passim.* Merritt and Yamada, p. 84; Statler (1), pp. 45–9; Kamon, Tozaka and Asahi, pp. 90–6, and colour reproductions of all his contributions to 'One Hundred New Views of Tokyo'; Sekino (1), pp. 49–56; Katō, 11, pls 41–9 (good colour reproductions of a selection of his prints); Michener, pp. 20–2.

MAKI Haku (b.1924)

Cat. 107–8

The artist uses this assumed name; his real name is Maejima Tadaaki. He was born in Asomachi, by Lake Kasumigaura in Ibaragi Prefecture, where he lived until around 1977, after which he moved to Ayase in Kanagawa Prefecture. He went to an ordinary school and had no formal art education. After the Pacific War he went to Tokyo and learned about prints at the Ichimoku-kai (First Thursday Society) meetings organised by Onchi (q.v.) but was too junior to contribute to its portfolios. He became a member of the Japanese Print Association in 1958 (first exhibited 1957) and exhibited with the College Women's Association of Japan annual show from 1970. In 1969 he produced woodblocks for the series *Matsuri to Shū* ('Festive Wine') based on old Japanese poems (Gallery Issai). His earlier prints are very much in the tradition of Onchi, whose youngest pupil he was, but in the early 1960s he began to experiment with embossing, the building up of textures on the block with concrete, and the use of oil-based pigments. His subjects turned increasingly to the shapes of Chinese characters, and later to deeply embossed prints reproducing the textures and shapes of teabowls. A man of very independent spirit, he has remained devoted to large editions at low prices available to ordinary people, in spite of the celebrity achieved by being selected for James Michener's portfolio *The Modern Japanese Print. An Appreciation* (1962).

Literature: Petit and Arboleda, pp. 62–9; Petit, I, pp. 210–11; Hasegawa, pp. 206–7; Michener, pp. 52–4; Brannen and Elliott.

MATSUBARA Naoko (b.1937)

Cat. 74

Matsubara left Japan for the USA in 1961 and has lived in the West ever since, though frequently revisiting her native country. Unlike most *émigré* Japanese artists, she has resolutely refused to become internationalised, and her technique and style remain close to those she developed as a young woman under the inspiration of Munakata Shikō whom she met after graduating. As a member of the Bangain founded by him, she came into contact with many of his pupils or associates, and in 1963 won his prestigious Kegon Prize at the annual group exhibition.

Matsubara was born in Tokushima Prefecture, Shikoku, daughter of a Shintō priest who eventually became chief priest of the Kenkun Jinja, Kyoto, a shrine which became a subject of her prints. The family moved to Kyoto in 1941, and she graduated in 1960 from the Design Department of Kyoto University of Applied Arts (Kyoto Geijutsu Daigaku). Already keen to work in the West, she studied for two years at the School of Fine Arts, Carnegie Institute of Technology, Pittsburgh, and for a year at the Royal College of Art, London. From 1962 onwards she held one-woman shows almost annually in North America and sometimes in Europe and Japan. Her first major series was 'Half Tame' in 1964, illustrating poems by Roger Shattuck, the first of many series and portfolios on literary themes both Western and East Asian. She taught at the Pratt Graphic Art Center, New York, from 1965 to 1966. Her position in the history of Japanese woodblock prints was recognised in the exhibition *Mokuhan: Woodcuts by Munakata and Matsubara* (Art Gallery of Great Victoria) in 1976. Her works vary from small portfolio items to very large woodblocks, almost all in black and white or one or more subdued colours, but all show a characteristic energy of design and cutting. Since 1974 she has lived in Ontario, Canada. Her portfolios, apart from 'Walden', include 'Matsubara Naoko's Kyoto', 1970.

Literature: Stanley-Baker; Matsubara; Merritt and Yamada, p. 86.

MATSUMOTO Akira (b.1936)

Cat. 134

Matsumoto, like Hagiwara (q.v.), obtained an early training in woodblock prints at artisan level from his relation Mitsumoto Ka'ichi, with whom he worked in his native Osaka from 1952 to 1957. In the latter year he moved to Tokyo where he worked for the great *Ukiyo-e* publisher Watanabe Shōzaburō from 1958 to 1968, and then, after an illness, he began making his own prints, using woodblock, silk screen, lithograph and mixtures of these media. Between 1964 and 1969 he experimented with combining newsprint with woodblock. He exhibited widely in Japan and the West and won the first prize at Ljubljana in 1975. In 1975–6 he travelled in the West on a scholarship from the Japanese Government (Agency for Cultural Affairs). His works have tended to be done in series which plot changes in visual perception of the same subjects. In later years he has increasingly used photographic separations as the basis of his silk-screen images and has, with a few exceptions moved away from woodblock.

Literature: Hasegawa, pp. 208–9; Smith (2), p. 34; *Gendai Hanga*, p. 79; Merritt and Yamada, p. 87; Petit, 11, pp. 220–1.

MIKI Suizan (1887–1957)

Cat. 40

Little information is recorded of this *Nihonga* artist, who was born in Hyōgō Prefecture and studied under Takeuchi Seihō (1864–1942) in Kyoto. He exhibited at the usual government-sponsored *Nihonga* exhibitions, such as the Bunten and its successor the Teiten. In 1924 he designed two sets of woodblock prints published by Satō Shōtarō, one of six beauties and one of eight landscapes. All of these were included in the first Toledo Exhibition in 1930. According to Katō, he also produced a series of 'Eight Views of Snow Viewing' after the Pacific War.

Literature: Stephens, p. 159; Katō, III, p. 267; Merritt, pp. 86–7; Blair (1).

MIZUFUNE Rokushū (1912–81)

Cat. 120–1

Like many sculptors in the twentieth century, Mizufune was also attracted to drawing and to graphic art. Although best known in Japan as a sculptor, his distinctive post-war prints (from 1955 onwards) added something new to both technique and style in the woodblock print, and his palette is unmistakable. He was born in Kure in Hiroshima Prefecture and studied sculpture at the Tokyo School of Fine Arts, graduating in 1936. Like so many others there, his interest in printmaking was nurtured by attending the side-courses given by Hiratsuka Un'ichi (q.v.). Already influenced as a boy by Edvard Munch, he became a co-founder in 1932 of the 'proletarian' Shin Hanga Shūdan (New Print Group) which also included Ono Tadashige (q.v.). Ono's post-war prints, densely pigmented over a black ground, are evidently the major inspiration for Mizufune's own technique. After the Pacific War he worked as an art teacher in Yokohama while gaining a good reputation as a sculptor and winning those prizes in official exhibitions necessary for success in twentieth-century Japan. After 1955 he began to exhibit his prints more widely, including the influential Tokyo International Print Biennales from 1960. He spent the year 1961–2 in the USA, where he was resident artist at the Putney School at Marlboro College, Vermont, confirming the international tendencies of his work, though their underlying sentiment is typically Japanese in their sense of loneliness. The dating of his works is very difficult, as he often printed impressions at long intervals after cutting the blocks, changed the colours as he felt appropriate, and maintained a very consistent style over the years. He rarely added dates to any of his prints.

Literature: Statler (2); Petit, 11, pp. 54–5; Merritt, pp. 255–6; Merritt and Yamada, pp. 93–4; Johnson and Hilton, pp. 72–9.

MORI Yoshitoshi (1898–1992)

Cat. 68–71

Mori was born in Tokyo and brought up by an aunt who taught *nagauta*, the songs which originally accompanied the action of the Kabuki drama. He lived most of his life in the Nihonbashi district of central Tokyo, or nearby districts. The street life of the area became another theme of his prints. As a teenager he had to work because of family poverty but took an active interest in art, especially *Ukiyo-e* prints. He began studying painting with the *Shin Hanga* artist Yamakawa Shūhō (1898–1944). Shūhō's father, a textile artist, took him as a pupil in textile dyeing and design. He was drafted into the Imperial Army in 1918 to 1920 and served in Korea. On his return he continued to study painting and meet artists; by 1925 he had his own textile design and dyeing business and quickly became known for his kimono designs. In 1938 he heard a lecture by Yanagi Sōetsu at the recently opened Japanese Folk Museum and became very interested in the Folk Art Movement. He participated in the founding of a group to study dyeing arts called Moeki-gai. In 1940 he first met Serizawa Keisuke (q.v.) as well as Munakata and Sasajima Jihei (q.v.). During the Pacific War he joined Serizawa in studying Okinawan *bingata* (stencil-dyeing) techniques. After the War he began to exhibit his textiles as works of art and achieved much recognition inside Japan. From 1951 he began to experiment with stencil-dyed prints, and by 1957, encouraged into this direction by Yanagi Sōetsu, had achieved much national and international success. He exhibited regularly at the Nihon Bangain (Japan Print Academy), thus placing himself firmly in Munakata's camp. From 1957 he also began to exhibit abroad. From 1960 he considered himself a printmaker, which brought him into disagreement with the idealistic craftsman Serizawa. Mori, however, had always wished to be a pictorial artist. One of his prints was chosen for Michener's portfolio *The Modern Japanese Print. An Appreciation* in 1962 and further increased his Western reputation. From 1965 until 1982 he distanced himself from all art associations. Travels in Europe in 1970 made him more aware of his Japanese roots and led him to even more characteristically Japanese cultural subjects – for example, *Heike Monogatari* ('Tales of Heike'), a set of thirty-four prints published in 1973. This was followed in 1976 by *Genji Monogatari* ('The Tale of Genji', forty-nine prints). In 1981 he recovered his failing sight after an operation and continued to work up to his last year. His exhibition *Mori Yoshitoshi Kappa-ban* was held in Leiden in 1985 and brought him further fame.

Mori became through his prints one of the major figures of the Folk Art Movement. His subjects are dominated by popular Buddhism, the Kabuki theatre, Japanese legends and traditional urban life. He also experimented with woodblock, painting on glass and calligraphy.

Literature: Mori Yoshitoshi Kappa-ban: Mori Yoshitoshi Hanga Sakuhin-shū (this biography is based mainly on the facts listed by Matsuoka Haruo on pp. 14–23 of the above); Petit, II, pp. 62–3; Hasegawa, pp. 214–15. Another print by Mori in the collection of the British Museum (*Shibaraku*) is reproduced in colour in Smith (2), no. 41.

MOROZUMI Osamu (b. 1948)

Cat. 133

Morozumi was born in Nagano Prefecture and with Kawachi Seikō (q.v.) was the first of the generation born after the Pacific War to come to prominence in the woodblock medium. He originally studied sculpture at Tama Art University, but before graduating in 1972 he had won the newcomer's prize at the Japanese Print Association and the main prize at the Nichidō Print Grand Prix Exhibition (both 1972). He was guided by Fukita Fumiaki, Professor of Printmaking at Tama. He began to exhibit at foreign exhibitions in 1975. His work since the early 1970s has been restricted mainly to monochrome prints produced by his own unique technique of punching numerous indentations into the block with nails of various sizes. The light and shade effects thus achieved are perfectly suited to his forms, which are basically sculptural with a strong sense of mystery. The prints are numbered serially and have no titles.

Literature: Hasegawa, pp. 216–17; Petit and Arboleda. Other prints by Morozumi in the British Museum's collections are illustrated in Smith (1), nos 124–5.

MUNAKATA Shikō (1903–75)

Cat. 59–65

The dominant figure in Japanese twentieth-century prints, and much the most celebrated internationally, Munakata is also the most thoroughly documented, both in his own extensive writings and in numerous studies, exhibitions, biographies and collections. Nevertheless, information on his early years up to 1933 (when he began to write regularly) is surprisingly patchy. This account is of necessity very selective but is drawn mainly from Tokyo National Museum of Modern Art (2) (Chronology by Tsuchiya Etsurō) and *Munakata Shikō Hanga Zenshū*, XII, (an eighty-page chronology). Munakata was also very active as a poet, writer on art, painter in both Western and Japanese techniques, calligrapher and book designer, but it is for his vast output of prints that he is at present most remembered.

Munakata was born in Aomori in northern Honshu, the sixth of fifteen children of a forger of steel blades. Leaving school at thirteen, he joined the family business, and moved to a lawyer's office in the Aomori District Court at seventeen, which gave him time to sketch. In 1921 he first saw reproductions of Van Gogh's works, which remained arguably his greatest inspiration throughout his life, and began to teach himself oil-painting. He moved to Tokyo in 1924, and lived by various means including drawing educational charts while continuing to paint and unsuccessfully to submit oils to the Teiten (Imperial Exhibition) until 1928 when he was first selected. He became inspired by woodblock prints after seeing Kawakami Sumio's *Wind in Early Summer* at the Creative Print Association Exhibition, and by 1927 was experimenting with woodblocks. The following year he had his first prints accepted at the same exhibition and was introduced to Hiratsuka Un'ichi (q.v.) who gave him instruction and encouragement. In 1930 he married for love Akajiro Chiya, a local girl in Aomori, but they had to live apart for some years until he could afford suitable accommodation in Tokyo. In 1931 he had his first one-man show of prints in Tokyo.

Munakata began to write in *Han Geijutsu* magazine in 1932, which brought him into contact with Maekawa Senpan and the folk style. The next year he had a whole number of the magazine to himself. About this time he came to know writers and poets such as Yasuda Yojūrō and to design books for them. His first really characteristic black and white prints, *Nohi* ('Moorland Fires', 1935), were rapidly followed by *Kojiki* and *Bandafū*. His meeting in 1936 with the Folk Art Movement *guru* Yanagi Sōetsu and its great potters Hamada Shōji and Kawai Kanjirō confirmed his confidence, and on a long visit to Kawai's house that year he developed a Buddhist dimension to add to his already strong folk and Shintō interests and subject-matter. *Kegonpū* (1937, Cat. 59–60) was the first of his Buddhist series. In 1939 he had the first of many exhibitions at the Mingeikan (Folk Art Museum) in Tokyo, which has a major collection of his works, and at Yanagi's suggestion began to experiment with colouring from the back of the paper. From 1943 he began to use the term 'board picture', rather than the more usual 'printed picture' (both romanised as *hanga*).

Munakata worked throughout the Pacific War, apparently little affected by censorship or shortages. He evacuated to Tōyama Prefecture early in 1945. His house in Tokyo and almost all his blocks were destroyed in May, and he stayed on in Tōyama until 1951. After the war he continued to work with enormous energy, beginning with *In Praise of the Valley of the Bell* (Cat. 63, December 1945). This he exhibited in São Paolo in 1951, which marks the beginning of his subsequent international career. In 1952 he joined in establishing the Nihon Hangain, often called Bangain (Japanese Print Institute), which included Azechi Umetarō (Cat. 87–9) and Sasajima Kihei (Cat. 66). In 1952 he won a prize at Lugano, in 1955 the first prize for prints at the São Paolo Biennale, and in 1956 at the Venice Biennale. These made his reputation not only internationally but also at home, where he now became a celebrity and was subsequently heaped with honours culminating with the *Kunshō* (Order of Merit) in 1970. In 1961 he received the old Buddhist title of *Hokkyō* ('Bridge of the Law') and in 1962 of *Hōgan* ('Eye of the Law'). Meanwhile, his visits to the USA and Europe in 1959 to lecture and attend his exhibitions marked the beginning of his late international period, and were followed by many more. The prints of these years were colourful and joyous and no less prolific than in earlier years, triggered especially by his commission in 1963 to produce a *Tōkaidō* series (Cat. 64). In 1972 he visited India; in 1974 he was taken ill on his last trip to the USA and Canada and died the following year. The Munakata Memorial Museum in Aomori opened the day after his funeral. There is also a museum devoted to his prints in Kamakura, while large collections of his works are in the Tokyo National Museum of Modern Art, the Folk Art Museum, Tokyo, and the Ōhara Museum Complex in Kurashiki.

Munakata had no formal pupils, but his influence on style was considerable, especially on Azechi, Sasajima, Kanamori (Cat. 67) and on the younger generation artists Akiyama Iwao (b.1921), Kida Yasuhiko (Cat. 75) and Matsubara Naoko (Cat. 74). His pioneering of large-scale and multi-sheet compositions influenced even Mori (Cat. 68–71) and Watanabe (Cat. 72–3).

Literature: *Munakata Shikō Hanga Zenshū* (vol. XII includes a very full bibliography of writings on and by Munakata); Tokyo National Museum of Modern Art (2); Yanagi; Stanley-Baker; *Shashin Munakata Shikō*; Mizuo; Hayward Gallery. Other prints by Munakata in the British Museum collections are reproduced in Smith (1), no. 22, and Smith, Harris and Clark, no. 239.

MURAI Maçanari (b.1905)
Cat. 118

Murai is a Western-style painter and has always thought of himself as such. He has also chosen to be known by the French spelling of his given name, Maçanari, a result of five years in France (1929–34). He was born in Ogaki, Gifu Prefecture, and was intended by his father to go to Germany to study medicine. Instead he joined the Bunka Gakuin (Culture Institute) in Tokyo and studied painting under Arishima Ikuma and Ishii Hakutei (q.v.). In later years he continued to teach there. During his French stay he travelled in Europe and had paintings accepted in the Salon des Indépendants. In 1935, after his return to Tokyo, he helped form the Jiyū Bijutsu Kyōkai (Free Artists' Association) which favoured abstract painting. This was revived after the Pacific War, when abstract art had been strongly discouraged, but Maçanari soon left it to form the Modern Art Association. According to Petit, he took up prints in order to give cheaper presents of his work to his many pupils, but in fact his atti-

tude to prints very much resembles that of twentieth-century French artists who have seen the medium as a profitable way of making their work more accessible. Maçanari has used woodblock, lithograph and silk screen, all of them being amenable to his very clear abstractions based mostly on the human face. He does the basic carving or other preparation but leaves the printing to others. Since around 1960 his work has become dominated by monochrome and his abstractions simpler and more monumental. He has also worked in stained glass and ceramic decoration.

Literature: Merritt and Yamada, p. 98; Kozaki, pp. 179–80; *Gendai Hanga* p. 125; Petit, II, pp. 70–1; *Murai Masanari Sakuhin-shū*.

NATORI Shunsen (1886–1960)
Cat. 43

Shunsen was born in Yamanashi Prefecture but his family moved to Tokyo the following year. Contemporaries at his first school included the future *Nihonga*-style artists Kawabata Ryūshi (1885–1966), Okamoto Ippei (1886–1948) and Okumura Dogyū (1889–1989). From 1897 he learned painting from Kubota Beisen (1852–1906) and his successor Kinsen (1875–1954). He also studied with Hirafuku Hyakusui (q.v.) who had great influence on him and led him to join the Museikai, a society dedicated to greater realism in *Nihonga* painting. With Hyakusui, Ogawa Usen (1868–1938) and others he founded the Sango-kai (Coral Society) and in 1917 won a prize for his handscroll *The Stage* at the Japan Art Institute Exhibition. However, he had lost faith in his painting career and gave it up by 1919, concentrating on newspaper illustrations (which he had first taken up in 1907), cartoons and actor portraits. From 1909 he worked for some years as a pictorial journalist with the literary section of *Asahi Shinbun* newspaper; as a result he built up a reputation as a book illustrator in the late Meiji era and worked with major writers of the period, including Natsume Sōseki (1867–1916). His career as a designer of woodblock prints of Kabuki actors began in 1915 with his participation in the five volumes of *Shibai Shin Nigao-e*, to which he contributed thirty portraits and two cover subjects, and with several prints for Watanabe from 1916. In 1930 he was secretary of the Nihon Gekiga Kyōkai (Japanese Theatrical Painters' Association). From 1925 to 1929 his series of thirty-six 'Portraits of Actors in Various Roles' was published monthly by subscription by Watanabe, mainly in the West, and all of them were shown in the first Toledo Exhibition in 1930. In all he produced over eighty actor prints in sheet form, which are considered the best and most genuinely theatrical of the *Shin Hanga* movement. His last set, 'Portraits of Contemporary Actors in Contemporary Plays', was published as late as 1951–4, but his powers were failing and he finally took his own life in a double

suicide with his second wife, profoundly affected by the sudden death of his daughter in 1958.

Literature: Kawakita (3), p. 262; Merritt and Yamada, pp. 107–8, and lists of the main series; Blair (1) and (2); Fujikake, pp. 102–3; Stephens, pp. 161–4. *Hanga Geijutsu*, 19, pp. 186–95. Other prints by Shunsen in the collections of the British Museum are reproduced in Smith (1), nos 50–3.

NODA Kyūho (1879–1971)
Cat. 4

Noda was born in Tokyo and studied under the *Nihonga*-style painter Terazaki Kōgyō (1866–1919) and for a year from 1896 at the Tokyo School of Fine Arts. The latter gave him the sketching ability to earn his living as an illustrator for the Osaka *Asahi Shinbun* newspaper, which he joined in 1907. In Osaka he did book illustrations, including those for the novel *Kōfū* by Natsume Sōseki (1867–1916), and became a friend of Kitano Tsunetomi (q.v.). Here he was in contact with the publisher Kanao Tanejirō (Cat. 4) and became a leading light in the artistic life of the city. He returned to Tokyo in 1917. Later in his career he concentrated more and more on pure *Nihonga* painting, specialising in religious and historical subjects of China and Japan. After the Pacific War he continued to live in the Tokyo area and was highly regarded in official artistic circles in Japan.

Literature: Mitchell; Kawakita (3), pp. 270–1; Maria Shobō, p. 230; Johnson; Sakamoto.

ONCHI Kōshirō (1891–1955)
Cat. 27–30, 76–80

Onchi was the most important figure in the *Sōsaku Hanga* movement from 1918 until his death, outstanding as a print artist, and active as a poet, founder and editor of magazines, an author on the subject of prints, art and literature, a leader and organiser of societies and encourager of other artists; and in book design, which was his actual profession. He was also the most internationally conscious of all the print artists of the period, in spite of never going to the West and hardly ever leaving Japan.

Onchi was the son of Onchi Tetsuo, an official of the Imperial Court in charge of ceremonies and of the education of two young princes, which education the young Kōshirō partly shared. Tetsuo was a calligrapher and scholar of the Chinese language; Onchi Kōshirō's mother was a skilled *koto* player. From 1904 to 1909 he was at the German Co-operative Middle School, as he was intended to be a physician, the profession of his mother's family. Although he dropped out of High School, his knowledge of German gave him a special sympathy with German art, which was to have as a result a major effect on *Sōsaku Hanga*. In 1909 with the reluctant permission of his father he took up Western art studies at the Hakuba-kai (White Horse Society) and in the same year became a friend of Takehisa Yumeji (q.v.) who was a major lifelong influence. In 1910 he entered the Tokyo School of Fine Arts but soon dropped out, and by 1911 had secured his first book-designing commission. He rejoined in 1911 but was finally asked to leave in 1915 since he was unable to agree with his teachers. By then he had founded the print and poetry magazine *Tsukuhae* (1914–15) with Tanaka Kyōkichi and Fujimori Shizuo (q.v.) and was working in abstract styles. He married in 1916 (unusually not an arranged marriage). He was a founder-member of the Creative Print Association in 1918, the year he began to work regularly as a book designer. In his career he designed over 1,000 volumes, taking a special interest in Western typefaces and the calligraphy of Chinese characters. The income from this work allowed him to spend time on poetry, prints and the founding, editing and designing of numerous coterie magazines such as *Shi to Hanga* ('Poetry and Prints', 1922–?5) and *Kaze* ('Wind', 1927–30).

From 1928 he was a leading organiser of the series 'One Hundred New Views of Tokyo' and through the 1930s produced many landscape and figurative prints. In 1934 he published his first art book *Umi no Dōwa* ('Fairy Tales of the Sea') with all his own illustrations in woodblock and the revolutionary *Hikō Kannō* ('Sense of Flight') combining graphic techniques with photographs. He was also a leading organiser for the uncompleted 'One Hundred New Views of Japan' (1938–40). In 1939 he was sent to China as a war artist. His Ichimoku-kai (First Thursday Society), founded 1939) was virtually the only body which kept the Creative Print Movement alive in the later days of the Pacific War.

From 1945 Onchi emerged unequivocally as the leader of the movement and contributed to two of the group portfolios which re-established it (*Tōkyō Kaikō Zue*, 1945, and *Nihon Jozoku sen*, 1946). His friendship with the American William Hartnett led to the appreciation of his work and that of his pupils in the USA. He exhibited at the São Paolo Biennale in 1951 and became Chairman of the Kokusai Hanga Kyōkai (International Print Association). He continued to design books, but the last eight years of his life saw him reverting to pure abstract prints of larger size and increasingly effective colour. Onchi's influence on his younger associates of his later years was very strong, and they dominated printmaking in Japan for another generation (see Hiratsuka Un'ichi, Sekino Jun'ichirō, Yamaguchi Gen, Azechi Umetarō, Takahashi Rikio, Maki Haku, and Yoshida Masaji in this catalogue).

Literature: There is more abundant published information on Onchi than any other artist from this catalogue except Munakata, and the following are only the most important. Merritt, ch. 8 and *passim*; Merritt and Yamada, pp. 121–2; Swinton (who includes the best bio-graphical information in English, and the most complete bibliography); Fuji; Onchi (1) reproduces most of his sheet-prints (but only some in colour); Kamon, Tozaka and Asahi reproduce in colour his prints contributed to 'One Hundred New Views of Tokyo'; Onchi, Kunio (a moderately exhaustive account of his book designs); Statler (1), pp. 21–30. Other prints by Onchi in the British Museum's collections are reproduced in Smith (1), nos 14–19, 88a–b, 90; Smith, Harris and Clark, no. 240; Carey, p. 43. The items in *Japon des Avant Gardes* and Onchi (1) listed as collections of Mrs Evans or Robert Vergez are also now in the British Museum.

ONO Tadashige (1909–90)

Cat. 11, 90–2

Ono was born in Tokyo in a then poor district (now called Mukōjima), the eldest son of the keeper of a food and drink shop. He went to Waseda School of Arts and Crafts in 1921. In 1923 the family house was destroyed in the great Kantō earthquake. In 1924 he joined a water-colourists' society called the Tsutahara-kai and soon began to study under Okada Saburōsuke (1869–1939) at the Hongō Painting Institute. Finishing his formal studies at Waseda in 1927, he joined the family business while continuing to paint. In 1929 he exhibited at the Proletarian Art Exhibition in Tokyo and began making woodblock prints, mostly in small portfolios in monochrome, for example, *Shigaisen* ('Street Battles', 1933), heavily influenced by German Expressionism. In 1932 he was a co-founder of the Shin Hanga Shūdan (New Print Group) with Fujimaki Yoshio (1909–35) whose obsession with the Sumida River left a lasting mark on his works, and in 1937 the Zōkei Hanga Kyōkai (Plastic Print Association), but could not work with the Japanese Print Association because of political disagreements. In 1941 he formed his own publishing company, Sōrinsha, and began issuing books on the history of Japanese printmaking, most of them by himself. Isolated by the Pacific War, his fortunes reached their lowest point in 1945 with the death of his wife, the second destruction of the family house, a brief period of conscription, and departure to the country where he became a teacher in Tsuyama. Returning to Tokyo in 1946, he worked in a publisher's, while taking up colour printmaking more seriously and developing from about 1948 his own special technique known as *inkoku tashoku-zuri mokuhan* ('colour negative woodblock printing'). From that year he began exhibiting in the Japan Independent Exhibition and continued to do so up to 1983. From the mid-1950s he became better known, exhibiting at the Tokyo Print Biennale (1957), in the USSR (1961), and travelling widely in the West in 1961. He also taught at several art universities, including Tokyo, and exhibited regularly at the College Women's Association of Japan annual print shows.

Ono is now remembered historically as one of the driving forces behind the *Sōsaku Hanga* movement, though always a little peripheral to its mainstream, as proved by his being ignored by Statler (1) and Sekino. He was a major writer on Japanese graphics. His early proletarian works are derivative, but his later production of colour prints in his best period, *c.*1955–75, with their distinctively glowing palette, seems likely to earn him a place as a minor classic.

Literature: Ono (4) (includes a full bibliography of Ono's own writings); Kawakita (3); Kubo; Tazawa, p. 335; Merritt (1), pp. 232–4; Merritt and Yamada, pp. 123–4; Katō, 11, nos 232–9, has some fine reproductions. Ono's print *Flying* from the collections of the British Museum is reproduced in colour in Smith (2), no. 46.

SAITŌ Kiyoshi (b.1907)

Cat. 93–4

Saitō experienced a considerable vogue in the West in the 1950s and 60s, combining an identifiably Oriental aesthetic with clear European influences. This popularity, which in the 1970s began to decline, has obscured the significance of his work taken as a whole; this lies in his ability to use the tactile, grainy qualities of woodblock with complete conviction for non-abstract subjects. A man of some individuality, he was born in Fukushima Prefecture and moved as a child to the northern island of Hokkaido. He moved to Tokyo in 1932. He began studying oil-painting at the private Hongō Painting Institute. In Tokyo Petit records that he was surprised to find the woodblock prints he had been experimenting with were a well-established form which could be produced in editions and could use more than one block. In 1937 he joined Ono Tadashige's Zōkei Hanga Kyōkai (Plastic Print Association). Saitō's history is essentially that of the gradual self-education of a natural artist into at one stage a teacher of printmaking at Ann Arbor, Michigan (1956–7). This process involved some loss of spontaneity which affected his work after that period.

Saitō was self-taught but associated with other artists of the *Sōsaku Hanga* movement, had a print accepted for the Kokuga-kai exhibition in 1937, and began showing with the Japanese Print Association in 1942. Munch and Onchi were early influences. He contributed to the three nostalgic albums published by Fūgaku Shuppansha in 1945–6 as an expression of the good side of Japanese art led by the *Sōsaku Hanga* movement. In 1948 his work came to the attention of American connoisseurs at the Salon Printemps exhibition which had been organised to help print artists in the post-war difficulties. In 1951 he surprised the Japanese art world by taking the first prize (together with the etcher Komai Tetsurō) for a Japanese work at the first São Paolo Biennale. It was this event that first brought the modern school of Japanese prints to prominence and was rapidly followed by other successes. Saitō was featured in Statler's *Modern Japanese Prints: An Art Reborn* (1956) by which time he was already popular in the West. His early prints were of winter scenes in his native Aizu, but he moved on to figure subjects in a rather European style, and then on to Buddhist subjects and the buildings and culture of Kyoto, in which the influence of Mondrian is very strong, as well as studies of ancient pottery, of cats and of flowers. His work is varied and prolific and subject to many changes in technique.

Literature: Statler (1), pp. 53–61; Merritt, pp. 243–7; Petit, pp. 104–5; Hasegawa, pp. 98–9; *Hanga Geijutsu*, 12, pp. 61–72 (special feature).

SAKAMOTO Hanjirō (1882–1969)
Cat. 6

Sakamoto was born in Kurume (Fukuoka Prefecture) and went in 1902 with his contemporary Aoki Shigeru (1882–1911) from the same place to study Western-style painting and sketching in Tokyo. He collaboratd with Yamamoto Kanae and Ishii Tsuruzō on the seminal magazine *Hosun* (1907–11), and with Kanae on an experimental set of actor prints (*Sōga Butai Sugata*). He became celebrated as a painter in 1912 when his painting *Usurebi* was praised by the novelist Natsume Sōseki (1867–1916). His artistic range was expanded by his visit to France in 1921–4. Following this he returned to live in Kyushu, where he stayed for the rest of his life. He was equally skilled in oils in landscape, still life and in compositions of horses and the Nō drama, for which he is best known. Late in his career he was much honoured within Japan as a painter. His early work in prints is limited but influential.

Literature: Merritt and Yamada, p. 130; Tazawa, pp. 215–16; Miyagawa, p. 123; Katō, I, pls 59–78, reproduces a number of reprints of his woodblock prints in colour.

SAKAMOTO Yoshinobu (b. 1895)
Cat. 12

Sakamoto was born in Kubokawa in Kōchi Prefecture (Shikoku) and graduated as a teacher in 1917. After seven years' service he went to Tokyo to study at the Taiheiyō-Gakai (Pacific Painting Association) under Ishikawa Toraji (q.v.) who also came from Kōchi and was experimenting with woodblock printing about that time. He returned to Kōchi and became a drawing teacher. With the encouragement of a local patron, Admiral Yamauchi, he undertook from 1932 onwards the series 'Thirty Pictures of Tosa'. After the Pacific War he was visited in his atelier by various Westerners, and as a result ten sets of the series went abroad. Sakamoto also produced other landscapes and still lifes in the print medium. According to Merritt and Yamada (p. 131), he contributed to the *Han Geijutsu* issues nos 18–

20 on folk toys (1934). His date of death has not been established.

Literature: Sakamoto Yoshinobu Hanga-shū. Another print from 'Thirty Pictures of Tosa' is reproduced in Smith (1), no. 12, incorrectly attributed to Sakamoto Hanjirō.

SASAJIMA Kihei (1906–93)
Cat. 66

Sasajima was born in Mashiko, the village in which Hamada Shōji settled in 1924. He thus came early in life into contact with the Folk Art Movement, of which he was always a supporter. He was able to take a sketching course while training to be a teacher in Tokyo. From 1927 to 1945 he earned his living as a teacher, but found some time to study prints, notably in 1935 at a printing course given by Hiratsuka, who gave him his taste for monochrome work. In 1938 he was introduced by Hamada to Munakata, who became the major influence on his art; and in 1940 he also met Mori Yoshitoshi. That year he first exhibited at the Kokuga-kai exhibition. From 1945 he worked as a print artist, occasionally using colour but mostly in monochrome; he first became a member of the Nihon Hanga Kyōkai in 1948 but withdrew to join Munakata in founding the Nihon Hangain in 1952. He began to be noticed internationally first when represented at the exhibition of contemporary Japanese prints in Yugoslavia in 1957; secondly when Oliver Statler mentioned him in *Modern Japanese Prints: An Art Reborn* (1956) and published two of his prints; and thirdly from exhibiting in the Tokyo Biennales 1957–66. In 1959 he held a two-man show in Washington, DC, with Hashimoto Okiie. In 1959 he became ill and lacked the strength to rub the impression into the paper with the traditional *baren*. As a result, and inspired by stone-rubbing, he developed a new technique of forcing paper into a deep-cut block with a press and dabbing the raised areas with ink by use of pads. This produced works of three-dimensional quality which made his prints instantly recognisable. From 1962 he worked only on religious themes, including many explorations of Mount Fuji, the Sacred Mountain, and of the Buddhist Deity Fudō Myō-ō (cf. Cat. 69). His book of essays on art, *Itchin*, was published in 1967.

Literature: Petit, II, pp. 112–13, and nos 189–94; Statler (1), pp. 166–7, and nos 93, 94; Merritt and Yamada, p. 131; Katō, II, nos 292–6; Kawakita (1), p. 184, and pls 68, 69; Kawakita (3), p. 171.

SEIMIYA Naobumi (b. 1917)
Cat. 117

Seimiya was born in Tokyo, the son of Seimiya Hitoshi (1886–1969), a painter in the Western manner and a minor *Sōsaku Hanga* artist who was a founder-member in 1931 of the Japanese Print Association. The son also studied West-

ern-style painting at the Tokyo School of Fine Arts, graduating in 1941; while there he took an extra course in etching. He took up woodblock printmaking after the Pacific War and first exhibited (at the Shunyō-kai) in 1954. He participated in a few international exhibitions up to 1967 but on the whole was content to sell his works (from 1960) through the perceptive Nantenshi Gallery in Tokyo. Seimiya's works, although they use the grain of the wood in ways that recall Edvard Munch and other early European Expressionists, are made with extreme precision, and his editions are therefore small. Each of his prints also tends to be dominated by one austere colour. Little regarded abroad, his reputation in Japan seems likely to survive his own lifetime because of its contemplative intensity.

Literature: Gendai Hanga, pp. 28–9; Merritt and Yamada, p. 133.

SEKINO Jun'ichirō (1914–88)
Cat. 98–9

Sekino was in his youth one of the work-horses of the *Sōsaku Hanga* movement, especially through his association with Onchi Kōshirō (q.v.). After Onchi's death, he developed quickly as an artist in his own right and achieved some celebrity through his prints of the Kabuki and Bunraku theatres, his portraits of artistic personalities such as Onchi and Munakata, his *Fifty-three Stations of the Tōkaidō Road* and his views of traditional Japanese roofs. He also wrote much about the print world.

Sekino was born in Aomori City (northern Honshu) and was from his youth inspired by Munakata, who came from the same city. In his youth he took up etching, which was his first passion, followed by woodblock. From that early period he was interested in the Bunraku theatre. He exhibited with the Japanese Print Association from 1932. In 1936 he did the printing for an illustrated book by Takei Takeo, a supporting role he was to repeat in the woodblock world. In 1939 he moved to Tokyo and became a pupil of Onchi, living close to his house in Ogikubo. That year he joined Onchi in the Ichimoku-kai (First Thursday Society). His life during the Pacific War is characteristically little described, but according to Petit he was involved in arranging entertainments by Kabuki actors and Bunraku troupes. These provided subjects for his later work. After the war he participated in all the Ichimoku-kai sets and the three nostalgic woodblock sets (1945–6) on Tokyo, Japanese customs and Japanese women, as well as doing reprints for Onchi or contributing to illustrated books in both etching and woodblock. In 1950 he originated a society to study etching, which formally became the Japanese Etchers' Society in 1953. He began to exhibit internationally from 1955 and from that time worked more in woodblock than in etching. In 1958 he toured in the USA and taught at the Pratt Graphic Centre. Again in 1963 he taught at Oregon State University and Washington University, and made lithographs at the Tamarind Studio. His celebrated portrait of Munakata was produced in 1968; he taught in Oregon again in 1969. *Fifty-three Stations on the Tōkaidō Road* was first exhibited in 1972. He visited France and Spain in 1976 and China in 1979. His last great series was *Oku no Hosomichi* ('The Road to the Deep North', sixty prints, 1985).

Literature: Morobushi (1); Statler (1), pp. 63–9; Sekino (1) and (2); Petit, II, pp. 120–1; Hasegawa, pp. 126–7; Tōbū Department Store, Tokyo (with very full bibliography in Japanese); Kuwabara.

SERIZAWA Keisuke (1895–1984)
Cat. 58

Serizawa was not strictly a printmaker, except in the form of illustrated books, but through those publications in folk styles he had considerable influence on graphic art, especially on Munakata, Watanabe Sadao and Mori Yoshitoshi. He was born in Shizuoka and graduated in 1917 from the Design Section at the Tokyo High School of Industry (Tōkyō Kōtō Kōgyō Gakkō). While working as a designer, he studied the techniques of dyeing. He was an early adherent of Yanagi Sōetsu and the Folk Art Movement. He made a special study of the Okinawan stencil-dyeing method called *bingata* and the Edo-period stencil technique of *komon* ('small patterns'). From these he developed his own more self-conscious style. Following the publication in 1937 of *Ehon Don Kihōte* (Cat. 58) his main field became stencil-dyed books of which the grandest was *Hōnen Shōnin Eden* ('Pictorial Legends of the Saint Hōnen', 1941). In 1940 he was visited by Mori Yoshitoshi (q.v.) with whom he had a lively subsequent association, and in the following year he was introduced to the group of young dyeing craftsmen called Moegi-kai, which included Watanabe Sadao. After the Pacific War recognition of his skills developed quickly, and in 1957 they were recognised by the Japanese Government as 'Intangible Cultural Assets'. In 1962 he had a celebrated dispute with Mori Yoshitoshi about whether craft and art are the same. In 1962 he was asked to design two panels for the rebuilding of the Imperial Palace. In 1977 he received the Award of Cultural Merit and in the same year had a major exhibition in Paris. In 1981 the Serizawa Keisuke Art Museum was opened in his native Shizuoka, which includes not only his books but many textile designs and his collection of folk art. Later in his career he taught at Tama University and the Women's Art University.

Literature: Serizawa Keisuke-ten; *Gendai Meikō Shokunin Jinmei Jiten*, pp. 268–9; *Serizawa Keisuke Zenshū*.

SHINAGAWA Takumi (b.1908)
Cat. 95

Shinagawa was born in Niigata Prefecture, the son-in-law of a traditional Buddhist sculptor, and has always remained interested in sculptural work. He originally studied metalwork and many other crafts at Tokyo City Craft School but got interested in *Shin Zōkeishugi* (New Formative) painting and printmaking, and became a pupil of Onchi to whom he went for advice and who encouraged him to make prints. In spite of a great personal interest in *Ukiyo-e*, he always worked in international styles and was particularly influenced by Picasso and Gauguin. In 1947 he contributed to the Ichimoku-kai print collection, and again in 1949 and 1950. His prints during this period are very similar to Onchi's late works.

Shinagawa achieved some Western celebrity by being included in Statler's *Modern Japanese Prints: An Art Reborn* (1956) and Michener's portfolio *The Modern Japanese Print. An Appreciation* (1962). He has been a restless experimenter in both style and technique, and his output is extremely varied. Many of his later prints are done partly or entirely by paper block.

Like many other *Sōsaku Hanga* artists he earned his living partly as a teacher in art colleges and partly as a commercial artist. He has worked not only on prints but also on photography, sculpture 'objets', colour photograms, posters and mobiles, which were published in book form by Bijutsu Shuppansha and Nichibō Shuppan in the 1970s.

Literature: Statler (1), pp. 71–8; Hasegawa, pp. 112–13; Blakemore, pp. 182–3; Merritt and Yamada, pp. 136–7.

SUWA Kanenori (1897–1932)
Cat. 9

Like Henmi Takashi, he was typical of the robust amateur spirit of the *Sōsaku Hanga* movement in its early days and the co-operative atmosphere among its members which brought out the best of a minor talent. Born, possibly in Kagoshima, his parents both died early and he spent his youth in Kobe, and began making prints from the age of sixteen. At seventeen (1914) he moved to Tokyo and entered the Hongō Painting Institute. He went on sketching tours in Japan in 1916–19 and from 1920 contributed prints to the magazine *Yomigaeri*, which brought him the admiration of Hiratsuka and to the notice of Fukazawa Sakuichi whom he helped with his woodblock technique. He first exhibited with the Sōsaku Hanga Kyōkai in 1921, and published a collection of his own prints in 1923 (*Suwa Kanenori Surie Awase*). The following year he participated in an exhibition of seventeen *Sōsaku Hanga* artists which also showed works by Bernard Leach, Käthe Kollwitz, Paul Klee, Marc Chagall, Wassily Kandinsky and Honoré Daumier. In June 1921 he joined the Shiseidō

Company and from 1928 participated in 'One Hundred New Views of Tokyo', contributing twelve prints, notable for their spiky, stark quality. He was also a contributor to international exhibitions and was particularly interested in the internationalisation of Japanese art. He continued to paint in water-colour throughout his career. He was becoming increasingly active in the Japanese print world when his life was ended suddenly by appendicitis.

Literature: Merritt and Yamada, p. 139; Kamon, Tozaka and Asahi, pp. 60–4; and reproductions there of all his contributions to 'One Hundred New Views of Tokyo'.

TAJIMA Hiroyuki (1911–84)
Cat. 127–8

Born in Tokyo, Tajima graduated from Nippon University (1932) and in 1934 from the Tokyo School of Fine Arts (Western Painting Faculty). He took a wide interest in many aspects of art, including textile dyeing (under Hirakawa Matsugorō) and printmaking under Nagase Yoshiro (1891–1978), one of the earliest *Sōsaku Hanga* artists. He began his career as a print artist in 1946 but gave it up temporarily in the 1950s to write. In the 1960s and 70s he developed his typical densely pigmented abstract style, which, however, was based on the ideals of East Asian calligraphy, traditional Japanese painting structure, and a sense of space derived partly from his Zen Buddhist beliefs. His abstract prints typically have complex surfaces achieved by building up the block with various materials such as crumpled paper. At this time he also made a living from producing more popular landscape prints under the name of Nagai Kiyoshi. In 1969 he began making prints on canvas using much the same techniques, but soon abandoned this. His prints were particularly promoted by the Red Lantern Shop in Kyoto and most of them can be found illustrated in their periodic English-language catalogues.

Literature: Merritt and Yamada, p. 44; Petit, II, pp. 134–5; Hasegawa, p. 135; Robertson. Other prints by Tajima in the British Museum collection are illustrated in Smith (1), nos 104 and 105.

TAKAHASHI Rikio (b.1917)
Cat. 114–15

Takahashi was born in Tokyo. His father was a *Nihonga* painter, and his uncle was Imaizumi Toshiji, a *Yōga* (Western style) artist, from whom he first learned art. He failed to graduate from middle school and quotes his artistic education as having taken place at the California Institute of Art in the 1960s, when he spent two years in the USA (1962–3). By then, however, he had studied informally for six years (1949–55) with Onchi Kōshirō (q.v.). His early works are very close to Onchi's late abstract style, with much use of heavily grained driftwood and strongly contrasted colours. Gradually his printing became smoother, his prints very large, and his colours more internally harmonious. His works have been inspired mostly by Kyoto gardens and locations, and are in a sense almost calligraphic reworkings of a few themes in a semi-abstract style. Takahashi has exhibited with the Japanese Print Association since 1950, and since the mid-1960s with the College Women's Association of Japan annual show. After his USA visit he had many one-man shows in that country and became popular in the West. He also worked in photographs.

Literature: Petit, II, pp. 148–9; Merritt and Yamada, pp. 143; Kawakita (1), pp. 38 and 186. Other prints by Takahashi in the British Museum collections are reproduced in Smith (1), nos 98–9.

TAKEHISA Yumeji (1884–1934)

Cat. 52–4

Yumeji was born in Okayama Prefecture, the son of a saké wholesaler; in 1900 the family moved to Fukuoka, where he worked briefly for a brush-maker and learned the art of line which was always to be the basis of his art. In 1901 he was sent to Tokyo to learn business, but by 1905 he gave up his studies to be an artist. He took up with a socialist group and did illustrations for the left-wing magazine *Hikari* and the newspaper *Heimin Shinbun*. This was closed down in 1907 by the authorities, and Yumeji began to retreat from active political comment, though remaining throughout his life a sympathiser with the oppressed and with some aspects of Christianity.

In 1907 Yumeji married Kishi Tamaki, who ran a postcard shop in Tokyo. Thereafter he did much design for postcards and other ephemera. Their relationship was extremely turbulent from the start and soon ended in divorce, though they remained attracted to each other and continued to work together. In 1909 his first book of sketches and poems was published (*Yumeji Gashū – Haru no Maki*), followed by many others, which were intended and accepted as a new sort of *Ukiyo-e*. The large-eyed, thin, sad beauties he created, based on Tamaki and on subsequent mistresses, became the standard romantic image for his generation. This style was heavily influenced by German *Jugendstil* in which Yumeji was keenly interested. His celebrated book of poetry *Dontaku* ('Holiday') came out in 1913, with book design by Onchi Kōshirō who had become a friend. It included the poem *Yoimachi-gusa* which was set to music in 1918 and became a big national success.

Between 1914 and 1916 Tamaki and Yumeji founded and ran the Minato-ya shop in Tokyo which sold sheet-prints (the only ones he designed as such) and all sorts of paper goods for which he acted as designer. In 1914 also he met Kasai Hikono, who became his

mistress, but who died early and tragically in 1920 aged twenty-four. From 1916, Minato-ya having failed mainly because of his lack of business sense, Yumeji began to design covers for sheet music, which eventually reached some 270 items. In 1919, after Hikono had gone into hospital, he met the third great female model in his life, Oyo, but this relationship too ended in 1925. In the decade 1920–30 he constantly travelled to hot-spring resorts and continued to paint and to design. His most celebrated paintings included the series *Naga-saki Jūnikei* ('Twelve Views of Nagasaki', 1920) and *Onna Jūdai* ('Twelve Female Subjects', 1921). These were water-colours, but he also worked in oils, brush and ink and *Nihonga* techniques.

Although he designed few sheet-prints, Yumeji was very influential on Japanese graphics, illustration and popular literature from 1909 onwards, when he published his first collection. His melancholic, poetic view of life, his ideals of the independence of the artist, and his own Bohemian and tragic lifestyle endeared him to many of his generation, including rather surprisingly Onchi Kōshirō; and his effects on both *Shin Hanga* and *Sōsaku Hanga* were considerable, as well as on graphic design and literary illustration in general. Having passed out of popularity by 1940, his reputation began to make a dramatic come-back in the 1970s, going hand in hand with renewed interest in the Taishō era of which he is now considered the representative figure.

Literature: Merritt, pp. 22–31; Yutaka; Takehisa Yumeji Ikaho Kinenkan; Kawai Bijutsu Kenkyūjo; Katō, III, pls 127–46; Swinton, pp. 15–19; Ogura (1).

TANINAKA Yasunori (1897–1946)

Cat. 19

Born in Nara Prefecture, Yasunori's mother died in 1903, and the following year his father moved to Korea and opened a food store in Kyŏngju. He was educated in Tokyo from 1915 to 1918 at a Buddhist school but withdrew because of sickness and for a while entered a temple. He also began to have poetry published in 1919. He briefly revisited Korea in 1921 but was depressed by his father's female relationships. The rest of his life was spent back in Japan as a writer and artist living a Bohemian existence. He discovered printmaking through Nagase Yoshio's *To People Who Want to Make Prints* (1922), became Nagase's pupil in 1927, and began exhibiting with the Creative Print Association in 1928. His work was much influenced by the Expressionist tendencies of Nagase's style, and he worked mainly in monochrome or very muted tones. No. 41 of the magazine *Shiro to Kuro* was devoted to his prints (1933) and he contributed to 'One Hundred New Views of Japan' (1940). He worked also on book design, illustrated novels and newspaper serial illustrations. His house was destroyed in the April 1945 air raids, and

he died the following year of malnutrition. A tragic yet often light-hearted and occasionally manic figure, he never married, most unusually for the Japan of that time.

Literature: Sekino (4); Merritt and Yamada, p. 150; Merritt, pp. 235–9; Kanagawa Prefectural Museum of Modern Art (1).

TOKURIKI Tomikichirō (b.1902)

Cat. 50

Tokuriki was born in Kyoto, where he has always worked. The last of a long line of traditional-style painters, he turned early to woodblock prints and became a leader of the Kyoto *Sōsaku Hanga*. He graduated from the Kyoto City School of Fine Arts and Crafts and then from the Kyoto City Specialist School of Painting in 1924. In 1928 he studied *Nihonga* painting under Tsuchida Bakusen (1887–1936) and Yamamoto Shunkyō (1871–1933), but about the same time he changed to woodblock printing under the influence of Hiratsuka Un'ichi and began to contribute to the early print magazine *Han*. He was a co-founder of the Kyoto magazine *Taishū Hanga* in 1932, which helped create the sense of a local school of the Creative Print Movement much encouraged by Hiratsuka. He produced many sets of prints before and during the Pacific War based on traditional subjects, such as *Shin Kyōto Fūkei* ('New View of Kyoto', 1933–4), which also included designs by Asada Benji (q.v.) and Asano Takeji (b.1900), and *Tōkyō Hakkei* ('Eight Views of Tokyo', 1942). Most of these were published by Uchida of Kyoto, but after the war Tokuriki set up his own publishing company called Matsukyū, which also began to teach block-carving to artisans and artists, in later years many of them foreigners. In 1948 he also set up a sub-company called Kōryokusha consisting of artists who would produce their prints under the financial umbrella of Matsukyū. Later sets include *Hanga Kyōto Hyakkei* ('One Hundred Print Views of Kyoto', 1975). Tokuriki has continued to be active in teaching and writing, producing a long series of articles on print techniques in *Hanga Geijutsu* magazine during the 1970s.

Literature: Statler, pp. 118–22; Tokuriki; Kanagawa Prefectural Museum of Modern Art (2); Merritt, pp. 88–92; Merritt and Yamada, pp. 253 and 260; Fujikake, pp. 110–11.

TORII Kotondo (1900–76)

Cat. 41

Kotondo was born in Tokyo as Saitō Akira, and adopted at the age of fifteen by Torii Kiyotada (1875–1941), fourth generation to use the name Kiyotada and the seventh to use that of Torii, an artist of a line of painters and designers for the Tokyo Kabuki theatre. He studied native-style painting (*Nihonga*) notably from 1917 under the influential Kaburagi Kiyokata (1878–1973) who also taught Shinsui, Kasamatsu and Hasui. Apart from designs for the Kabuki magazine *Engei Gahō* and Kabuki scenery, programmes and posters, he painted *bijinga* (portraits of beautiful women). This side of his work was taken up by the publishers Sakai/Kawaguchi who issued most of his small output of woodblock prints on that subject, which was largely restricted to the years 1927 to about 1935. His prints appealed strongly to Westerners and were shown in both Toledo Exhibitions (1930 and 1936). Around 1935 he changed his art name to Kiyokoto. On his father's death in 1941 he became Torii VIII and Kiyotada V.

Literature: Merritt, pp. 81–4; Merritt and Yamada, p. 155; Blair (2), nos 131–43; *Kabuki Jiten*, p. 296; Katō, III, nos 107–14 (good colour reproductions of his female portraits); Stephens, pp. 198–203.

TSURUYA Kōkei (b.1946)

Cat. 139–40

Kōkei was born in Chigasaki, Kanagawa Prefecture, but was brought up in Shinjuku Ward, Tokyo. His real name is Mitsui Gen. His father was an unsuccessful painter; his grandfather, who lived next door, was the Western-style painter and print artist Nakazawa Hiromitsu (1874–1964) who specialised in landscape series. Kōkei graduatd from Fuji Junior College and then worked as a company 'salaryman' until turning suddenly in 1978 to the production of woodblock prints of actors performing at the Kabuki-za, Tokyo. He began with bust portraits (*ōkubie*) inspired by the work of Sharaku (worked 1794–5). The early series were in editions of thirty-six or forty-five, but he did not always complete them, sometimes defacing the blocks even before the announced number was produced. His earlier works also included flower pieces and the series *Hachi Dai-Jigoku Zu* ('Eight Types of Hell') in an edition of two. He almost gave up, but was taken up by the President of Shōchiku, the company which runs the Kabuki-za, who gradually interested others, until the editions reached seventy-two. In 1922 Kōkei changed his brightly coloured style to a semi-monochrome palette. He uses extremely thin paper made from *ganpi* and does all his own cutting and printing. His perceptive, slightly grotesque studies of contemporary actors have made him the most notable artist of Kabuki prints since Natori Shunsen (q.v.). His exhibition in 1988 at the Pacific Asia Museum, Pasadena, made him widely appreciated by Western connoisseurs.

Literature: Kabuki-za; Matsuya Department Store. Another print by Kōkei in the British Museum's collection (*Onoe Baikō VII as Moku-zume*) is reproduced in colour in Smith, Harris and Clark, no. 250.

UEHARA Konen (1878–1940)

Cat. 44

Konen was born in Tokyo, and studied first under Kajita Hanko (1870–1917) and then with Matsumoto Fūko (1840–1923). He spent most of his painting career on landscape, showing at official exhibitions and receiving prizes and awards regularly. He was influenced by the moist brushwork of Imamura Shiko (1880–1916). According to Watanabe (1), he worked as an official in the Imperial Household and the Foreign Ministry, and at one time was associated with Okakura Tenshin (1862–1913). Only a handful of woodblock prints by him are known, a few published before the Kantō earthquake by Kobayashi Bunshichi, the remainder by Watanabe. All are landscape or townscape subjects.

Literature: Kawakita (3), p. 52; Watanabe (1), p. 42; Stephens, pp. 102–3.

WATANABE Sadao (b.1913)

Cat. 72–3

Watanabe has always avoided publicity and worked on prints of remarkable consistency in style, technique and subject. His themes are invariably Christian, and this combined with the expressive clarity of his work has made him relatively well known internationally, although his visual vocabulary is very largely drawn from Japanese folk traditions. He was born in Tokyo and had no formal artistic education but became involved in his twenties with figures in the Folk Art Movement, including its leader Yanagi Sōetsu, and took up dyeing textiles. He was a member at that time of a group of young textile dyers called Moegi-kai. In 1941 he met Serizawa Keisuke (q.v.) and began to learn from him. Serizawa's pictorial influence is very evident in his post-war work. Watanabe began to make his distinctive prints after 1945 and first exhibited in 1947 at the Mingeikan (Folk Art Museum) in Tokyo. Through these connections he became influenced by Munakata and exhibited at his *Nihon Hangain* (Japanese Print Institute) exhibitions. He became known in the West first through a Japanese contemporary print exhibition in 1958 at St James's Church in New York and through his print *Listening* being included in Michener's *The Modern Japanese Print. An Appreciation* (1962) where he explained that he was unwilling to comment on his work, a practice he has maintained. In 1966 one of his designs was printed to form the cover of the College Women's Association of Japan print show catalogue and he has exhibited with them annually ever since. In 1976 he did a major tour of the USA exhibiting his prints. Watanabe works in a very distinctive style in bright but harmonious colours, usually on hand-crumpled *momigami* paper.

Literature: Michener, pp. 28–30. Other prints by Watanabe in the British Museum collection are reproduced in Smith (1), nos 91b, 106.

YAMAGUCHI Gen (1896–1976)

Cat. 100–2

Yamaguchi's date of birth is sometimes incorrectly given as 1903. He was born in Shizuoka Prefecture in what is now Fuji City, spent part of his youth in Tokyo and part back in Shizuoka (Shimizu City). His father was a well-off liquor merchant, and Yamaguchi was throughout his life able to follow an artistic career. He partly reacted against this in his youth by joining a religious sect devoted to poverty, and always remained of a strongly religious temperament. His parents took him with them to Taiwan in 1914, and while there he met Fujimori Shizuo (q.v.) who interested him in printmaking; on his return to Tokyo in 1923 he was introduced to Onchi (q.v.) and became his pupil. From then on he worked as a *Sōsaku Hanga* print artist, associating particularly with Onchi, Azechi (q.v.) and Maeda Masao (q.v.), though from around 1935 he spent several years wandering on foot, mainly in Shikoku and Kyushu, possibly as an underground activist, before resuming printmaking in 1937 and joining Onchi's Ichimoku-kai (First Thursday Society) in 1939. He contributed to all the Ichimoku-kai print collections, and to 'Recollections of Tokyo' (1945) and 'Picture Album of Native Customs' (1946). He evacuated to Enoura (Numazu City, Shūzuoka Prefecture) in 1944 and lived there the rest of his life. His international career began with a prize at Ljubljana in 1956 and he was the first Japanese to win the Grand Prix at Lugano (1958). A Christian, a political liberal, widely read, highly independent in outlook, Yamaguchi resembled Onchi most closely of all his pupils, and his free and emotional abstraction is also close to his master's, with a similar interest in incorporating natural and man-made objects into the printing process. His family presented 228 of his works to the City of Numazu in 1981. His printing methods are described with photographs in Petit and Arboleda.

Literature: Statler (1), pp. 154–8; Petit, II, pp. 174–5; *Yamaguchi Gen Hanga-shū*; Yamaguchi Gen Kenshō-kai (with extensive life history); Sekino (1), pp. 156–66; Merritt, pp. 251–3; Petit and Arboleda, pp. 45–54.

YAMAGUCHI Susumu (1897–1983)

Cat. 86

Yamaguchi was born in Nagano Prefecture and remained devoted to the mountains all his life. As a boy he taught himself woodblock printing. He went to Tokyo in 1920 and until 1922 studied Western-style painting, when he began to work as an art teacher and school counsellor and also tried running a hostel for impoverished men from the country. He exhibited at many different sorts of exhibitions (oil-paintings, water-colours, cartoons, prints), but from 1920 was already being accepted for the

Creative Print Association shows and contributed to a number of *Sōsaku Hanga* magazines. Forty-nine of his prints were chosen for the Paris exhibition of 1934 and sold very well. This determined him to specialise in prints from then on. He was evacuated at the very end of the Pacific War back to his home district, where he remained and took up farming, continued producing prints, and was very active in the promotion of local art education. His prints of the mountains proved very popular with foreigners, especially after he was featured in Statler's *Modern Japanese Prints: An Art Reborn* (1956). His views of mountains have some similarities to those of his close friend Azechi Umetarō (q.v.) but are more forbidding. His technique was characterised by very dense colours achieved by repeated printings on thick paper, using much water.

Literature: Katō, II, nos 89–95 and p.276; Merritt and Yamada, p.170; Merritt, pp.228–9; Statler (I). pp.109–14.

YAMAMOTO Kanae (1882–1946)

Cat. 1–2

Born in Okazaki in Aichi Prefecture, Yamamoto was apprenticed to the wood-engraving workshop of Sakurai Torakichi in Tokyo in his teenage years. This gave him a lifelong insight into Western-style representation of light and shade and a persistent ambition to be an oil-painter, which was always at odds with an instinctive Japanese taste for simple composition and flat planes. From 1902 to 1906 he studied oil-painting at the Tokyo School of Fine Arts and during this time produced the first acknowledged *Sōsaku Hanga* (creative print), published and publicised by Ishii Hakutei (q.v.) in the magazine *Myōjō* in 1904. With Hakutei and Morita Tsunetomo (1881–1933) he founded the important art and literature magazine *Hōsun* (1907–11), which promoted among many other things contemporary Westernising prints; in 1908–11 he belonged to the Bohemian 'Pan' Society, which became suspected by the police of socialist activities. He worked with Sakamoto Hanjirō (q.v.) on a series of actor prints (*Sōga Butai Sugata*), issued in 1911, with the unsuccessful intention of reviving the *Ukiyo-e* print tradition of Kabuki theatre subjects in a modern style.

In 1912 Yamamoto went to France and produced a few pioneering woodblock prints which were sold back in Japan by subscription, while studying oil-painting and earning his living partly by wood-engraving. Returning via Moscow, his latent interest in children's art and the cultural lives of farmers was aroused there and he visited Tolstoy's widow. In 1918 he was leader of the group which founded the Creative Print Association and thereafter became moral leader of the *Sōsaku Hanga* movement. From 1919 until his death he devoted himself first to children's art, helping found the Japan Children's Free Painting Society in that year and encouraging children

to learn woodblock printing; and then to the Farmers' Art Foundation, founded in 1920, teaching for many years at an idealistic farmers' art and craft school in Kangawa village. Here he continued to promote woodblock printing as a 'people's art' until his return to Tokyo in 1935. After 1920 Yamamoto produced few prints. His total production of woodblock prints was small but their influence was very considerable, and his intellectual breadth of interests and dynamic energy were a major factor in the ultimate success of the *Sōsaku Hanga* movement after the Pacific War.

Literature: Statler (I), ch. 2; Merritt, chs 6 and 7; Katō, I, pls 121–36; Ono (2); Kozaki; Merritt and Yamada, pp.170–1; Oka, pp. 5–6; Onchi (2), pp.13–14; Sekino (I), pp.19–32.

YOSHIDA Hiroshi (1876–1950)

Cat. 47–8

The life of Yoshida is covered in authoritative detail in Japanese and English in Yoshida (I) ('Chronological History', pp.178–93). The facts in this account are derived mainly from that source.

Yoshida was born as the second son of Ueda Tsukane in Kurume, Fukuoka Prefecture, a schoolteacher from an old samurai family. In 1891 he was adopted by his art teacher Yoshida Kasaburō in Fukuoka and took his surname. In 1893 he went to Kyoto to study painting, and the following year to Tokyo to join Koyama Shōtarō's Fudōsha private school; he also joined the Meiji Fine Arts Society. These institutions were all teaching and encouraging Western-style painting. From 1899 to 1901 he made the first of many visits to the USA and Europe and was successful in selling his watercolours in the former. In 1902 he helped re-organise the Meiji Fine Arts Society as the *Taiheiyō-Gakai* (Pacific Painting Association) for which he suggested the name. He was again in the USA, Europe and north Africa in 1903–7, with his stepsister and fellow-artist Fujio, whom he married on their return. From then until 1920 he became a very successful painter in oils and water-colour in the light, airy style he had learned in the West, but his independent spirit led him into many quarrels with the artistic establishment in Japan.

In 1920 Yoshida began to design woodblock prints for Watanabe, who was keen to have a Western-style artist in his stable. In September 1923 all the blocks for his prints and existing stock were lost in the Kantō earthquake when Watanabe's shop was destroyed. Soon after he left for the USA once more to raise funds for himself and for others; he toured the west of the country and realised that good prints were eagerly sought after in North America. On his return he set up his own establishment to produce his designs in print form.

From 1925 onwards Yoshida devoted his career mainly to prints, supervising all aspects of their production to very high standards. Many of his sets were on foreign subjects,

including the USA and Canada, Europe, Egypt, India (visited 1930–1), and Korea and China (visited 1936). In 1938 he went on the first of three further trips to China as an official war artist. He designed his last print in 1946 but continued to paint. He was the prime Japanese organiser of the Toledo Exhibitions in 1930 and 1936, and as a result many of his prints were included: nine were shown in the first (Blair (I)) and sixty-six in the second (Blair (2)). Both exhibitions increased his existing popularity in the USA and led to his being widely collected there. His orientation towards a Western audience is shown in his publication of the book *Japanese Woodblock Printing* (Sanseido, Tokyo and Osaka, 1939) in English. Yoshida's sons Tōshi (Cat.51) and Hodaka both became print artists, the latter mainly in mixed media, as is his wife, Chizuko. Yoshida's wife, Fujio, also produced a few prints.

Literature: Yoshida (I); Yoshida (2); Paechter, pp. 31–7; Blair (I) and (2); Merritt, pp. 75–80, 94–5; Statler (I), pp.167–72; Riccar Art Museum, Tokyo (I). Other prints by Yoshida from the British Museum collections are reproduced in Smith (I), no.81; Smith, Harris and Clark, no.237.

YOSHIDA Masaji (1917–71)

Cat. 103–6

Masaji, usually so called to distinguish him from other artists with the name Yoshida, died relatively early. Since them, his reputation as an abstract printmaker has continually risen, and he is now considered the best of the post-war artists inspired by Onchi Kōshirō. He was born in Wakayama, went to Tokyo in 1934 to study at the Kawabata Art Academy, and in 1936 joined the Western painting faculty of the Tokyo School of Fine Arts, graduating in 1941. While there, like so many others, he became interested in printmaking after attending Hiratsuka's side-class. He joined the Imperial Army in 1942, was wounded, and eventually returned from China as a prisoner of war. In 1946 he did a further year's research at the renamed Tokyo University of Fine Arts and Music before becoming a teacher. He met Onchi around 1948, began making woodblock prints, and first exhibited with the Japanese Print Association in 1949. He joined the Modern Art Society in 1953. From 1955 to 1964 he taught a Sunday print course at his atelier in Tokyo. His work was publicised in the West through Statler's *Modern Japanese Prints: An Art Reborn* (1956), by selection for Michener's portfolio *The Modern Japanese Print. An Appreciation* (1962), and through exhibiting at Lugano (1956). The death in infancy of his son (October 1956) added further tragic depth to his work, which became denser in tone and more complex in its surface patterns. In 1957 he won a newcomer's prize at the Tokyo International Print Biennale, and thereafter exhibited regularly there and at international exhibitions throughout the world. He also designed occasionally for modern ballet productions in Tokyo, while still earning his living as a teacher. He produced little after his fatal illness began in October 1969.

Literature: Wakayama Kenritsu Kindai Bijutsukan (1); Statler (1), pp. 149–51; Michener, pp. 48–50; Merritt and Yamada, pp. 177.

YOSHIDA Tōshi (b.1911)

Cat. 51

Yoshida was born in 1911, the eldest son of Yoshida Hiroshi (q.v.) who began teaching him when he was fourteen. At an early age he absorbed the techniques of old-style woodblock printing from the artisans in his father's studio. He studied from 1932 to 1935 at the Taiheiyō-Gakai (Pacific Painting Association) which had been co-founded by his father. Before the Pacific War he travelled widely with him in Asia, Europe, Egypt and the USA; he continued to travel after it, especially in Mexico, the USA and Canada and Africa. He remained in his father's studio until Hiroshi's death in 1950, after which he took over. His early works, such as *Tokyo at Night* (1938), are very close to his father's and continue up to the 1950s. In 1952 he began to make larger abstract prints in the *Sōsaku Hanga* manner without the help of his workshop. From the early 1960s he returned to representational art but this time on a larger scale, concentrating on scenes of wildlife in its natural habitat, especially in Africa. In 1984 he published the first of many illustrated children's books on African wildlife (*Dōbutsu Ehon Shirizu*) which have continued up to the early 1990s. In 1966 he published a book together with Yuki Rei, *Japanese Print Making: A Handbook of Traditional and Modern Techniques*, which has been influential throughout the printmaking world. His workshop has continued to produce reprints of his father's and his own early prints.

Literature: Statler (1), pp. 168–9; Merritt and Yamada, pp. 177–8; Petit, 11, pp. 206–7; Yoshida and Yuki.

YOSHIKAWA Kanpō (1894–1979)

Cat. 42

Also often known as Kenjirō, Kanpō was born in Kyoto, where he lived all his life. He studied native-style painting at the Kyoto City Specialist School of Painting from 1914 to 1918 (1914–20 according to Stephens) and later with Takeuchi Seihō (1864–1944). As a young man he was deeply interested in *Ukiyo-e* prints and the Kabuki theatre, and began to design small printed actor portraits about 1916, moving on to larger subjects with mica grounds in 1918. He became adviser on design to the Shōchiku Kabuki Company on his graduation, and eventually a writer on *Ukiyo-e*, traditional music, history of costume, the theatre and old Kyoto. He was commissioned by the Kyoto publisher Satō Shōtarō to produce designs of Kabuki actors for prints, which were published around 1923–4. He designed a few other prints, especially townscapes of Kyoto, also in the 1920s. In 1925 he held a joint exhibition with Miki Suizan (q.v.). After this he did no prints but became increasingly well known as author, collector, antiquarian and connoisseur of the theatre, producing paintings only on commission. His publications included *Nihon Fūzoku-shi* ('History of Japanese Folk Customs') and *Obi no Hensen-shi* ('History of Changes in Sash Design'). His collection of paintings is now divided between Nara Prefectural Museum and the Kyoto City Archives.

Literature: Blair (1); Merritt and Yamada, p. 178; Stephens, pp. 172–4; Kyoto Municipal Museum of Fine Arts, unpaginated biographies section; Nara Kenritsu Bijutsukan. Other prints by Yoshikawa in the collections of the British Museum are reproduced in Smith (1), nos 55 and 69.

Catalogue

PLATE 1

1 YAMAMOTO Kanae
(1882–1946)

French Pastoral in Spring

?1913

Annotations: (printed in blue on image, bottom right) *Kanae*; (on reverse) seal of Vergez Collection

Colour woodblock print, 262×355 mm

Provenance: Robert Vergez Collection

1988.3–15.03

The title is as given by Statler (1), pl. 4, though he reports that in the case of this artist information was gained mostly 'from colleagues and contemporary periodicals and catalogues' (p. 185). The date is assumed to be that of the artist's visit to Brittany in 1913, since it does not bear the signature Kanae in the Roman letters he used on prints made after his return to Japan (Cat. 2). Yamamoto also uses clear, flat blocks of colour in the manner of his early French period prints such as *Bathers in Brittany* and *A Small Bay in Brittany*, both executed in 1913. Both the style and the palette of blue, green and orange owe much to Cézanne, who was the only French artist he wholeheartedly admired; but the almost pastel-like surfaces are equally influenced by recent or contemporary French woodcuts and lithographs. The particular combination of style, palette and technique was transmitted through Yamamoto to the early *Sōsaku Hanga* artists, especially Onchi Kōshirō and the other contributors to 'One Hundred New Views of Tokyo' (Cat. 8 and 9), who, however, used them almost exclusively to record Japanese landscape and townscape.

PLATE 2

2 YAMAMOTO Kanae
(1882–1946)

Bathing

1918

Annotations: (printed in red on image, bottom left) 'Kanae'; (on reverse) seal of Vergez Collection

Colour woodblock print, 348×260 mm

Provenance: Robert Vergez Collection

1988.3–15.04

In contrast to no. 1 Yamamoto designed this print to reflect the naturalism, sense of movement, and expresssion of light and shade he admired in some European painting of the Impressionist and Post-Impressionist movements. On his return to Japan from France in 1916 he continued to paint in oils. In this print he succeeded in transmitting his painting style into the woodblock medium by the rapid use of the curved chisel known as the *komasuki*, which allowed a more flowing, brush-like line to be cut into the block. This side of his work was to have wide influence on the early works of Onchi Kōshirō and eventually on Munakata Shikō. The rather Expressionist pictoral style of this print contrasts strongly with his much flatter bathing-scene *Bathers in Brittany* of 1913 (illustrated in colour in Katō, 1, pl. 136). The rugged coastline here, however, is clearly Japanese in inspiration, and the artist's high point of view, eliminating the horizon, is an ancient Japanese artistic device going back to at least as early as the twelfth century. The younger Onchi's prints *A Spring* and *Hilltop* (Onchi (1), nos 68 and 69) seem to have been an inspiration for Yamamoto's design, both in pictorial construction and intensity of colour. This print was made to subscription and seemingly produced entirely in Japan.

PLATE 4

3 ISHII Hakutei (1882–1958)
Nihonbashi ('Japan Bridge'), from *Tōkyō Jūnikei* ('Twelve Views of Tokyo')

1916

Annotations: (printed in black on image, bottom right) *Hakutei Ga* ('Drawn by Hakutei'); (printed seal on image, bottom right) *Bonkotsu tō* ('Carved by Bonkotsu'); (printed in red cartouche on image, top left) *Tōkyō Jūnikei*; (printed on image, to left of geisha) *Nihonbashi*; (on reverse) seal of Vergez Collection

Colour woodblock print, 381×252 mm

Provenance: Robert Vergez Collection; Mitsukoshi Sale, Tokyo, 1980 (no. 564)

1987.3–16.0498

This is one of the last of the nine subjects Ishii completed from this series, in which he tried to revive in a more modern style the glories of the *Ukiyo-e* prints of the eighteenth and nineteenth centuries. In the magazine *Hōsun* for August 1910 he advertised the series, claiming that the co-operative *Ukiyo-e* print tradition (which had so impressed Westerners) was capable of returning to its old vigour. In the advertisement the first subject (*Yoshichō*) was illustrated. Like *Nihonbashi* and all the others in the series, it pairs an unnamed contemporary geisha with a modern Tokyo scene, including in this case telegraph wires, set in a cartouche, the style of the scene being noticeably French. This old *Ukiyo-e* device of pairing and comparing had been very popular in the late eighteenth century, but Ishii's half-Japanese, half-Western mixture against a blank background attracted few customers and the series was abandoned in 1916 after nine prints had been offered by the publisher and bookseller Takamura Kōtarō. Ishii used his friend Igami Bonkotsu (1877–1933) to cut the blocks, which he was unable to do well himself, so that he could keep control over the artistic production of the print in keeping with the ideals of the *Sōsaku Hanga* school. The printing was done by Nishimura Kumakichi. Another subject from the series in the British Museum collection (*Asakusa*) is illustrated in Smith (1), no. 5. Nihonbashi was the point in Tokyo from which distances were measured. Ishii illustrates the Westernised buildings which had grown up near it in the Meiji era (1868–1912).

PLATE 3

4 NODA Kyūho (1879–1971)
Ōwada, from *Hanshin Meisho Zue* ('Pictures of Celebrated Places in Osaka and Kobe')

Dated October 1916 on title page but published 1917
Annotations: (printed on image, bottom right) signature and seal *Kyūho*; (printed in brown on lower left-hand margin, as follows):

Hanshin Meisho Zue-Ichi ('No. 1')
Ōwada
Noda Kyūho
Hanmoto ('Publisher') *Bun'endō*
Chōkoku ('Carver') *Ōkura*
Insatsu ('Printer') *Nishimura*

Colour woodblock print, 345×245 mm
Provenance: seal of Seika Bunkō Library on contents page. Purchased in Tokyo, 1990
1991.8–5.022

The set consisted of thirty views near or in Kobe and Osaka, plus a map in antique Japanese style showing the location of the scenes depicted and a list of contents. Information comparable with the annotations on *Ōwada* are found on each print from the set.

This example is in folding-album format, but Mitchell guessed correctly that the set was first issued in a series of portfolios. This was later confirmed by Johnson (p. 28). The present author has seen a complete set of six portfolios of five prints each on sale in London, and the British Museum has examples of three of the portfolio covers, each of which has a small printed landscape by Akamatsu Rinsaku pasted to it.

This was one of the ambitiously illustrated travel-books produced by the publisher Kanao Tanejirō under his Bunendō imprint (at that time based in Tokyo). Here he used five artists all employed as illustrators by the Osaka *Asahi Shinbun* newspaper; the other four are Akamatsu Rinsaku (1878–1953, Cat. 26), Hata Tsuneharu (1883–?), Mizushima Nihofu (sometimes called Nihou, 1884–1958) and Nagai Hyōsai (1882–1945). Noda's view shows fishing boats at Ōwada, on the coast of Osaka bay where it turns south. Like his other designs in the series, it is in the revived traditionalist *Nihonga* style, with the artist's point of view placed very high.

Other prints from *Hanshin Meisho Zue* are published in Mitchell (including Noda's *Ashiya*) Johnson, Hillier (1) and Merritt (1).

PLATE 5

5 HIRAFUKU Hyakusui
(1877–1933)
Naruko, from *Nihon Fūkei Hanga* ('Prints of Japanese Landscape'), set 3 (*Tōhoku*)

1917
Annotations: (printed on image, bottom left) *Naruko*; (on image, bottom left) unread seal of artist; (on reverse) seal of Vergez Collection
Woodblock print, 188×252 mm
Provenance: Robert Vergez Collection
1987.3–16.0494

The turbulent Naruko River in Miyagi Prefecture has long been a venue for Japanese tourists. Earlier in the twentieth century the wilder landscapes of the Tōhoku area north from Tokyo became popular as subjects for artists of the revivalist *Nihonga* movement, of which Hyakusui was an important activist. This may account for his choosing the Tōhoku district for his contribution of one portfolio to the *Nihon Fūkei Hanga* series, as well as a natural preference for the north of Japan where he was born. The style has the lightness of touch and sense of movement characteristic of one aspect of the work of this many-sided artist. The series was published from 1917 to 1920 by Nakajima Jūtarō, with blocks cut by Igami Bonkotsu (1877–1933). The motivator seems to have been Ishii Hakutei (no. 3), who produced three of the ten sets of each of the series of five small prints; each was sold originally in a cover with a small print pasted on it (an example by Morita Tsunetomo is published in Jenkins *et al.*, no. 44).

The other contributors were Sakamoto Hanjirō (no. 6), Morita Tsunetomo (1881–1933), Kosugi Misei (1881–1964) and Ishii Tsuruzō (1887–1973), elder brother of Ishii Hakutei. At least two later sets were issued (by Maekawa Senpan and Kawakami Sumio) in 1929 by the same publisher.

PLATE 6

6 SAKAMOTO Hanjirō
(1882–1969)
Chikugo-gawa ('The Chikugo River'), from *Nihon Fūkei Hanga* ('Prints of Japanese Landscape'), set 6 (*Tsukushi*)

1918
Annotations: (on image, bottom left) unread oblong seal of artist; (printed on image, bottom left) *Chikugo-gawa*; (on reverse) seal of Vergez Collection
Colour woodblock print, 182×250 mm
Provenance: Robert Vergez Collection
1987.3–16.0557

For an explanation of this series see Cat. 5. Tsukushi is the ancient name of the area of north-west Kyushu where Sakamoto was born. Sakamoto was rarely involved with

sheet-prints, but like his colleagues on this series he had worked as a cartoonist and illustrator and had been a collaborator on the magazine *Hōsun*; hence he was well used to graphic techniques. Indeed, his set is the most strikingly designed in the series, combining Impressionist, abstract and Expressionistic elements into a characteristically forceful blend. The complete prints of the set are published in full-size colour in Katō (pls 69–73) but not identified there as such. According to Robert Vergez (personal communication to the present writer) the Katō illustrations are not from the original series but from his own reprint of it issued in 1970.

PLATE 8

7 HIRATSUKA Un'ichi (b.1895)
Izu Yugano Onsen ('The Spa at Izu Yugano')

Undated
Annotations: (printed in red, right margin) *Hiratsuka Un'ichi*; (printed on image, top right) *Un*; (on reverse) seal of Vergez Collection
Black and white woodblock print, 295×265 mm
Provenance: Robert Vergez Collection
1987.3–16.0478

This early work is said on an accompanying note in English to have been shown at the third Kitsutsuki print exhibition. Kitsutsuki ('Woodpecker') was the name given to several groups beginning in the late 1920s who followed Hiratsuka in his enthusiasm for European-style wood-engraving, which he maintained sporadically for many years, and in his dedicated pursuit of Japanese-style woodblock printing in black and white. In the latter he was the true pioneer among the *Sōsaku Hanga* artists, inspired particularly by early Japanese Buddhist monochrome prints, and, most significantly, passing his interest on to the young Munakata Shikō. Magazines called *Kitsutsuki* were issued from July 1930 to June 1931 and print collections under the same name in 1942 and 1943, all associated with Hiratsuka. Even at this early stage Hiratsuka's appreciation of the contrasts of the white of the paper with deeply and repeatedly printed black ink is clearly seen, as is the artist's characteristic love of his native scene and customs. In this view a woman is shown washing clothes in a natural pool at Yugano, one of the many spas in the Izu Peninsula, a few hours by train from Tokyo, which the artist so loved. The date 1920 is given by Hiratsuka himself in his collected prints (1978), but there is some difficulty in accepting a year so early, and a date nearer to 1930 seems likely.

PLATE 7

8 HENMI Takashi (1895–1944)
Yotsuya Mitsuke Ukei ('Rain at Yotsuya Mitsuke'), no. 22 from *Shin Tōkyō Hyakkei* ('One Hundred New Views of Tokyo')

1930
Annotations: (stamped on lower right margin in arabic numerals) 18; (printed in red on image, bottom right) *Henmi Takashi*; (on reverse) seal of Vergez Collection
Colour woodblock print, 18/50, 210×263 mm
Provenance: Robert Vergez Collection
1987.3–16.0491

The original descriptive label is missing from this example. The rather melancholic view of life in central Tokyo as known by impoverished artists at this period is poignantly brought out in this desolate view by a bus-stop in the rain. The scene is set in an area now dominated by the New Otani Hotel and Sophia University, but was at that time rather more Bohemian in flavour. In common with many prints of the period 1930–40 the main figure has her back turned to the viewer, as if unable even to present to the world that half-face which had been characteristic of *Ukiyo-e* prints in the eighteenth and nineteenth centuries.

PLATE 9

9 SUWA Kanenori (1897–1932)
Asakusa Rokku, no. 67 from *Shin Tōkyō Hyakkei* ('One Hundred New Views of Tokyo')

1930
Annotations: (in pencil on image, bottom left, in arabic numerals) 17; (in pencil in Roman) Kanenori; (printed in black on image, lower left) KANE 30; (on reverse) seal of Vergez Collection
Colour woodblock print, 265×210 mm
Provenance: Robert Vergez Collection
1987.3–16.0562

The sixth district (*Rokku*) of Asakusa is shown in its heyday as one of the principal entertainment districts of the downtown end of Tokyo, a position it had held since the late Edo period (1603–1867) and had consolidated in the Meiji era (1868–1912). In post-Second World War times, however, Asakusa has lost its status as an entertainment centre to Ginza, Shinjuku and Akasaka, except in its continuing feeling for low life and for national *sumō* wrestling tournaments at Ryōgoku. Suwa's view is obviously influenced by contemporary German graphic art, with its somewhat despairing view of an automatised popular culture. The inherent bleakness is emphasised by the stark colour world of red, black and grey, though the red picks up to good effect the garishness of the hanging banners advertising

shops and events. The original descriptive label is missing from this example, as from Cat. 8.

PLATE 11

10 FUJIMORI Shizuo (1891–1943)
Anemones in July

1934 (printed in ?1933)
Annotations: (in pencil, right lower margin) S. Fudimori [*sic*] 1934, with red seal of Henri Vever; (printed in red on image, bottom left) *Fujimori sei*; (on reverse) seal of Vergez Collection
Colour woodblock print, 319×245 mm
Provenance: Exhibited at the Musée des Arts Décoratifs, Paris, 1934, no.418. Robert Vergez Collection. Purchased at the Henri Vever sale, Part III, Sotheby's, London, 24 March 1977
1987.3–16.0469

This print was one of 246 contemporary works shown by the recently formed (or re-formed) Japanese Print Association shown at a specially selected exhibition at the Musée des Arts Décoratifs in Paris in 1934. The show was dedicated to 'self-carved, self-printed' works, and those made specifically for foreign taste (for example, Torii Kotondo's *Rain*, Cat. 41) were excluded from this part of the exhibition. However, the modern works were preceded by over 400 prints, mostly from the *Ukiyo-e* tradition, dating from the 1740s up to and including works by Goyō (q.v.). This print clearly appealed to Vever, who was the foremost connoisseur of *Ukiyo-e* prints in Europe at that time. The vitality of the composition comes partly from the vase, which is in the Folk Art (*mingei*) style perfected by the potter Tomimoto Kenkichi (1886–1973), who also between 1911 and 1931 publicised his designs through the print medium.

PLATE 10

11 ONO Tadashige (1909–90)
Komagata Bridge

1933
Annotations: none; (on reverse) seal of Vergez Collection
Woodblock print, 245×305 mm
Provenance: Robert Vergez Collection (purchased directly from the artist)
1987.3–16.0216

The date is sometimes given as 1935, but here we follow the opinion in the Machida Municipal Museum of International Graphic Art's exhibition catalogue *Ono Tadashige Mokuhanga-ten* (1993).

Komagata is a district in Tokyo on the right bank of the Sumida River, looking across at the more industrialised left bank of Higashi-Komagata. The bridge marks the end of Asakusa-dōri, which leads from Ueno. Even in so early a work Ono is seen experimenting with the light on dark technique which later became

the most recognisable feature of his print style, though he had not yet hit on the idea of dyeing the paper to a dark colour all over before printing. It is also one of his bleakest industrial landscapes, rather unusual in his work in lacking any figures, and typically expressing more strongly than any other *Sōsaku Hanga* artist a dehumanised urban environment, especially at night as shown here.

PLATE 13

12 SAKAMOTO Yoshinobu (b.1895)
Harimaya-chō, no. 6 from *Tosa Sanjū Ezu* ('Thirty Pictures of Tosa')

c.1935
Annotations: (printed in black on image, lower right) '*Sakamoto*' (signature) and *Harimaya-chō* (title); (on image, lower right) *Saka* (artist's seal)
Colour woodblock print, 260×375 mm
Provenance: Purchased at Sotheby's, London, 12 December 1967, lots 130–1
1968.2–12–09 (Coldwell Fund)

Tosa is the old name of the province now called Kōchi Prefecture on the south coast of the Island of Shikoku. Sakamoto's series is a mixture of coastal, mountain and urban scenes, the last being mainly of the old castle-town and provincial capital of Kōchi, where he worked as a teacher. This night-scene in winter in the then shopping and business district of the city expresses poignantly the atmosphere of the period, with its semi-Westernised culture symbolised by men wearing Western hats with traditional dress. The view today would be as looking north-east from the Shikoku Bank Buildings.

According to the facsimile *Tosa Sanjū Ezu* fifty sets were printed before the Pacific War, and by implication a further number after it, including the ten sets which went abroad about 1947. For these, two missing prints or blocks (*Yamauchi Jinja* and *Katsurahama*) were replaced by *Kagamigawa* and *Yaesu*. The British Museum's collection has fifteen scenes plus the title-sheet from apparently the pre-war series, since they include *Katsurahama* and are all from the same source. The 1979 facsimile portfolio shows an extra pinkish block around the lamp-post to the right.

This print and *Kenchō-Mae* ('In front of the Prefectural Offices') from the series were formerly incorrectly attributed by the present writer to Sakamoto Hanjirō (Smith (1), nos 11 and 12). The series is incorrectly dated '*c.*1925' in Merritt and Yamada, and the date of the artist's death is as yet unverified. The modesty and obscurity of this Sakamoto may account for these misrepresentations, but it is hoped he will fare better in the future.

PLATE 12

13 KOIZUMI Kishio (1893–1945)
Ueno Fūkei ('Ueno View'), no. 9 from *Shōwa Dai-Tōkyō Hyaku Zu-e* ('One Hundred Pictures of Great Tokyo in the Shōwa Era')

April 1937
Annotations: (printed in Japanese in black on image, top right) *Izumi*, with (printed in red) KOIZUMI KISIO; (printed in black, top left margin) full title *Ueno Fūkei: Hyōkeikan to Bijutsukan* ('Ueno View – the Hyōkeikan and the Art Museum'); (printed in purple, right margin) full series title and date: *Shōwa Dai-Tōkyō Hyaku Zu-e Hanga Kansei-han* ('Complete publication of prints of "One Hundred Pictures of Great Tokyo in the Shōwa Era"') with date *Dai-Jūninen Shigatsu* ('Number for April, 1937') and serial number *Kyūjukei* ('Scene 90'). Relevant numbers and dates are added in pencil, as is the signature *Koizumi Kishio* below; (on reverse) seal of Vergez Collection
Colour woodblock print, 302×392 mm
Provenance: Robert Vergez Collection
1987.3–16.0527

This view at the top end of Ueno Park shows cherry blossom on a cold spring day, with visitors round one of the fountains. To the left is the Tokyo City Art Museum (built in 1926) where so many exhibitions by *Sōsaku Hanga* groups were held, and which is still the most important centre for contemporary art in the city. To the right is a Meiji-era building then forming part of the Tokyo Imperial Museum. This Hyōkeikan was built in 1900 to celebrate the marriage of the Crown Prince (the future Emperor Taishō). Koizumi has used only four blocks for this effectively introspective composition, very typical of that period of Japanese history. As the artist did all the processes himself for this ambitious series, he had to economise in this way on effort.

PLATE 15

14 MAEKAWA Senpan (1888–1960)
Kishū Dorohatchō ('River Pool at Dorohatchō, Kishū'), no. 61 from *Shin Nihon Hyakkei* ('One Hundred New Views of Japan')

December 1938
Annotations: (printed in black on white cartouche on print) *Kishū Dorohatchō* (title); (below title) *Sen* (artist's seal); (on reverse) seal of Vergez Collection
Colour woodblock print, 249×326 mm
Provenance: Robert Vergez Collection
1987.3–16.0594

This example of the first scene of the series lacks the margin titles and imprints found on most of the later views. It shows a famous river gorge with whirlpools on the Kitayama River on the borders of Wakayama, Mie and Nara Prefectures (the province formerly known as Kishū), with a sightseeing propeller-launch also used for postal communication. Senpan's rugged, folky style is well-suited to the rough cutting of the blocks, which he normally did himself, and set the rather severe tone of the remainder of the series, of which thirty-nine were eventually published.

PLATE 14

15 ASADA Benji (1899–1984)
Biwa-ko ('Lake Biwa'), no. 12 from *Shin Nihon Hyakkei* ('One Hundred New Views of Japan')

April 1939
Annotations: (printed in red-brown on image, upper right) *Biwako* (title); (printed in grey below) *Ben*; (on reverse) seal of Vergez Collection
Woodblock print, 352×327 mm
Provenance: Robert Vergez Collection; Mitsukoshi Sale, Tokyo, 1980, no. 59
1987.3–16.0459

This example, like no. 14, lacks the marginal inscriptions of most of the series. The original printed slip, on transparent paper, in the same format as that of Cat. 16, 18 and 19, records the artist's warm feelings as a Kyoto man about nearby Lake Biwa, Japan's largest inland water, which he explains was also loved by his master Nishimura Goun. Lake Biwa is in fact separated from Kyoto by hills and lies entirely in Shiga Prefecture, but was loved since the Middle Ages by Kyoto poets, artists and musicians. In spite of the artist's traditionally poetic sentiments, his style in this print is very French, and the palette is closer to that of lithography than of woodblock printing.

PLATE 16

16 FUKAZAWA Sakuichi (1896–1947)
Ura Fuji ('The Back of Fuji'), no. 19 from *Shin Nihon Hyakkei* ('One Hundred New Views of Japan')

October 1939
Annotations: (on image, bottom right) *Saku* (artist's seal); (printed in red, upper right margin) *Shin Nihon Hyakkei* (series title); (printed in red, lower left margin) *Nihon Hanga Kyōkai sen* ('Selected by the Japanese Print Association'); (on reverse) seal of Vergez Collection
Colour woodblock print, 250×331 mm
Provenance: Robert Vergez Collection
1987.3–16.0473

The printed slip (same format as Cat. 15, 18 and 19) has an eulogy on the mountain by the artist, relating his composition to the celebrated print *Red Fuji* by Katsushika Hokusai (1760–1849) from 'Thirty six Views of Mount Fuji'. The dawn scene is taken from high up on the north side in Yamanashi Prefecture near Lake Kawaguchi. Fukazawa graphically describes his hard journey there in February and the circumstances of the composition. He uses just five colours to achieve his desired effect. The whorling marks of the artist's *baren* are clearly visible in the sky, especially on the left.

PLATE 17

17 KURIYAMA Shigeru (b.1912), also known as Matsunaga Shigeru
Ashi-no-ko shoshū ('Early Autumn at Lake Hakone'), no. 30 from *Shin Nihon Hyakkei* ('One Hundred New Views of Japan')

April 1940
Annotations: (printed in blue on image, bottom right) *Ashi-no-ko shoshū* (title); (next to title) *Kuri* (artist's seal); (printed in red, upper right margin) *Shin Nihon Hyakkei* (series title); *Nihon Hanga Kyōkai sen* ('Selected by the Japanese Print Association'); (on reverse) seal of Vergez Collection
Colour woodblock print, 252×336 mm
Provenance: Robert Vergez Collection
1987.3–16.0529

The original descriptive slip is missing from this example. *Ashi-no-ko* ('Lake of Reeds') is the name normally used by the Japanese for what foreigners call 'Lake Hakone' in Kanagawa Prefecture. The artist emphasises the reeds blowing in the wind in the foreground, suggesting the last line of many autumn *haiku* poems, 'The Winds of Autumn'. The bleakness and loneliness of the scene, like many in the series, seem to reflect the artist's well-found apprehensions about future events, which indeed were soon to bring the series to a premature end.

PLATE 18

18 MAEDA Tōshirō (1904–90)
Shirahama 'Engetsutō' ('"Round Moon Island" at Shirahama'), no. 35 from *Shin Nihon Hyakkei* ('One Hundred New Views of Japan')

November 1940
Annotations: (printed in green on image, upper right) *Shirahama 'Engetsutō'* (title); (printed in purple on image, lower right) T. MAEDA; (printed in red, upper right margin) *Shin Nihon Hyakkei* (series title); (printed in red, lower left margin) *Nihon Hanga Kyōkai sen* ('Selected by the Japanese Print Association'); (on reverse) seal of Vergez Collection
Colour woodblock print, 255×318 mm
Provenance: Robert Vergez Collection
1987.3–16.0538

The original printed slip includes a long and lyrical description of the pleasures of Wakayama Prefecture for the tourist. This is an area to the south of Osaka where Maeda lived and which remains relatively unspoilt even today because of difficult communications. The artist in particular mentions the hot springs in the Shirahama area, and its popularity for weekend stays by people from Osaka and Kobe. The island with the 'full moon' aperture cut right through it by the sea is one of the great tourist sights of the district, equally beautiful, according to the aritst, in all seasons. In spite of the lushness of his verbal description, Maeda succumbs in this print to the introverted loneliness of most of the series.

PLATE 19

19 TANINAKA Yasunori
(1897–1946)

Ōkawabata, no. 33 from *Shin Nihon Hyakkei* ('One Hundred New Views of Japan')

July 1940
Annotations: (printed in red, upper right margin) *Shin Nihon Hyakkei* (series title); (printed in red, lower left margin) *Nihon Hanga Kyōkai sen* ('Selected by the Japanese Print Association'); (printed on image, lower right) *Yasunori saku* ('made by Yasunori') *Ōkawabata*; (on reverse) seal of Vergez Collection
Colour woodblock print, 259×331 mm
Provenance: Robert Vergez Collection
1987.3–16.0574

The original printed slip on translucent paper gives a rather unclear account, typical of the artist's fanciful imagination, of how he came to choose this snowy scene at night, overlooking a small public garden in Hama-chō by the river. The bleakness of the scene is heightened by the use of just two colours – yellow and a cold blue – apart from the black key-block. He has also inserted the picture in a thick black line like a picture- or window-frame. The title of the print means simply 'By the Big River', an alternative name for the Sumida River. The slip also records that Maekawa Senpan (q.v.) supervised the printing.

PLATE 21

20 KAWANISHI Hide
(1894–1965)

Kōbe Minato ('Kobe Port'), no. 27 from *Shin Nihon Hyakkei* ('One Hundred New Views of Japan')

February 1940
Annotations: (printed in white in red cartouche on image, top right) *Kōbe Minato* (title); (printed in black on image, top right) *Hide* (signature); (on image, top right) *Hide* (artist's seal); (printed in red, top right margin) *Shin Nihon Hyakkei* (series title); (printed in red, bottom left margin) *Nihon Hanga Kyōkai sen* ('Selected by the Japanese

Print Association'); (on reverse) seal of Vergez Collection
Colour woodblock print, 252×330 mm
Provenance: Robert Vergez Collection
1987.3–16.0519

The outgoing Kawanishi, who spent all of his life in the city of Kobe, characteristically produced the most cheerful of all the prints in this series. Adopting and adapting the international Art Deco poster style, he found a simply colourful means of describing his much-loved home city in all its moods. Kobe had been since the later nineteenth century the most international of Japanese cities, a position it retains, and Kawanishi understood that its character derived from its being a very narrow strip between the mountains and the sea, the latter dominant. It has perhaps not been noticed that the artist's use of simple, unmixed colours is a reversion to Japanese aesthetic principles, although the colours themselves are different from traditional ones.

PLATE 20

21 KAWANISHI Hide
(1894–1965)

Girl on the Verandah

1944
Annotations: (printed in black in cartouche on image, bottom right) *Hide* (artist's signature); (printed below signature) *Hide* (artist's seal); (on reverse) seal of Vergez Collection
Colour woodblock print, 240×167 mm
Provenance: Robert Vergez Collection
1987.3–16.0520

The date is supplied by Robert Vergez. Kawanishi's works are almost entirely restricted to his native Kobe, and it is assumed that this scene is set there also. It is included in this catalogue as a rare example of a non-propaganda *Sōsaku Hanga* print from the late war year of 1944, when most print exhibitions and magazines had been shut down. The normally expansive and colourful work of Kawanishi is replaced here by deep introspection; his subject, like Japan herself at the time, turns her back on the world and stares inward at the inner garden of a typical Japanese house, with a tree and stone water-basin with a bamboo ladle for washing the hands. Western-style chairs were sometimes placed in corridors looking out over wooden verandahs at this period, and this was particularly common in Kobe.

PLATE 22

22 MAEDA Masao (1904–74)
Black Cat

1940
Annotations: (on image, bottom left) *Masao* (artist's seal); (in pencil, lower margin) Masao Maeda 15/50; (on reverse) seal of Vergez Collection

Colour woodblock print, 15/50, 409×490 mm
Provenance: Robert Vergez Collection. Regular staining round the margins of the back of the print suggests it had been framed for some time before coming into Vergez's hands
1987.3–16.0414

Statler (1) states that by then (1956) only ten out of the proposed edition of fifty had been produced. It is not clear whether the edition was completed. He also records that the artist made this print after seeing a neighbour's cat in a pine-tree. This story strangely echoes that about the origin of the painting *Black Cat* (1910) by Hishida Shunsō (Smith (4), p. 88). In Maeda's print the cat is a strikingly sinister presence in the great pine-tree, a traditional symbol in East Asia of stability, fortitude and the spirit of the scholar, and seems to suggest considerable unease. The treatment of the tree suggests the influence of the oil-painting *East Wind* by Kojima Zenzaburō (*Fauvism and Modern Painting*, no. 172: the catalogue entry quotes Zenzaburō's difficulties with his native pine-trees as a subject for oils). Yet the simple, solid shapes which the boughs typically present translate simply and easily into the woodblock medium.

PLATE 24

23 HIRATSUKA Un'ichi (b.1895)
The Innermost Temple of Kōyasan

1941
Annotations: (in pencil, lower margin) *Kōyasan Oku no In* (title) *Un'ichi Hiratsuka* 1941; (on image, bottom left) *Un* (artist's seal); (on reverse) seal of Vergez Collection
Monochrome woodblock print, 428×511 mm
Provenance: Robert Vergez Collection
1987.3–16.0394

Mount Kōya in the depths of the mountains in Wakayama Prefecture is the generic name for a group of temples of the Shingon School of Buddhism, originally founded in AD 819 by Japan's most revered Buddhist patriarch Kōbō Daishi (774–835). The scene is dominated by stone monuments to priests of the past and by the huge forest cypresses and cryptomerias which flourish in the area. Hiratsuka was turning at this time to the larger monochrome prints which were to become the most noticeable aspect of his output, distinguished by their perfect balance of black and white. The artist was evidently attracted by Kōyasan, a central symbol of Japanese peace and spirituality, at a time of approaching strife and disaster.

PLATE 23

24 HIRATSUKA Un'ichi (b.1895)
Hida Kokubunji

1942
Annotations: (printed on bottom right margin) *Hiratsuka Un'ichi*; (on image, bottom right) *Un* (artist's seal); (in pencil, lower margin)

Un'ichi Hiratsuka 1942 57/100; (on reverse) seal of Vergez Collection
Colour woodblock print, 57/100, 384×319 mm
Provenance: Robert Vergez Collection; Mankyūdō Shoten Sale, Hiratsuka City, 1983, no. 156
1987.3-16.0486

This is one of Hiratsuka's rare larger colour prints, which within a few years he abandoned almost entirely for monochrome works. It shows him nevertheless as a subtly warm colourist, clearly influenced by the colour skills of his older contemporary Onchi Kōshirō. The *Kokubunji* are Buddhist temples founded in each province of Japan by the order of the Emperor Shōmu in AD 741 as guardians of the nation, though none of them now has buildings surviving from that period. As in Cat. 23 Hiratsuka turns to this symbol of natural stability in troubled times. Hida is an old province of Japan, now Gifu Prefecture.

PLATE 25

25 HASHIMOTO Okiie
(1899–1993)
Nagoya-jō ('Nagoya Castle'), from the book *Nihon no Shiro* ('Castles of Japan')

June 1944
Annotations: (printed on image, left) *Nagoya-jō* (title); (printed, right and left margins) *Nihon no Shiro* (title), *Katō Hanga Kenkyūjo* ('Katō Print Research Institute')
Colour woodblock-printed page, opening 289×380 mm
Provenance: Robert Vergez Collection
JA RV 57

Hillier (1) reproduces in colour (p. 217) another opening from this book but from a later edition of 1950. The text is by Kashida Hidetō. Hashimoto cut his own blocks for the twelve expansive double-page subjects and three vignettes, but the printing was done by Yokoi Yoshikazu. The daring designs and bold but unliteral colour work betray the benign influence of the artist's great friend Hiratsuka Un'ichi and can claim to be his finest landscapes, preferred for this catalogue to his single sheet-prints. In spite of the nationalistic text, obligatory under the censorship of the time, the scenes themselves have a poetic poignancy which goes far beyond Japan's then military society. The 'Katō Print Research Institute' was in fact a publisher of woodblock prints founded in 1930.

PLATE 26

26 AKAMATSU Rinsaku
(1878–1953)
Dōtonbori ('Dōtonbori, theater street'), from *Osaka Sanjūrokkei* ('Thirty-six Views of Osaka')

March 1947
Annotations: (printed on image, bottom left) *Dōtonbori* (title), *Rinsaku* (signature); (printed on bottom right margin) 6
Colour woodblock print, 245×361 mm
Provenance: Scott Johnson, Kyoto. Purchased in London, 1986
1986.10-21.01 (6)

This portfolio was published as the last venture of Kanao Tanejirō, now based in Kyoto, who also published *Hanshin Meisho Zue* (Cat. 4) and a list of superbly illustrated travel-books. According to Mitchell, a series of views of his adopted city of Osaka was announced by Kanao as early as 1903, but did not appear as this portfolio until after the Pacific War forty-four years later. It was an exercise in nostalgia for the old Japan and the old city, much of which had been destroyed in the bombing. Kanao's old colleague Akamatsu rose nobly to the occasion, making effective use of the limited colours available at the time and combining them skilfully with the loose ink outline which he had perfected for many years as a newspaper illustrator in the city. The English-language captions and introduction of the portfolio are obviously aimed at hoped-for new customers among the occupation forces. The introduction on the contents page is self-explanatory: 'The artist Rinsaku Akamatsu, being an authority of modern western style painting, selected the thirty-six views of Osaka in order to represent them as they were before the recent war damages, and made the pictures in wood prints.'

The portfolio also included *haiku* poems on Osaka by Aoki Gettō, reproducing his calligraphy. The colophon of the portfolio quotes the block cutter as Monjū Keitarō and the printer as Nishimura Kumakichi.

PLATE 29

27 ONCHI Kōshirō (1891–1955)
Mannequin in the Studio

1936
Annotations: (in pencil, lower margin) *Koshiro Onzi-36*; (block-printed on image, top) *KO. ONZI*; (on reverse) seal of Vergez Collection
Colour woodblock print, 540×416 mm
Provenance: Robert Vergez Collection. This copy was exhibited at the National Museum of Modern Art, Tokyo, July–August 1976, and at the Shōtō Art Museum, Shibuya, Tokyo, July–August 1982
1989.3-14.066

The copy from the Statler Collection (formerly in Chicago) is published in Onchi (1), pl. 180, with slightly different colours; notably 'KO. ONZI' is brown and not pale grey. The edition is stated to be two only. This was Onchi's biggest print to date, and one of the largest yet produced by a *Sōsaku Hanga* artist. It shows a grasp of contemporary European abstract style far beyond that of any of his fellow print

artists and a new confidence in his print technique which presages his triumphs during and after the Pacific War.

PLATE 27

28 ONCHI Kōshirō (1891–1955)
The Sea

1937 (left sheet)
Annotations: none; (on reverse) seal of Vergez Collection
Colour woodblock print, 496×479 mm
Provenance: Robert Vergez Collection
1989.3-14.067

PLATE 28

29 ONCHI Kōshirō (1891–1955)
The Sea

1937 (right sheet)
Annotations: none; (on reverse) seal of Vergez Collection
Colour woodblock print, 491×459 mm
Provenance: Robert Vergez Collection
1989.3-14.068

These are the wings of a startlingly ambitious triptych, of which the even bigger missing vertical centre panel (880×505 mm) depicts two semi-nude female bathers by hot red rocks. The only complete set is in the Juda Collection, California, and is the one reproduced in Onchi (1), pls 187–9. If the central sheet represents Onchi's grandest piece of printed figural art, then the wings are the beginning of a flowering of that typical abstraction deeply rooted in natural forms which is found again and again in his later years. Onchi's artistic interest in the sea goes back to his youth, but a more intense involvement begins with his book *Umi no dōwa* (1934) which links the sea with the female body, as does this triptych. The central panel is derived from one of his own oil-paintings, a most unusual practice for this artist, who aimed to create prints as original works of art in themselves. It is no surprise that the print carries more conviction than the painting. Onchi's fondness for fish and shells reasserts itself in the more abstracted book of prints *Insects, fish, shells* (*Chūgyōkai*) published in 1943. This triptych is perhaps his finest achievement to date as a colourist, looking forward to the intensely pigmented post-war abstracts such as Cat. 77 and 78.

PLATE 30

30 ONCHI Kōshirō (1891–1955)
Portrait of the Poet Hagiwara Sakutarō

1943
Annotations: none; (on reverse) seal of Vergez Collection
Colour woodblock print, 541×403 mm
Provenance: Robert Vergez Collection
1989.3-14.069

Onchi had illustrated and designed Hagiwara's first collection of poems *Tsuki ni Hoeru* ('Howling at the moon') in 1917 and remained closely associated with him. This intense portrait, the most powerful yet produced by a twentieth-century Japanese print artist, is one of only seven produced by the artist himself (Statler (1), pp.187–8). There were seven blocks and fifteen printing stages, resulting in a densely sombre palette. Onchi himself referred to this print as *The Author of the Ice Island* – the name of one of Hagiwara's best-known works, published in 1934. The artist regarded printing as a form of painting and equally valid as a means of individual expression. However, in 1949 he allowed his close colleague Sekino (Cat. 98–9) to make an edition of fifty; while in 1955 Onchi's family commissioned an unlimited edition from the printer Hirai Kōichi. In 1987 Onchi's son Kunio produced in his own workshop a further edition of ten. One of Sekino's in the British Museum collection is reproduced in Smith (1), no.19. All three versions, from the Juda Collection, are reproduced together in Merritt, p.191.

Hagiwara Sakutarō (1886–1942) was the first Japanese poet to write successfully in the modern colloquial language and in completely free forms. As can be seen in this haunting portrait, he was afflicted by a depressive sensibility which led him to alcoholism and death in 1942, brought on by despair over the deepening tragedy of the Second World War. Onchi, himself a considerable poet, wrote in 1947 a poem about Hagiwara called *The Author of The Ice Iceland* which is translated in Statler (1), p.188.

PLATE 31

31 HASHIGUCHI Goyō
(1880–1921)
Woman Making Up
April 1918
Annotations: (printed on image, right) *Taishō Shichinen* ('Seventh Year of Taishō'), *Goyō Ga* (signature); (below signature) *Go* with representation of leaf (artist's seal); (printed in red, bottom left margin) cartouche for edition number, not filled in. Cartouche with names *Shō* ('Printer') *Somekawa? Kinzo* ('? Respectfully done by Somekawa') and *Chō* ('Carver') *Takano Shichinosuke*
Colour woodblock print with gold leaf and powdered mica background, 550×390mm
Provenance: Purchased in London, 1981
1981.4–10.04

This is the grandest of the portraits of which Goyō personally supervised the printing. According to Blair (1), the blocks and surviving print stocks of Goyō's small output were destroyed in the 1923 earthquake and are very rare. All of his female subjects are known to be geishas or waitresses in high-class restaurants or tea-houses, and hence professional beauties. In the *Ukiyo-e* tradition of which he was a

student he has concentrated the skills of the printer on the hair and the tie-dyed textile, as well as on the gilt back of the hand-mirror.

PLATE 32

32 HASHIGUCHI Goyō
(1880–1921)
Nakatani Tsuru Dressing
June 1920
Annotations: (printed on image, right) *Taishō Kunen Rokugatsu* ('Sixth Month, Ninth Year of Taishō'), *Goyō Ga* (signature); (below signature) GY (artist's seal)
Colour woodblock print with powdered mica background, 452×296mm
Provenance: Purchased in London, 1981
1981.4.10.02

The title is given by Merritt, p.72 (reproduced in unpaginated colour plates between pp.68 and 69). Clearly a professional beauty, by name and by appearance, Tsuru sits before a traditional dressing-table and mirror-stand on a *zabuton* (flat cushion), wearing a transparent summer bathrobe (*yukata*). This was an old *Ukiyo-e* device designed both to titillate and to show the skill of the printer. As in Cat.31, Goyō walks a tight line between the flatness of *Ukiyo-e* style and the modelling of flesh he had learned as a student of Western art.

PLATE 33

33 ITŌ Shinsui (1898–1972)
Awazu, from *Ōmi Hakkei* ('Eight Views of Ōmi')
May 1917
Annotations: (printed on image, bottom right) *Ōmi Hakkei no Uchi: Awazu* ('Awazu from Eight Views of Ōmi'), *Taishō Rokunen Gogatsu* ('Fifth Month, Sixth Year of Taishō'), *Shinsui* (signature)
Colour woodblock print, from an edition of 200, 224×315mm
Provenance: Bequeathed by Arthur Morrison
1946.2–9.077

This is no.3 from the series published by Watanabe Shōzaburō in 1917–18. The title is given in *Itō Shinsui Zen Mokuhanga* as *Morning at Awazu*. Some copies have a seal of Watanabe on the back and a seal incorporating the edition number out of 200. This set is based on a traditional series (said to have been initiated in AD 1500) of eight views or poems on Lake Biwa near Kyoto, Japan's largest inland water. Ōmi is the name of the old province in which Lake Biwa lies (now Shiga Prefecture). This set of eight was in turn based on an older Chinese prototype called 'Eight Views of the Xiaoxiang Rivers', each of which was attached to a subject, such as *Returning Sails* and *Night Rain*. Andō Hiroshige (1797–1858) had designed an almost unsurpassable set of prints on this subject, but the young Shinsui was not deterred from trying to emulate him, and indeed

they are among the best landscapes of the *Shin Hanga* movement. Where Hiroshige on the whole took the more usual high viewpoint of Japanese art, Shinsui came down to ground level in the Western tradition. His view of the spit of land at the source of the lake, with its striking line of pine-trees, is even more dramatic than Hiroshige's aerial overview, and its abbreviated style, with simple, clean colours, is most obviously influenced by the recent set of eight hanging scrolls 'Eight Views of Ōmi' by Imamura Shikō (1880–1916). The relationship to the *Clearing Mist at Awazu* of the conventional series of subjects is rather tenuous.

PLATE 35

34 ITŌ Shinsui (1898–1972)
The Ukimidō at Katata, from *Ōmi Hakkei* ('Eight Views of Ōmi')
May 1918
Annotations: (printed on image, top right) *Ōmi Hakkei no Uchi: Katata Ukimidō* ('The Ukimidō at Katata from Eight Views of Ōmi'), *Taishō Shichinen Gogatsu* ('Fifth Month, Seventh Year of Taishō'), *Shinsui* (signature)
Colour woodblock print, from an edition of 200, 322×219mm
Provenance: Bequeathed by Arthur Morrison
1946.2–9.074

For information on the series see no.33. This romantic snow-scene is the closest to the spirit of Hiroshige of all the set and one of the landscape masterpieces of the *Shin Hanga* movement. The Ukimidō is a picturesque sixteenth-century pavilion set in the water at the narrowest part of Lake Biwa. According to the artist, he made this composition from a photograph, not having visited the pavilion itself.

PLATE 34

35 ITŌ Shinsui (1898–1972)
Yukata ('Summer Kimono'), from *Shin Bijin Jūnishi* ('Twelve Figures of Modern Beauties')
Summer 1922
Annotations: (printed on image, top left) *Taishō Jūichi-nen Shoka* ('Early summer, Eleventh Year of Taishō'), *Shinsui* (signature); (below signature) *Itō* (artist's seal); (on image, bottom left) *Watanabe* (publisher's seal); (printed in red in cartouche on reverse) *Nihyaku-mai Kagiri Zeppan Dai-Hyaku Hachi-jū Nana-Ban* ('No.187 from a limited edition of 200 sheets')
Colour woodblock print, 187/200, 440×266cm
Provenance: Purchased in London, 1981
1981.7–31.01

This series (1922–3) was the most important produced by the young Shinsui for Watanabe before the 1923 earthquake and fire, which destroyed the blocks and existing stocks of prints. Those done after the resumption of production rarely recaptured the tactile quality of printing, which can be seen very clearly in this example in the whorling marks of the printer's *baren* on the background grey, as well as the almost three-dimensional feeling of the kimono with its tie-dyed patterns. A thicker paper was also used by the publisher Watanabe for these pre-earthquake works. The subject of this print is sitting outside on a slatted-bamboo verandah, by implication overlooking a garden.

PLATE 33

36 ITŌ Shinsui (1898–1972)
Yuki no Yo ('Snowy Night'), from *Shin Bijin Jūnishi* ('Twelve Figures of Modern Beauties')

July 1923

Annotations: (printed in black on image, lower left) *Taishō Jūni-nen Ichigatsu* ('First Month of Twelfth Year of Taishō'), *Shinsui Ga* ('Designed by Shinsui'); (below signature) *Itō* (artist's seal); (next to signature, almost invisible) *Watanabe* (publisher's seal); (printed in red in cartouche on reverse) *Nihyaku-mai Kagiri Zeppan Dai Jūrōku-ban* ('No. 16 from a limited edition of 200 sheets')
Colour woodblock print, 16/200, 434×258mm
Provenance: Purchased in London, 1982
1982.10.7.09

This copy was published in black and white in Smith (1), no. 33. A sombre masterpiece of the printer's art, it shows the clear influence of Shinsui's teacher Kaburagi Kiyokata in its underlying steeliness of mood and also in the highly decorative pictorial use of the great umbrella. Like Kiyokata, Shinsui tended to have real women in mind as the subjects of his paintings. It is not known who this is, but she is obviously a professional beauty, probably a geisha.

PLATE 36

37 ITŌ Shinsui (1898–1972)
Gifu Chōchin ('Gifu Lantern'), from the first series (*Dai-isshū*) of *Gendai Bijin-Shū* ('A Collection of Today's Beauties')

Annotations: (printed in black on image, bottom right) *Shōwa Gonen Kanoe Uma Natsu* ('Summer of the Fifth Year of Shōwa, Cyclical Year Kanoe Uma'), *Shinsui* (signature); (below signature) unread artist's seal; (on image, bottom right) *Watanabe* (publisher's seal); (printed in red cartouche on reverse) *Nihyaku Gojū-mai Kagiri Zeppan Dai Hyaku Rokujū-roku Ban* ('no. 166 from a limited edition of 250 sheets'); (printed below cartouche) *Watanabe* (publisher's seal in square form)

Colour woodblock print, 166/250, 425×280mm
Provenance: Purchased in London, 1980
1980.12–27.03

This copy was published in black and white in Smith (1), no. 36. The print is named from the most prized type of paper lantern called the *Gifu Chōchin*, which is covered in very fine-quality paper and hand-painted. The fittings are usually lacquered, with silk braid tassels. The lantern took a candle and was hung under the eaves of a house or restaurant. In this example a mature beauty with heavily lacquered hair is seen hanging the lantern by the rattan blind of what seems to be a restaurant or house of entertainment. The flowers painted on it indicate late summer or early autumn. The lantern and blind both provide the cutter and printer with a traditional display for their finer skills. The successive stages of original drawing, block proofs and colour proofs have been preserved for this design and are repoduced in *Itō Shinsui Zen Mokuhanga*, p. 258.

PLATE 41

38 KAWASE Hasui (1883–1957)
Okayama, Uchi Yamashita ('Rain at Uchi Yamashita, Okayama'), from the series *Nihon Fūkei Senshū* ('Selected Views of Japan')

1923

Annotations: (printed in black, bottom left margin) *Okayama Uchi Yamashita* (title), *Taishō Juninen Saku* ('Made in the Twelfth Year of Taishō'); (printed on image) *Hasui* (signature); (below signature) *Sui* (artist's seal)
Colour woodblock print, 300×225mm
Provenance: Bequeathed by Arthur Morrison
1946.2–9.071

This copy was published in black and white in Smith (1), no. 43, as *Rain at Uchisange* (an alternative reading), *Okayama*. The series (1922–6) consisted of thirty-six sheets, each of which was originally issued with a titled paper folder. Some others from the series in the British Museum's collection include these original wrappers. All of the sheets are in this comparatively small format, which encouraged denser and sharper compositions than the larger format Shinsui tended to use later (see Cat. 39). Like his great nineteenth-century predecessor in the landscape print Hiroshige, Hasui was at his best as a master of atmosphere, especially of snow, rain and mist. This rainy scene in the old castle-town of Okayama on the Inland Sea is one of his most poignant.

PLATE 38

39 KAWASE Hasui (1883–1957)
Ba'nyū-gawa ('Ba'nyū River'), from the series *Tōkaidō Fūkei Senshū* ('Selected Views along the Tōkaidō')

January 1931

Annotations: (printed in black, right margin) *Ba'nyū-gawa* (title), *Shōwa Roku-nen Ichigatsu Saku* ('Made in January of the Sixth Year of Shōwa'); (printed in black in cartouche, lower left margin) *Hanmoto Watanabe Hanga-ten* ('Print establishment of the Publisher Watanabe'); (printed in black on image, bottom right) *Hasui* (signature); (below signature) *Sui* (artist's seal)
Colour woodblock print, 265×395mm
Provenance: Bequeathed by Arthur Morrison
1946.2–9.072

This copy was published in black and white in Smith (1), no. 73. Merritt and Yamada list twenty-nine sheets in this series (1931–47). The more expansive style and format reflects the influence of the recent work of Yoshida Hiroshi. This is especially noticeable in the less enclosed view and the use of a developed skyscape as an important element of the design. Since Hirōshige's 'Fifty-three Stations on the Tōkaidō Road' was published in the early 1830s, Japanese artists have from time to time sought to emulate his achievement by producing their own sets of views along the old road between Tokyo and Kyoto. Although much of it had been built up by Hasui's time, it still had the advantage of a very long passage past Mount Fuji which he fully exploited, as in this winter scene in the Ba'nyū River. This is the popular name for the Sagami River, which rises in Lake Yamanaka in Yamanashi Prefecture and runs through Kanagawa Prefecture to Sagami Bay. The artist produced two scenes with this title in the series.

PLATE 39

40 MIKI Suizan (1887–1957)
Kiyomizu Kei ('Visiting Kiyomizu Temple')

1924

Annotations: (printed on image, bottom left) *Kiyomizu Kei* (title), *Suizan* (signature); (next to signature) *Satō Shō Han* (seal of the publisher Satō Shōzaburō)
Colour woodblock print with embossing, 420×278mm
Provenance: Purchased in London, 1984
1984.5–15.02

This is one of a set of six subjects made for the reproductive Kyoto publisher Satō by this *Nihonga*-style painter, a pupil of Takeuchi Seihō (1864–1942). Miki is known to have designed as prints only this set and one other of eight landscapes. An elegantly dressed young woman is seen about to wash her hands before entering the hilltop Kiyomizu Temple in Higashiyama, Kyoto, on a moonlit night in autumn. By her head looms the figure of one of the gigantic wooden guardians called *Niō*. The temple remains one of the most visited in all of Japan, especially in spring and autumn.

PLATE 40

41 TORII Kotondo (1900–76)
Ame ('Rain')

1929

Annotations: (printed in black on image, centre right) *Shōwa Yonen Jūgatsu* ('Tenth Month of the Fourth Year of Shōwa') *Kotondo Ga* ('designed by Kotondo'); (below signature) *Kotondo* (artist's seal); (blind-stamped on lower margin) *Ame* ('Rain'); (blind-stamped in two cartouches on lower left margin) *Sakai Kawaguchi Gōhan* ('Joint publication of Sakai and Kawaguchi'); (on printed label on reverse, filled in in brush and ink) *Gaikoku-yuki Nihyaku-mai-kagiri Zeppan Dai Hyaku Sanjūyon-ban Torii Kotondo* ('For foreign consumption, no. 134 from a limited edition of 200 sheets; Torii Kotondo'), *Kotondo* (artist's seal)
Colour woodblock print, 134/200, 383×264 mm
Provenance: Purchased in London, 1981
1981.8–1.04

This example was reproduced in black and white in Smith (1), no. 45. As the attached label suggests, it was designed very much with the Western market in mind, presenting an image of the Japanese woman which foreigners preferred to see. It was shown at the Toledo Exhibition in 1930. This taste for young women with parasols or umbrellas had been nurtured by the *Nihonga* painters Uemura Shōen (1875–1949) and Kaburagi Kiyokata (1878–1973), the latter passing it on to his pupils Shinsui and Kotondo himself. The artist uses here a much older Japanese convention in paintings and prints of representing rain by straight lines, but the low, dramatic point of view shows strong Western influence.

PLATE 43

42 YOSHIKAWA Kanpō
(1894–1979)

The Actor Kataoka Gadō, as Miyuki in the play Shoutsushi Asagao Nikki

1924

Annotations: (printed in black on image, top right) *Kanpō* (artist's signature); (below signature) *Satō Shō han* (seal of publisher, Satō Shōtarō); (printed on label on reverse) *Nihyaku-mai Zeppan Satō Shōtarō Kyōto-shi Nawatedōri Benzaiten-chō. Dai gojūhachi-go* ('Limited edition of 200 sheets, Satō Shōtarō of Benzaiten-chō, Nawate Street, Kyoto City, no. 150'); (stamped in blue on reverse) MADE IN JAPAN
Colour woodblock print, with powdered mica background, 401×275 mm

Provenance: Purchased in London, 1981
1981.10–21.06

The most striking portrait, reproduced in black and white in Smith (1), no. 54, shows the *onnagata* (female impersonator) Kataoka Gadō as the tragic heroine Miyuki in the play first performed as a Kabuki drama in 1850. Miyuki flees her parents' house mistakenly believing she is to be made to marry a man different from her lover Miyagi. In Act III he discovers her blind and destitute in an inn, where she plays the *koto* for him without knowing him. In this print she is shown blind, with plectra on her fingers for plucking the stings. (The story is related fully in Halford, pp. 295–9.) The actor is shown with the traditional headband of female impersonators. Kataoka Gadō (1882–1946) was known by this name in 1924, but succeeded to the senior family name of Nizae-mon in 1936. He played in both Tokyo and the Kansai area, and it was probably in the latter that he came to the attention of the Kyoto artist Kanpō. This de-luxe print uses powdered mica as a background, a device used in fine Kabuki theatre prints since the works of Sharaku in 1794–5, which at that period had considerable prestige among Western scholars and connoisseurs. According to the first Toledo catalogue of 1930 (Blair (1), no. 329), the blocks were cut by Maeda (?Kentarō) and printed by Oiwa (Tokuzō).

PLATE 42

43 NATORI Shunsen (1886–1960)
The Actor Ichikawa Ennosuke, as Kakudayū in the play Tōyama Seidan, *from the series* Shunsen Nigao-e-Shū ('Collection of Shunsen Portraits')

Annotations: (printed in white on image, top right) *Shōwa Ninen Shunyō Saku* ('Made in the spring of the Second Year of Shōwa') *Shunsen* (signature); (below signature) *Kajichō* (artist's seal); (printed in cartouche, bottom right) *Watanabe Kō* ('Production of Watanabe'); (half on image, half on margin, bottom right) *Natori* (artist's seal of approval). There is also an accompanying printed label with the basic details typed by C. H. Mitchell (as Editorial Secretary of the Japan Ukiyoe Society).
Colour woodblock print, unnumbered copy from an edition of 150 sheets, 390×272 mm
Provenance: Purchased in London, 1966
1966.6–13.04

This example was reproduced in black and white in Smith (1). no. 49. The actor is seen in the role of Ikuda Kakudayū in the play *Tōyama Seidan* performed at New Year 1926 at the Shōchiku-za, Asakusa, Tokyo. He is seen in a photograph in this precise pose in the magazine *Engeki Shashin-chō* for February 1926. It seems clear that Shunsen must have used this photograph as a basis for his print, and perhaps used the same method for many others.

The print is from the series of thirty-six

by Shunsen published monthly by Watanabe from 1925 to 1928, each in a separate cover which is generally now lost, as in this example. All the prints were shown in the first Toledo exhibition in 1930 (Blair (1)), and a supplementary series in the second exhibition in 1936 (Blair (2)).

The actor Ichikawa Ennosuke (1886–1963), from the old Edo (modern Tokyo) line of Ichikawa actors, acquired the prestigious name of Ennosuke in 1910. In the early Taishō era he visited Europe and returned with an innovative attitude to the traditional Kabuki theatre. His appearance as the pistol-waving robber Kakudayū caused a sensation in 1926, though the pistol is not shown in Shunsen's print. In his later years Ennosuke became one of the grand old men of the Kabuki stage.

PLATE 44

44 UEHARA Konen (1878–1940)
Dōtonbori

1928

Annotations: (printed, bottom left margin) *Dōtonbori* (title), *Shōwa Sannen* ('Third Year of Shōwa'); (printed in cartouche, bottom right margin) *Hangon Shoyū Watanabe Shōzaburō* ('Copyright of Watanabe Shōzaburō'); (on image, bottom left) *Konen* (artist's seal)
Colour woodblock print, 362×240 mm
Provenance: Purchased in London, 1983
1983.3–12.06

This example was reproduced in black and white in Smith (1), no. 72. The subject is listed by Watanabe himself as *Night Scene at Dōtonbori, Osaka*. Dōtonbori is the name of a canal in Osaka which also gave its name to the theatre and entertainment district (see Keyes, pp. 32–40, for an account of the district as it was in the first half of the nineteenth century). A racier, more journalistic view of the district between the Wars by Akamatsu Rinsaku is reproduced in Cat. 26.

As in Konen's few other prints the influence of Hirgoshige (1797–1858) is dominant, clearly seen here in the device of looking at the building across the canal through a very prominent foreground feature, in this instance a willow tree. The use of artificial lights in a night-scene, though, is more typical of *Shin Hanga* style, and succeeds in conveying a rather Westernised atmosphere. The building, which on a casual glance might also seem Westernised, is in fact a traditional multi-storey type still found in the entertainment districts of larger towns in Japan, each floor consisting mainly of private banqueting rooms. A strangely similar design by Tokuriki (Cat. 50) called *Spring Evening on the Kamo River* is reproduced in the Kyoto Municipal Museum of Fine Arts exhibition catalogue, no. 159.

PLATE 45

45 ISHIWATA Kōitsu (1897-1987)
Barber's Shop, Koyasuhama

September 1931
Annotations: (printed on image, bottom right) *Kōitsu* (signature); (below signature) *?Ishiwata* (artist's seal); (printed, left margin) *Kanagawa Koyasuhama Shoken* ('Impression of Koyasuhama in Kanagawa Prefecture), *Tokoba* ('Barber'), *Shōwa Rokunen Kugatsu Saku* ('Made in the Ninth Month of the Sixth Year of Shōwa'); (printed, bottom right margin) *Hanmoto Watanabe Hanga-ten* ('Print establishment of the publisher Watanabe') Colour woodblock print, 386×260mm
Provenance: Purchased in London, 1981
1981.10–21.03

This copy was illustrated in black and white in Smith (1), no. 76. Like his colleague Hasui, Kōitsu enjoyed the added range which the use of light and shade gave to the traditional landscape-print style, and especially the night-scenes which had been rare in earlier *Ukiyo-e* prints. The majority of his known print subjects up to the Pacific War are of night or twilight or rainy scenes, and usually intimate and domestic in nature. This old-style barber's shop is in a district of Yokohama now dominated by heavy industry. The rainfall is represented by broken straight lines, almost in the style traditionally used in Japanese prints from the seventeenth century onwards.

PLATE 48

46 KASAMATSU Shirō (b.1898)
Morning at the Spa: Nozawa

Summer 1933
Annotations: (printed on image, bottom right) *Shirō* (signature); (below signature) *Shirō Saku* ('Made by Shirō') (artist's seal); (printed, left margin) *Shinshū Nozawa* ('Nozawa in Shinano'), *Shōwa Hachinen Natsu* ('Summer, Eighth Year of Shōwa'); (printed in cartouche, bottom right margin) *Hanken Shoyū Watanabe Shōzaburō* ('Copyright owner Watanabe Shōzaburō')
Colour woodblock print, 387×262mm
Provenance: Bequeathed by Arthur Morrison
1946.2–9.085

This copy was illustrated in black and white in Smith (1), no. 78. Nozawa in the mountains in Nagano Prefecture (previously called Shinshū or Shinano) is celebrated as a hot-spring resort, and to this day the individual houses and inns have no baths because of the abundance of public ones. In this print an old-style bath-house is shown in spring (the blooms in the wooden bucket are cherry blossom). The natural hot water is running into it through a wooden pipe. The women's clothes are lying in a large woven-bamboo basket on the raised platform, and the wooden tubs used to wash outside the bath itself lie about. The nearer of the women still has her elaborate geisha-style

hair arrangement, suggesting that she has had a long night providing the entertainments traditionally available in hot-spring resorts in Japan. Shirō's detailed treatment contrasts strongly with Maekawa Senpan's starker bath-house scene (Cat. 83) and a comparison shows the opposed characteristics of *Shin Hanga* and *Sōsaku Hanga.*

PLATE 49

47 YOSHIDA Hiroshi (1876–1950)
Ōmuro

1940
Annotations: (printed on image, bottom left) *Yoshida* (signature); (below signature) *Hiroshi* (artist's seal); (printed, left margin) *Jizuri* ('Self-printed'), *Shōwa Jūgonen Saku* ('Made in the Fifteenth Year of Shōwa'), *Ōmuro* (title) Colour woodblock print, 267×395mm
Provenance: Purchased in London, 1980
1980.12–27.011

This copy was illustrated in black and white in Smith (1), no. 74. The view shown is in fact the main gateway of the Ninnaji Temple in Kyoto, which is in the district called Ōmuro. The special variety of cherry called Ōmuro is known in Japan as the latest of all to bloom, and Yoshida has chosen that time of year for his scene. The rather heavy construction of this composition is typical of Yoshida's prints in the last years leading up to the Pacific War. According to Paechter (p. 37), quoting the artist's son Tōshi, the term 'Self-printed' should not be taken literally. It means that the printing was carefully supervised by the artist, which is virtually the same attitude taken by many *Sōsaku Hanga* artists.

PLATE 50

48 YOSHIDA Hiroshi (1876–1950)
Spring at a Spa

1940
Annotations: (printed on image, bottom left) *Yoshida* (signature); (below signature) *Hiroshi* (artist's seal); (printed, left margin) *Jizuri* ('Self-printed'), *Shōwa Jūgonen Saku* ('Made in the Fifteenth Year of Shōwa'), *Onsen no Haru* ('Spring at a Spa'); (in pencil, lower margin) 'Spring in a Hot Spring. Hiroshi Yoshida'; (on reverse) seal of Vergez Collection. Also with separate printed and typescript label of a dealer, M. Nakazawa, Tokyo, with relevant details.
Colour woodblock print, 277×415mm
Provenance: M. Nakazawa; Robert Vergez Collection
1987.3–16.0580

According to Yoshida (1), p. 161, this is in fact a view of Shūzenji, a celebrated *onsen* (hot-spring spa) in the Izu Peninsula in Shizuoka Prefecture. It is in the artist's favourite densely luscious cherry-blossom style, and is similar in treatment to his series *Sakura Hakkei* ('Eight Scenes of Cherry Blossom') published in 1935.

PLATE 46

49 KAWASE Hasui (1883–1957)
Shiobara

1946
Annotations: (printed, left margin) *Shiobara Hataori: Shōwa Nijūichi-nen saku* ('Hataori in Shiobara: made in the Twenty-first Year of Shōwa'); (printed on image, lower right) *Hasui* (signature); (on image lower right) *Sui* (artist's seal), *Watanabe* (publisher's seal); (on reverse) seal of Vergez Collection
Woodblock print, 402×269mm
Provenance: Robert Vergez Collection
1987.3–16.0518

After the interruptions caused by the Pacific War, Hasui resumed designing landscape and townscape prints with unabated energy and continued up to the last year of his life. This view (one of two with the same title published in 1946) is of a district of the hot-spring resort of Shiobara in the mountains of Tochigi Prefecture, now equally well known for skiing. Artistically it is a reversion to the concentrated, romantic style of his earliest series, especially 'Twelve Tokyo Subjects' (*Tōkyō Jūni-dai*, 1919–21) and 'Twelve Months of Tokyo' (*Tōkyō Jūnikagetsu*, 1920–1). It is not difficult to see the comforting symbolism of the lone, warm light glowing in the frozen but familiar landscape of old rural Japan for Japanese in the year following defeat and occupation. For the artist, it was doubly powerful as an image, since he had spent some of his childhood in Shiobara and was also evacuated there during the Pacific War.

PLATE 47

50 TOKURIKI Tomikichirō (b.1902)
Rain at Yoshida-guchi, from the series *Fūgaku Sanjūrokkei* ('Thirty-six Views of Mount Fuji')

?1947
Annotations: ('printed on image, right) *Tomikichirō Saku* ('Made by Tomikichirō); (below, in seal form) *Sanjūrokkei* ('Thirty-six Views'); (below, in seal form) *Hanmoto Uchida* ('Publisher Uchida'); (printed, right margin, top) *Yoshida-guchi Yongōme no Ame* ('Rain at the Fourth [Stage] of Yoshida-guchi'); (printed, right margin, centre) *Tomikichirō Saku* ('Made by Tomikichirō); (below, in seal form) *Kiwame* ('Examined'); (printed, right margin, bottom) *Uchida Bijutsu Shoshi* ('Uchida Fine Art Shop'); (below, in seal form) *Fukyō Fukusei* ('Reproduction forbidden'). Also with separate typed slip '109. Subject: the Fourth Stage of Mt Fuji from the Yoshida Ascent. Artist TOKURIKI, Tomikichirō. Done: Circa 1947. Publisher: Uchida' (with addition in ink) 'VII 229'.
Colour woodblock print, 289×415mm
Provenance: Purchased in London, 1983
1983.11–18.01

The standard ascent of Mount Fuji by both Buddhist and Shintō pilgrims begins from Yoshida in Yamanashi Prefecture, and consists of ten stages, of which this view shows the fourth. The standing wooden pillar in the foreground reads '*Yongōme Daikoku-shitsu*' ('Daikoku Room at the fourth stage'). This refers to the Buddhist deity Daikoku who is also one of the 'Seven Gods of Fortune'. The banners of religious groups hang top right. As in other prints in this catalogue, the artist has chosen to represent rain by straight lines in the old *Ukiyo-e* convention. Thirty-six had been a conventional number for a series of landscape prints since Hokusai's 'Thirty-six Views of Mount Fuji' (*c.*1830). The seal 'Examined' is an enlarged copy of the one used by government-appointed censors from 1790 onwards.

PLATE 51

51 YOSHIDA Tōshi (b.1911)
Mendocino, Sunrise

1982
Annotations: (in pencil, lower margin) Mendocino, Sunrise 20/300 Tōshi Yoshida, 1982
Colour woodblock print, 1210×850mm
Provenance: Purchased in London, 1985
1985.6–14.014

The work, printed on a single sheet of handmade *washi* (Japanese paper), is one of several extremely large prints made by Yoshida and his assistants in the early 1980s to demonstrate the virtuosity of his development of the traditional techniques inherited from his father. The scene is in northern California. The romantic style of the print is very close to that he was developing at the time for his extensive series of children's books on African animals. These in turn were inspired by his involvement in the World Wildlife Fund and a series of increasingly large prints of wildlife begun in the mid-1970s in often very big editions, sometimes as many as 1,200. The linear technique of the sun's rays is very much related to these prints, where the large dimensions made a more individually characterised method of cutting impractical. However, the most striking aspect of this print – the rising sun glaring through the trees – is derived, perhaps unconsciously, from his father's early woodblock print *Sailing Boats, Morning Sunlight*, published by Watanabe in 1921.

PLATE 52

52 TAKEHISA Yumeji
(1884–1934)

Illustration from the book *Samisen Gusa* ('Samisen Leaves')

1915 (tenth printing, 1919)
Annotations: (on image, bottom left) s (artist's seal – probably first letter in Roman of his given name Shigehiko)
Colour woodblock print, 170×112mm

Provenance: Inscribed in ink on endpaper 'March 16th 1919 M Furukawa'. Purchased from Scott Johnson, Kyoto, 1991
SJ 191

This immensely popular book typified the melancholy view of fragilely beautiful women which was Yumeji's special contribution to the culture of the Taishō era (1912–26) and which helped establish the atmosphere of the period. The six individual small-scale woodblock prints bound into the volume are not major pieces, but the cumulative effect of the book, which also includes many illustrations in line process, collotype and halftone, is significant. All are of young geishas and other professional female players of the *samisen*, a three-stringed instrument plucked by ivory plectra (see reproduction for an example), which had been the most used instrument in popular entertainment since its introduction from the Ryūkyū Islands in the seventeenth century. All the illustrations are after Yumeji's paintings or sketches, and the selection of poems was also made by him. These are *ko-uta*, short romantic songs sung to a *samisen* accompaniment. Yumeji writes in the preface 'This volume is dedicated to the young women of the land where the *samisen* blooms with cherry blossom'. The volume was published by Satō Yoshikatsu at Shinchōsha, Tokyo.

PLATE 53

53 TAKEHISA Yumeji
(1884–1934)

Tanabata Festival (Dinner Menu)

1929
Annotations: (printed on image, bottom right) Yumeji; (woodblock-printed on central cartouche) N.Y.K. (Nihon Yūsen Kaisha); (pasted in cartouche) printed menu (transcribed below); (printed label pasted below menu) '"Tanabata matsuri", or the star festival. On the branches of freshly erected bamboo are huge coloured paper strips bearing poems dedicated to the stars.'
Colour woodblock print with gold, 370×240mm
Provenance: Purchased in the USA, 1981
1981.10.23.01

The menu is in English and reads [sic]:

MENU
Hors-d'Oeuvre
Mary Widow Crab Cocktail
Ripe Olives   Heart of Celery   Mixed Nuts
Veloute of Rafraiche
Delice Mahimahi Florida
Supreme Breast of Capon Clamart
Cauliflower Hollandaise   Mignonette Potatoes
Racing King Salad
Royale Souffle Pudding   Sauce Sabayon
(Ice Cream) Olga Plaza   Friandaises
Corbeille de Fruits
Demi Tasse
M.S. 'Asama Maru'
Tuesday, October 22, 1929

The passenger linear traffic between Japan and the USA and Europe was very active during this period, and this menu gives a good indication of the luxurious attention to detail employed by the Japanese companies. The menu itself is printed on thick paper over woodblock designs of fallen pine needles. The main design is on even thicker paper which would stand up to handling. It shows a young woman, probably a waitress, hanging a lantern on the verandah of her establishment for the night of Tanabata (7 July or 7 August). This festival commemorates an ancient Chinese story that the stars Altair and Vega represent two lovers who can meet only on that one night in the year. In its most popular form in Japan young women hang poem-slips on bamboo fronds which have been placed on poles outside houses, temples or shrines. These are thought to help success in love and the acquisition of a good husband.

This rather sumptuous design on special paper with much applied gold is typical of Yumeji's design work for ephemera, which enabled him to earn a living and at the same time propagated his style widely through Japan. Apart from his work for his Minato-ya shop in 1912–14, he was rarely closely involved with the reproduction of his work in the various graphic processes used at the time.

PLATE 54

54 TAKEHISA Yumeji
(1884–1934)

Asa no Hikari e ('To the Morning Light'), from *Onna Jūdai* ('Ten Female Subjects')

Printed 1938, after a water-colour of 1925
Annotations: (printed on image, top left) *Asa no Hikari e* (title), *Yumeji* (signature); (below signature) ?Takehisa Yumeji no in (artist's seal); (printed in cartouche, bottom left margin) Hanmoto Katō Junji ('Publisher Katō Junji'); (below cartouche) *Hyaku Gojūmai Zeppan Dai Yonjūroku-go* ('No. 46 from an edition limited to 150 sheets'); (on reverse, in seal form) ?Hōrō [. . .]
Colour woodblock print, 46/150, 432×305mm
Provenance: Purchased in London, 1981
1981.7–30.08

This set of prints was published posthumously by Katō, reproducing extremely closely the set of water-colours of the same name produced by the artist in 1921–2, and in almost the same dimensions. The cutters and printers have reproduced with extraordinary skill the typically dry brushwork of the artist. According to Kawamura Kōjirō (Kawamura Collection, p. 39), this is a newly married young woman of the 'Yamanote Set' (that is, central Tokyo), whose husband is a 'Morning Salaryman', a phrase which had recently come into use. She is well dressed, with a Westernised haircut and a chic silk appliqué hair ornament attached to a ribbon, instead of a traditional comb. Looking out of her window after her husband's morning departure, her distressed expression belies the supposed happiness of her circumstances. Katō produced this set after Yumeji's death to meet the demand for his images, which remained popular up to the Pacific War.

PLATE 55

55 KITANO Tsunetomi
(1880–1947)

Keikōnoma ('In the Practice-Room (Spring)'), from the series *Kuruwa no Shunshū* ('The Seasons in the Entertainment Districts')

July 1918
Annotations: (printed on image, bottom right) *Tsunetomi Hitsu* ('The Brush of Tsunetomi')
Colour woodblock print, 390×259 mm
Provenance: Scott Johnson, Kyoto. Purchased in London, 1983
1983.6–9.02

This series of four prints was published by Nakajima Jūtarō in Tokyo, but the artist was an Osaka man, and so was the printer Tadokoro Rikimatsu and hence no doubt also the block cutter, who is not named on the decorated folder in which the four prints were originally issued as a set in an edition of 500. These folders have usually been broken up, but a complete set is in the collection of Scott Johnson in Kyoto. Among much other information on the folder it is stated that *Before the Mirror* (Winter) could also be bought separately, implying that more than 500 copies of that particular subject might have been printed (the British Museum's copy is illustrated in Smith, Harris and Clark, no. 236). The remaining two subjects are *After the Bath* (Autumn) and *Dusk* (Summer). Each of the four prints shows a professional woman of one of four entertainment districts in Osaka. *In the Practice-Room* is associated with the Shinmachi area. The subject wears a kimono decorated with portraits of Kabuki actors. Like all of the set this print is derived and simplified into graphic form from an earlier painting. Nakajima's comments on *Ukiyo-e* and the modern print, expressed at some length on the folder, are discussed on p. 17. Katō (III, no. 103), apparently mistakenly, gives the title *In the Afternoon* for this print and the date *c.*1923.

PLATE 56

56 ISHIKAWA Toraji (1875–1964)
Yokushitsu nite ('In the Bathroom'), no. 5 from the series *Rajo Jūshū no Uchi* ('Ten Types of Female Nude')

1934
Annotations: (printed on image, top right) Ishikawa (signature); (below signature) *Tora* (artist's seal); (in printed cartouche, bottom

left margin) *Yamagishi Kazue Tō* ('Carved by Yamagishi Kazue')
Colour woodblock print, 480×372 mm
Provenance: Purchased in London, 1981
1981.7–30.02

This copy was reproduced in black and white in Smith (1), no. 66. The original protective sheet covering the print survives and has the title and series as quoted (in Japanese) printed on it. This scene makes an interesting comparison with the bath-house scenes by Kasamatsu Shirō (Cat. 46) and Maekawa Senpan (Cat. 83). Ishikawa, as a *Yōga* (Western-style painting) artist, places much more emphasis on the woman and less on the atmosphere of the setting. This young woman, with her modern hair-style, is seen in a very modernised version of the traditional Japanese bath, using tiles and marble. This was Ishikawa's only series designed specifically for woodblock prints and was published by himself, but it has made his name better known in the West than it would otherwise have been, doubtless because of its subject-matter and racy style. The block cutter Yamagishi Kazue had also worked for Ishikawa's younger colleague Yoshida Hiroshi (q.v.) and Kitano Tsunetomi.

PLATE 57

57 DŌMOTO Inshō (1891–1975)
Hatsu Keshō ('New Year Toilette')

January 1935
Annotations: (on image, bottom right) *Inshō* (signature); (below signature) *Inshō* (artist's seal); (printed, left margin) *Gentei Shuppan Dai-Shichi Go* ('No. 7 from a limited edition'), *Hangen Shoyū Kanete Seisakusha Baba Nobuhiko* ('Baba Nobuhiko, copyright holder and producer'); ('printed in cartouches, bottom left margin) *Suri Satō* ('Printer Satō'), *Hori Katsumura* ('Cutter Katsumura'); (printed, right margin) *Hatsu Keshō* (title), *Shōwa Jūnen Ichigatsu* ('First Month of Tenth Year of Shōwa')
Colour woodblock print, 7/?, 507×375 mm
Provenance: Purchased in London, 1981
1981.4–10.5

This image was one of Inshō's very rare print subjects but was most successful in its day. The publisher's decision not to reveal how many sheets his 'limited edition' was restricted to was therefore prudent. A young Kyoto *maiko* is shown arranging her hair on New Year's Day. Her under-kimono is decorated with pine fronds and plum blossoms, both symbols of the festival. On New Year's Day it was the custom for young *maiko* (the Kyoto version of young geishas) to visit their older teachers and give them presents.

PLATE 61

58 SERIZAWA Keisuke
(1895–1984)

Osore o Shiranu Don Kihōte ('Don Quixote knows no fear'), from the book *Ehon Don Kihōte* ('Picture Book of Don Quixote')

Published October 1936 by Kōnichian ('Sunward Press'), Kyoto
Annotations: (printed in cartouche on image, bottom right) *Sono Nijū-ni* ('No. 22')
Stencil-printed opening with hand-colouring, 285×370 mm
Provenance: Given to the British Museum by Carl T. Keller. Transferred from the British Library, 1973
JA XBL 83

The scene seems to be from Chapter 17 of Part 2 of *Don Quixote*, where the knight meets a carter and keeper delivering a lion and lioness to the King. The knight demands that the cage be opened so that he might fight the lion, and as always finally gets his way. The lion, however, turns his back on the knight while still in his cage, and the carter persuades him that the beast has therefore conceded the victory and is allowed to lock up the cage again, promising to report Don Quixote's courage to the King.

This book, which was the third produced by Serizawa, includes thirty-one illustrations in black and white stencil, all coloured by hand in green and orange-red, the traditional colours of the early seventeenth-century *tanrokubon* ('red and green books') which Serizawa was here imitating. He also added a yellow to give greater variety. There is no descriptive text, but simply a list of the illustrations' titles. A colophon states that seventy-five impressions were made but a further twenty-five were then printed, of which this copy is no. 17, and that it was published at the request of Carl T. Keller. This copy is sewn up in traditional Japanese style and has covers with designs of cloud and other patterns in light brown and vermilion lacquer, with added gold leaf. The lacquerer was Suzuki Shigeo. The *chitsu* wrapper is covered with a stencilled cloth in indigo and yellow. The paper stencils for the book are in the collection of the Fogg Art Museum, Boston.

Carl Tilden Keller, a collector and bibliographer of materials relating to *Don Quixote*, commissioned this Japanese version from Serizawa on the recommendation of Yanagi Sōetsu and Kawai Kanjirō. Serizawa illustrated the story in the style of Japanese books of the early seventeenth century which were in turn popularised versions of the *Nara Ehon*, cheaply produced hand-painted versions of medieval romances. In this style the Don appears as a high-ranking samurai. The complete book is reproduced in colour in *Serizawa Keisuke Zenshū*, I. The artist produced a new version, *Shinpan Ehon Don Kihōte*, in 1976, with colours closely resembling those of his textile designs. It is reproduced in full in *Serizawa Keisuke Zenshū*, VI. For *tanrokubon* see Yoshida, Kogorō.

PLATE 58

59 MUNAKATA Shikō (1903–75)
Joshin ('Goddess'), from the series
Kegonpū ('A Record of the Kegon
Sutra')

1937
Annotations: (on sheet) none
Black and white woodblock print,
530×725 mm
Provenance: Given by the artist to Bernard
Leach. Purchased from Philip W. Leach, 1983
1983.7–2.04

The complete set of *Kegonpū* consists of twenty-three sheets, namely nineteen Buddhist divinities, representations of sunrise and sunset, a title page and a decorative contents list. Both the latter are a combination of text and decoration which became typical of much of Munakata's later work. The nineteen divinities are listed on the contents page in a symmetrical arrangement, with the Buddha Birushana at the centre, flanked each side by lesser Buddhas, Bodhisattvas, Myō-ō ('Shining Kings'), minor divinities such as Fūjin, the Wind God, and sunrise and sunset. This arrangement is a type of *mandala*, a pictorial representation of the whole of existence in the form of deities and symbols. This is in fact what Munakata was trying to do using the doctrine of the *Kegon Sutra* (a *sutra* is a Buddhist scripture) that all existence is totally unified in the greatest Buddha Vairocana (Japanese *Dainichi* or *Birushana*), while all existence is conversely present in every part of itself, down to a grain of sand or even smaller. This broad and positive view of life was very sympathetic to the ebullient artist. He was also attracted by the possible reading of *Kegon* as 'Brilliant and awesome', and explored both these aspects in the series. The unnamed female deity here, enmeshed in and emerging from a vibrant tangle of plum blossom, has much of the feeling of a fertility goddess, and is deliberately placed near the 'sunrise' end of the arrangement.

Five of the deities exist in earlier forms, which were then altered for the final set. One of these (*Yakushi Nyorai*) was added to the final twenty-three to make a set of twenty-four mounted as a pair of twofold screens (now in the Munakata Shikō Kinenkan in Kamakura). The British Museum's incomplete set includes one of the earlier versions (see Cat. 60) but lacks five of the subjects. Presumably the pencilled note 'Children to select' on the portfolio box explains this. It does, however, include a sheet with a small figure of a running multi-armed and -legged deity printed in red on blue-grey paper not apparently recorded elsewhere. One or more versions also exist of *Kegonpū* with tan hand-colouring in the style of his series on the Bodhisattva Kannon produced in 1938.

Like almost all of Munakata's blocks then in existence these were destroyed in 1945, and the survival of this set, albeit broken up, is due to his giving it to his friend Bernard

Leach, who made visits to Japan before the Pacific War.

For the *Kegon Sutra* see Eliot, pp. 108–14.

PLATE 59

60 MUNAKATA Shikō (1903–75)
Ashura-Ō, from the series *Kegonpū*
('A Record of the Kegon Sutra')

1937
Annotations: (on sheet) none
Black and white woodblock print,
530×725 mm
Provenance: Given by the artist to Bernard
Leach. Purchased from Philip W. Leach in
1983
1983.7–2.07

For an explanation of the series see no. 59. Ashura-Ō, originally an Indian deity, is associated in the Buddhist pantheon with war and is usually shown with six arms and three faces. He is also one of the group of 'Eight Guardians of the Buddhist Law'. This is the earlier version of the design. In the altered version the area on the right beyond Ashura-Ō's last hand is left black and his feet are cut out. The complete set and the five earlier sheets are all reproduced together in *Munakata Shikō Hanga Zenshū*, II, pp. 182–3.

PLATE 60

61 MUNAKATA Shikō (1903–75)
The disciple Subodai, from *Shaka Jū
Dai Deshi* ('Ten Great Followers of
Shaka')

1939 (printed in or after January 1962)
Annotations: (in pencil on image, bottom left)
Shikō with cipher, Munakata (signature);
(above signature) *Hōgan Muna Shikō* (artist's
seal); (in pencil on reverse, apparently in
Munakata's hand) *Subodai* and SUBODAI
Paper watermarked 181
Black and white woodblock print,
1023×396 mm
Provenance: Purchased in London, 1981
1981.3–31.02

This example was reproduced in black and white in Smith (1), no. 20.

Following his two great 1938 series *Utō* and *Kannon-kyō*, Munakata considered making much bigger prints. He decided to create a set on the ten great disciples of Shaka (the historical Buddha) after seeing a sculpture of Subodai, the subject of this print, which belonged to the Kōfukuji Temple, Kyoto, and which was on display in the Imperial Museum in Tokyo (now the Tokyo National Museum). According to his own account in *Hanga no Michi* ('The Way of Prints', 1956), he came across some suitable large woodblocks which he carved quickly without even using drawings, compressing the extremes of the bodies into the edges of the blocks as if they were

bursting out of them spontaneously. The set was made to put on to a pair of sixfold screens, as it was the artist's custom to design his works for traditional painting formats. Each subject was thus conceived for a specific place on the screen, and the variety of stances in the set is fully understandable only in that light. As ten subjects looked unbalanced, he enclosed them each end (with typical lack of regard for canonical correctness) with two extra subjects, the Bodhisattvas Fūgen and Monjū. The title of the series is sometimes, therefore, quoted as 'Two Bodhisattvas and the Ten Great Followers of Shaka'. The disciples themselves are all shown as Buddhist monks, more or less in Japanese folk style, but retaining some of the Indian characteristics they were by tradition given. Subodai was the disciple said to have the greatest understanding of the doctrine of the void, or nothingness.

Most of Munakata's blocks were destroyed with his house in an air raid on Tokyo on 25 May 1945, but those for the 'Ten Disciples' survived because he had used them to shore up his air-raid shelter. He was thus able to take new pulls as demand increased, especially after his standing in the world rose after his 1955 success at the São Paolo Biennale. This example is presumed to be after January 1962, when Munakata received the Buddhist title of *Hōgan* ('Eye of the Law'), which is incorporated in the seal, though it is possible he proudly added the new seal to an older pull.

PLATE 62

62 MUNAKATA Shikō (1903–75)
Dust-jacket for the book *Hankei*
('Strength of the Board')

1944
Annotations: (printed in black, front of dust-jacket and spine) *Hankei* (title), *Munakata
Shikō Chō* ('Author Munakata Shikō');
(printed in black, front) *Kawade Shobō*
(publisher)
Brown and white woodblock print,
245×390 mm
Provenance: Robert Vergez Collection
JA RV 156

The title refers to Munakata's idea that the 'board', or woodblock, is full of energy waiting to be released by the cutter. The book was published by Kawade Shobō, Tokyo, in a declared edition of 2,500 copies. In astonishing defiance of the austerity regulations and the desperate national situation at the time, it has the same design printed on the boards, another print in brown on purple paper as endpapers, a print hand-coloured from behind as a frontispiece, a further twenty monochrome woodblock prints bound in, as well as eight small colour offset lithographs of the artist's prints tipped on to handmade grey paper. The book is completed by fourteen essays in letterpress by Munakata on various artistic topics, including his own works. In the last of them (*Hankei Goki*, dated 10 May) he acknowledges the generous help of his publisher Yamaguchi Shigetarō. He also states that apart from the reproductions and the cover subject all the prints are newly done for the book. The style of this jacket is close to that of prints in his most recently produced series, such as *Utō* ('The Tale of the Cormorant', 1938), but its subject is not explained.

PLATE 64

63 MUNAKATA Shikō (1903–75)
Kai ('Shells'), from *Shōkeishō* ('In Praise of the Valley of the Bell')

1945; this example printed 1956
Annotations: (in pencil, lower margin) *Shikō Munakata* 1956-4-20; (in pencil, bottom left) cipher and letter H; (on image, centre right) *Muna Shikō* (artist's seal, in the shape of a three-legged bronze vessel), *Muna* (artist's seal); (on reverse) label inscribed in ink *Kaizoku* ('family of shells'), the remainder obscured by marks in blue including the number 27 but probably reading *Munakata Shikō*; (impressed partly over label) *Muna Shikō* (artist's seal)
Black and white woodblock print with hand-colouring applied from reverse, 550×390 mm
Provenance: Purchased in London, 1980
1980-12-27.01

This series of twenty-four prints is a tribute to Munakata's friend and supporter in the Folk Art Movement, Kawai Kanjirō (1890–1966), now acknowledged as one of Japan's great twentieth-century potters. His kiln in the Gojō district of Kyoto was called *Shōkei* ('Valley of the Bell'). After meeting him in 1936, Muna-kata spent forty days in his house, where he learned much about the Buddhist scriptures from the master. The series was Munakata's first after the Pacific War, and shows a typically unabated vigour, each print dominated by an energetic but primitive human or near-human figure almost filling the block, half expressed as a flat black shape and half as a white; the latter is generally coloured wholly or partly in tan. All of the prints are further unified by hand-colouring in blue, purple and tan.

As in the series 'Ten Great Followers of Shaka' (Cat. 61), the artist conceived these prints both as a pair of sixfold screens (two to each leaf) and also as a Buddhist *mandala* or pictorial representation of a scheme of spiritual reality, and the subjects are designed in relation to their position on the screens and paired as black or white/coloured. Twenty of the figures are female, each representing an aspect of the natural world such as 'Morning Chrysanthemums' or 'Shells', shown in dynamic patterns in the background, and the set is completed by one Buddhist divinity (A-ō) and three figures of *rakan* (ascetics) representing this world, the intermediate stage, and the final state of nirvana. This set was Munakata's first attempt at the solid black human shapes with

white lines cut into them in reverse which became a notable feature of his work after this time. He spent many years settling the final colouring and titles of the prints, and they were not completed as a screen until 1969.

PLATE 65

64 MUNAKATA Shikō (1903–75)
Kanya, no. 25 from the series *Tōkaidō Munakata Hanga* ('Munakata's Prints of the Tōkaidō Road')

1964
Annotations: ('printed in cartouche on image, top right) *Kanaya* (title); (in pencil, lower margin) *Shikō Munakata Hatsu* ('first') 5/10, with a cipher; (in pencil, upper right margin) *Shikō ? Saku* ('? Made by Shikō'), and *Hōgan Muna Shikō* ('Eye of the Law Muna[kata] Shikō') (artist's seal); (printed red cartouche filled in in pencil, top right margin) *Kyōkin Bogaku* (?'Dark Peak of the Heart') (subtitle); (below) *Zatsukadō* ('Hall of Varied Flowers') (artist's seal)
Black and white woodblock print, with hand-colouring front and back, 5/10, 630×480 mm
Provenance: Collection of James Austin (Stanley-Baker, no. 39). Purchased in London, 1981
1981.7-30.012

Most sources state that Munakata applied colour by hand almost entirely from the back, but this example has colours applied from both sides. It is strikingly different in its tonal schemes from the example published in *Munakata Shikō Hanga Zenshū*, XI (frontispiece), where the composition is dominated by red and yellow. In this series Munakata attempted to revive a subject which had been used by artists and writers since the later seventeenth century, originally recording the posting-stations along the mainly coastal road between Edo (Tokyo) and the old capital of Kyoto. Its best-known example was the series of prints by Andō Hiroshige (1797–1858) 'Fifty-three Posting Stations on the Tōkaidō, published in the early 1830s. By the early twentieth century rural mountain and maritime scenes poetically described by Hiroshige had already been much altered by industrial and population growth, but Munakata overcame these potential difficulties by concentrating on either close-up views (as in no. 7, *Fujisawa*, a view of a massive tree trunk) or on the grand vista, as in this example dominated by Mount Fuji, and by the Expressionistic energy of his treatment. Where he used colour, he could also introduce much variation into each individual print, and indeed used different subtitles (in pencil) for those variations.

He was commissioned in 1963 to do this series by the Suruga Bank, Suruga Province (modern Shizuoku Prefecture), which includes the most dramatic part of the Tōkaidō Road where it passed near to Mount Fuji. The artist

made seven sketching trips and completed the series of sixty-two in 1964, a mixture of black and white and hand-coloured prints. Using the same sets of sketches, he made a second series of black and white prints in 1966 (*Tsuikai Munakata Hanga Tōkaidō Myōtai Byōbu*).

PLATE 63

65 MUNAKATA Shikō (1903–75)
Manten no Hoshi ('Stars of the Whole Sky')

1987
Annotations: (in pencil, lower margin) *Shikō Munakata* with cipher; (over signature) *Muna* (artist's seal); (on reverse) seal of Vergez Collection
Black and white woodblock print with hand-colouring, 347×307 mm
Provenance: Robert Vergez Collection
1986.3-21.0661

The print shows the sky above buildings in the old Shintō style, illustrating a thirty-one-syllable *waka* poem by Sadaaki Kuraku (b. 1932) whom Munakata knew. The poem is printed as part of the key-block in *katakana* script in the sky, and may tentatively be translated:

Entranced, we are strong
Entranced, we are weak
The sky filled with stars!

However, the poem is deliberately written in the *katakana* syllabary, leaving unclarified the maximum ambiguity which is inherent in the text. The poem is followed by the words *Kuraku Sadaaki Uta* ('A poem of Sadaaki Kuraku'). The ecstatic sentiments of wonder so succinctly expressed in Sadaaki's poem are typical also of Munakata's attitude to the created universe.

PLATE 66

66 SASAJIMA Kihei (1906–93)
Wind God B

1963
Annotations: (in pencil, lower margin) 4/100 K. Sasajima. 1963. *Fujin B*; (on image, lower left) *Sasa* (artist's seal)
Black and white woodblock print, 4/100, 386×524 mm
Provenance: Gaston Petit Collection
1986.3-21.0661

This copy is reproduced in black and white in Petit, II, no. 191.

Sasajima was overwhelmingly influenced by the monochrome prints of Munakata, whom he knew well; but he did not follow the master into colour prints, preferring to concentrate on black and white Buddhist and Shintō subjects with an increasingly religious intensity. The fragmentation and reintegration of his pictorial subjects are akin to certain styles of ink calligraphy which he particularly admired. This image is of the Wind God, who with the Thunder God (Raijin) is one of the most popular figures of Japanese religion, shown here as normal with a huge bag of wind across his shoulders. By 1963 Sasajima had developed a new technique of printing from a woodblock (see Introduction), but this example is printed with ink in the standard manner. According to Petit (no.191), the paper is unbleached *nisōshi*; this is particularly absorbent and accounts for the slightly blurred edges to the printed areas.

PLATE 67

67 KANAMORI Yoshio (b.1922)
Lake 38–4

1963
Annotations: (in pencil, lower margin) 4/30 *Mizu-umi –4* YOSHIO KANAMORI; (on lower margin) *Yo* (artist's seal); (on reverse) seal of Vergez Collection
Colour woodblock print, with mineral dusts, 250×326 mm
Provenance: Robert Vergez Collection
1987.3–16.0100

The scene is a very small Shintō shrine on a lake promontory or island, with a modest fence and *torii* (ceremonial gateway). It is printed in black and blue, with a pale green over which brass dust has in part been sprinkled, and an area of powdered mica bottom left, applied over an adhesive. The simplicity of the design is typical of Folk Art Movement prints, which were much influenced by the stencilled style used in textiles.

PLATE 69

68 MORI Yoshitoshi (1898–1992)
Mie o kiru ('Posturize')

1967
Annotations: ('in pencil on image) Yoshitoshi Mori '67. 16/50; (above signature) *Yoshitoshi* (artist's seal); (on image, bottom right) seal of Gaston Petit Collection; (on reverse in pencil) 1–822 Posturize (*Mie o kiru*)
Stencil print in two colours, 16/50, 696×852 mm
Provenance: Gaston Petit Collection
1986.3–21.0661

This copy is reproduced in colour in Petit, II, c.53.

The print is done on specially textured paper (*hosokawa-gami* from Sendai) with fibres of the bark of the paper mulberry showing prominently in its surface. The design is achieved through one red-ochre stencil over which another in black is partly superimposed. The black contains an adhesive giving the appearance of lacquer in the manner of the 'lacquer prints' (*urushi-e*) popular in the eighteenth century. Another version of this print uses a darker red, plus a beige and a grey stencil (Mori Yoshitoshi Kappa-ban, no.88). The Japanese title *Mie o kiru* is the phrase used of Kabuki actors when they hold a pose at a climactic point in the drama, usually to the accompaniment of a drum roll. This pose is the most famous in all Kabuki, where the hero Kamakura no Gongorō Kagemasa (always played by a member of the Ichikawa family) in samurai armour and brandishing his huge sword shouts *Shibaraku* ('Wait a moment . . .') at the villain Kiyohara no Takehira. The title of the play consequently became *Shibaraku* also. The action and history of the play are described in Halford, pp.259–62.

PLATE 68

69 MORI Yoshitoshi (1898–1992)
Bonji Fudō ('Sanskrit Fudō Myō-ō')

1968
Annotations: (in pencil on image) Yoshitoshi Mori '68 10/50; (above signature) *Yoshitoshi* (artist's seal)
Stencil print in three colours on paper brushed with grey wash, 10/50, 894×578 mm
Provenance: Gaston Petit Collection
1986.3–21.0485

The print is executed on *hosokawa-gami* paper from Sendai, which the artist has filled with a grey-wash background broadly applied with a brush. The main figure is stencilled in three colours, its whole shape first done in yellow, then green and black in the appropriate areas. The yellow subtly suggests the fire which comes from the body of Fudō, who is one of the 'Five Shining Kings', a group of deities below the rank of Buddha or Bodhisattva. Fudō ('the Immovable') was especially popular in Japan among the common people, his sword and noose at the ready to restrain evil, his ferocious demeanour frightening only to the enemies of good, and his image appears frequently in Japanese Buddhist folk art. It is not clear why Mori links this particular image to *Bonji* (the form of Sanskrit used in some schools of Japanese Buddhism).

PLATE 71

70 MORI Yoshitoshi (1898–1992)
Geisha

1970
Annotations: (in pencil on image) Yoshitoshi Mori '70; (next to signature) *Yoshitoshi* (artist's seal); (on reverse) seal of Vergez Collection
Colour woodblock print, 477×304 mm
Provenance: Robert Vergez Collection
1987.3–16.0179

The artist did use woodblock occasionally, although most of his work is stencilled, but the style was very little affected. This work is typical of his series on professional women produced mostly in the years 1976–9, illustrating geishas and the like, the majority in the costume of the later Edo period. In this example his subject is playing with an elaborately woven silken ball of a type which was recognised as a specially feminine accomplishment. As always, Mori's treatment is genially humorous, verging on the bawdy.

PLATE 70

71 MORI Yoshitoshi (1898–1992)
Kagura Dancers

1978
Annotations: (in white pigment on image) Y Mori '78 3/50; (above signature) *Yoshitoshi* (artist's seal); (on reverse) seal of Vergez Collection
Colour stencil print, 3/50, 690×515 mm
Provenance: Rober Vergez Collection
1987.3–16.0428

Mori showed a particular taste for the popular Japanese festivals, theatre and dance forms from early in his career as a print artist, beginning with *Kagura A* in 1957, which still had the crowded visual style derived from his textile designs. This example has the energetic simplicity and humour found in most of his work from 1960 onwards when he had found his true graphic manner. *Kagura* is an ancient religious dance form performed at Shintō festivals, usually in shrines themselves. It is in essence an invocation of Shintō deities (*kami*), normally including masked dances telling legends about them, but other dancers, also masked, play supporting roles. There are numerous local variations and styles over much of Japan. The humour and vitality found in most Kagura peformances appealed greatly to Mori as did their rumbustious nature. A print on a similar theme, *Futari no Dōke* (B), was one of the ten chosen by Michener and two juries for *The Modern Japanese Print. An Appreciation* (1962) under the title 'Kagura Buffoonery'; there the artist explained that the idea came from his childhood memories of such 'fools' dances in Shintō shrines.

PLATE 74

72 WATANABE Sadao (b.1913)
The Three Wise Men

1972
Annotations: (in pencil on image) SADAO WATANABE; (on reverse) seal of Vergez Collection
Colour woodblock print, 303×398 mm
Provenance: Robert Vergez Collection
1987.3–16.0346

The paper is not hand-crumpled *momigami* as in no.73 and is thinner, and the artist has, unusually for him, used woodblock. The result is a greater clarity but less depth of texture. The paper has been completely dyed or printed yellow on the facing surface; there are no brush marks as in no.73; and the colour is unvaryingly even. In spite of the low viewpoint from which the scene is taken, betraying some Western influence, the dramatically curved lines of the hills are in pure Japanese folk style, itself a popular version of the earlier *Yamato-e* painting manner. This curvilinear, patterned style is found in the hand-coloured *tanrokubon* of the first half of the seventeenth century, where the basic colours of orange, green and yellow are clearly an inspiration for Watanabe's palette, though his is not the nearly direct copy of it found in Serizawa's *Ehon Don Kihōte* (Cat. 58). Close approximations to the style and composition of *The Three Wise Men* are found, for example, in the 1646 *tanrokubon Soga Monogatari*, especially in the scenes of travel. The simplified eyes, connected across the nose, appear in many of Watanabe's works and are also derived from the Buddhist folk style which was first widely publicised in the prints of Munakata.

PLATE 72

73 WATANABE Sadao (b.1913)
The Flight into Egypt

1974
Annotations: (handwritten in white pigment, lower margin) 14/70 SADAO WATANABE 1974; (on reverse in pencil, top left) *Tōhi* ('flight'); (on reverse, bottom right) seal of Vergez Collection
Colour stencil print on hand-crumpled paper, 14/70, 630×531 mm
Provenance: Robert Vergez Collection
1987.3-16.0453

The top of the print clearly shows the brush marks with which deep red was applied over the front surface of the whole sheet. All of the other colours are applied over this (green, yellow, white and black). It is not clear from observation alone whether these are all applied by stencil. It is stated of the similarly pigmented print *Listening* (1960) 'First, red background applied to the entire paper surface with a red brush. Second, white, green and yellow colors applied by hand with a brush. Third, black overprinted in one impression by means of a stencil of *shibugami* . . .' (Michener, p. 30). (*Shibugami* is a special layered paper treated with persimmon juice used for stencils.) This is not a direct quotation from the artist and may not be correct. The overall design is defined, as is usual, by the black stencil. The hand-crumpled *momigami* paper and the brush marks give a much greater sense of depth and vitality than in Cat. 72. The manner of the landscape background is very close to the dyed textile styles of the Folk Art Movement and of *tanrokubon* (see Cat. 58).

PLATE 75

74 MATSUBARA Naoko (b.1937)
Walden Pond (cover for the portfolio box for 'Solitude')

1971
Annotations: (printed on label pasted to bottom right corner) SOLITUDE Matsubara,

with *Nao* (artist's seal)
Green and white woodblock print, pasted on to board, II/XXV, 420×805 mm
Provenance: Purchased from the artist, 1980
1980.12.24.01

'Solitude' is an essay from *Walden* by the American writer Henry David Thoreau (1817–62) and is separately printed, as part of the portfolio, on *kōzo* paper decorated with monochrome woodblock vignettes by Matsubara, sewn up in the traditional Japanese *fukuro-tōji* manner. The portfolio itself includes eleven woodblock prints illustrating ideas from the essay (apart from a portrait of Thoreau himself), while the twelfth is this cover subject of Walden Pond, printed in two colours of green which subtly reproduce the effects of the gradations of ink-painting. The text speaks in terms of a deep sense of spiritual integration with the pond near to which the reclusive Thoreau lived alone in the woods, and has a contemplative concentration which has obvious affinities with some Japanese religious attitudes. The prints, austere in tone, are notable for their sensitivity to Thoreau's lyrical text.

The colophon helpfully gives all the history of the project. It was published by Aquarius Press, Baltimore and New York, in an edition of 200. A further twenty-five sets of a 'preferred edition' were issued, with all the prints and the text signed by the artist (of which this is one) and a further edition of 100 of the prints alone, including their cover subject, were issued, also signed by the artist. All the prints but one were done on *hōsho* paper made by Iwano Ichibei, designated as a 'Possessor of Intangible Cultural Assets' by the Japanese Government (*hōsho* was the customary paper of *Ukiyo-e* prints in the seventeenth to nineteenth centuries.)

Much of Matsubara's work is close in style to Munakata's – vigorous, with surprising perspectives and a sense of movement – but here she has added to it a sense of texture reminiscent of East Asian ink-painting and also an elegant patterning of landscape typical of later twentieth-century *Nihonga* painting. The result is a classic of print design.

PLATE 73

75 KIDA Yasuhiko (b.1944)
Yakushiji Hana Eshiki ('Yakushiji Flower Ceremony')

1985
Annotations: (in ink, lower margin) 13/50 1985 *Yakushiji Hana Eshiki* Y. Kida; (next to signature) *Yasu* (artist's seal); (embossed on lower margin, left) Y. KIDA enclosed in the character *Ki*
Colour woodblock print, 370×359 mm
Provenance: Given by the artist, 1989
1989.2-3.07

The Yakushiji is one of the most venerable Buddhist temples in Japan, situated in the

Nishinokyō district outside Nara, which was Japan's capital in the years AD 710–84. It is the national headquarters of the now small but then influential Hossō School of Buddhism. Its Main Hall (*Kondō*), originally eighth century but rebuilt, houses the great bronze triad of Yakushi, the Buddha associated with healing, flanked by images of the Bodhisattvas Nikkō and Gekkō associated with the sun and moon. These images are late seventh to eighth century in date and one of Japan's most famous and revered religious sculptural groups. It is the main image (over two metres tall) that Kida shows with banks of artificial flowers presented at the annual flower ceremony from 30 March to 5 April. The print is one of a large series in varying formats on festivals all over Japan which the artist treats in an affectionate, sometimes gently ironic, folk style. His own contributions to this style are a sense of energy and movement, and a tendency to visually dramatic close-ups, as in this example.

The flower ceremony was inaugurated by the Emperor Horikawa in AD 1107 after the Empress's recovery from illness following prayers to Yakushi at the temple. He ordered the court ladies to make artificial flowers (it then being winter) and presented twelve vases of them to the Yakushiji, which subsequently repeated the event annually by making its own flowers. Ten types of flower are now presented, made of paper rather than the silk which was first used.

PLATE 76

76 ONCHI Kōshirō (1891–1955)
Ginza no Tasogare-doki ('Dusk in Ginza'), from Fujisawa Calendar

1948
Annotations: (woodblock-printed below image) calendar for September and October 1949; advertisements for products of Fujisawa Yakuhin Kōgyō Company and Company's name and logo; (on reverse in movable-type printing) artist's description of print; (on reverse) seal of Vergez Collection
Colour woodblock print, 360×245 mm
Provenance: Robert Vergez Collection
1989.3-14.0876

This is one of three prints by Onchi contributed to this portfolio calendar, a type still common in Japan. The other three are by Hiratsuka Un'ichi, who seems to have been the more active partner and also designed the cover sheet and calendars themselves. All six designs were also issued separately as sheet-prints. One of these, *Kyoto in the snow* (January–February), is in the British Museum's collection and was published by Smith (1), no. 19, under the title *Young Woman on a Verandah*. Onchi's other contribution is *On the Inland Sea* (May–June). Hiratsuka's are *By Lake Shinji* (March–April), *Sapporo in Summer* (September–October) and *Late Autumn on Mount Aso* (November–December). The three images by Onchi are published in Onchi (1), supplement nos 18–20, where they are dated 1947. The artist's poetic prose piece on the reverse describes the strange twilight world of the Ginza entertainment district of Tokyo under the post-war occupation, here represented by two American women.

PLATE 77

77 ONCHI Kōshirō (1891–1955)
Poème No. 7: Landscape of May

1948
Annotations: (stencilled on image, top right) Onzi; (on reverse) seal of Vergez Collection
Woodblock print, 385×487 mm
Provenance: Robert Vergez Collection. This copy was exhibited at the National Museum of Modern Art, Tokyo, July–August 1976
1989.3–14.075

As with the portrait of Hagiwara (Cat. 30) and several others, a memorial edition was made after Onchi's death by Hirai Kōichi (1967), based on the original blocks but considerably tidied up, and with clear, simple, elegant colours far removed from the artist's turbulent, impassioned tones, which recall the effects of brush and oil paint rather than woodblock. The reprint was published in black and white in Smith (1), no. 14. The intensely lyrical composition bears some resemblance to the layout of a Japanese rock and sand garden, and seems to have inspired a whole body of work by Onchi's pupil Takahashi Rikio (Cat. 114–15).

PLATE 78

78 ONCHI Kōshirō (1891–1955)
Form No. 3: Uprise of Blue

1948
Annotations: (stencilled on image, bottom right) form nr. 3 Koshiro Onchi; (in red) G; (on reverse) seal of Vergez Collection
Colour woodblock print, 557×456 mm
Provenance: Mrs M. Evans Collection; Robert Vergez Collection. This copy was exhibited at the National Museum of Modern Art, Tokyo, July–August 1976, and the Shōtō Art Museum, Shibuya, Tokyo, July–August 1982
1989.3–14.076

This example is reproduced in Onchi (1), no. 298, and no other copy seems to be recorded. *Form No. 3* is one of a series of reverberantly coloured abstracts beginning in 1947, each of them triumphantly celebrating one dominant tone. Others are *Forme No. 2: Symphony of Green* (1947), *Poème No. 7: Landscape of May* (Cat. 77) and *Forme No. 7: Grotesque (1) b*. All of these are in the collection of the British Museum. Onchi was apt to use European words such as 'form' and 'forme' indiscriminately.

PLATE 80

79 ONCHI Kōshirō (1891–1955)
Poème No. 7 (?10): Nihil

1949
Annotations: (stencilled on image, bottom right) onzi poeme no 7; (in pencil) 'Nihil' – 49; (on reverse in ink on label) Poem No 7. Nihil 5. – 49 *Mōshi Aato Ten*; (on reverse) seal of Vergez Collection
Colour woodblock print, 605×511 mm
Provenance: Mrs M. Evans Collection; Robert Vergez Collection. This copy was exhibited at the National Museum of Modern Art, Tokyo, July–August 1982, and the Centre Georges Pompidou, Paris, December 1981–March 1982 (catalogue, p. 74).
1989.3–14.063

This example is reproduced in Onchi (1), no. 310, and called 'Poème No. 10'. This may be correct, in spite of the evidence on the print itself, since the earlier Cat. 77 is apparently genuinely *Poème No. 7*. (*Japon des Avant Gardes* also calls it 'Poème No. 7'). This rather grand piece might be regarded as a happy return by Onchi to the Futurist and Constructivist styles he had been so profoundly influenced by in his youth, especially in the days when he was co-editing the poetry and art magazine *Tsukuhae* (1914–15). Such works had never found much of a public in Japan, and abstraction had been virtually banned during the Pacific War.

PLATE 79

80 ONCHI Kōshirō (1891–1955)
Image No. 7: Black Cat (a)

1952
Annotations: none; (on reverse) seal of Vergez Collection
Colour paperblock print, 499×361 mm
Provenance: Mrs M. Evans Collection; Robert Vergez Collection. This copy was exhibited at the Shōtō Art Museum, Shibuya, Tokyo, July–August 1982
1989.3–14.081

There is an *Image No. 7: Black Cat (b)* from the same year, which is a completely different design (Honolulu Academy of Arts). The *(a)* version catalogued here was the one used for Onchi (1), no. 384. The extraordinary simplicity of this design, printed from just two cut-out blocks of paper, is closer to the starkness of traditional Japanese calligraphy. The results of this experimental technique are technically messy, but the famously self-critical Onchi was all the same content to let it survive. There is an account of Onchi's method of printing with paperblocks in Statler (1), pp. 26–7. The tendency for the colour to ooze outside the block is described there and is visible in this example.

PLATE 83

81 HIRATSUKA Un'ichi (b.1895)
Matsue Tsuda no Matsubara ('View of Pines in Matsue Tsuda')

1947
Annotations: (on image, bottom right) *Un* (artist's seal); (printed, top right margin) *Matsue Tsuda no Matsubara* (title); (printed, bottom right margin) *Hiratsuka Un'ichi*; (on reverse) seal of Vergez Collection
Colour woodblock print, 400×325 mm
Provenance: Robert Vergez Collection
1987.3–16.0487

One of the artist's most ambitious colour prints, and one of his last in colour, this work shows an avenue of Japanese red pines at Tsuda in his native city of Matsue (Shimane Prefecture). As in Cat. 24, he shows himself to have been one of the most distinguished colourists of the *Sōsaku Hanga* movement, avoiding the lavishness of colour work so noticeable in some later woodblock landscapists such as Unno Mitsuhiro (1939–79).

PLATE 84

82 HIRATSUKA Un'ichi (b.1895)
Steps to the Jakkōin, Kyoto

1960
Annotations: (in pencil, lower margin) *Jakkoin Sandō, Kyōto* (title), Un-ichi Hiratsuka 1960 40/80; (on image, lower left) *Un* (artist's seal); (on reverse) seal of Vergez Collection
Woodblock print, 40/80, 479×322 mm
Provenance: Robert Vergez Collection
1987.3–16.0396

This print represents the artist at the peak of his powers in the monochrome medium and on the larger scale he adopted in the post-war years, shortly before his departure to live in the USA. The density of the black, the result of constant overprinting, almost overwhelms the white of the paper, and the result partly recalls the wood-engraving style he favoured in the 1920s and 30s. The Jakkōin is a very picturesque Imperial Buddhist temple at Ōhara to the north-east of Kyoto, set in a wooded hillside, with a tradition since the later nineteenth century of patronising artists, especially local ones.

PLATE 81

83 MAEKAWA Senpan
(1888–1960)
Woman in Hot Spring Bathroom

1949
Annotations: (printed in red on image) Maekawa Senpan
Colour woodblock print, 503×432 mm
Provenance: Robert Vergez Collection (purchased by him directly from the artist's widow)
1987.3–16.0416

In common with many of his countrymen Maekawa was devoted to the bath-houses which abound in every area of the country where there are *onsen* (natural hot springs), and which he enthusiastically toured and recorded. The classic type of bath-house was made of cypress wood, including the bath itself, giving off a rich scent when in contact with hot water or steam. It is this almost tangible atmosphere which the artist has vividly captured in a few simple colours. According to Statler (1), no. 26, this is a bath in the *onsen* town of Beppu in Ōita Prefecture on the east coast of Kyushu. Statler also states that the edition was of five only, after which the artist destroyed the three colour blocks, though not the key-block which was of *katsura*. There is a much more common reprint of this famous subject by Katō, presumably made with recut colour blocks, as prophesied by Statler.

PLATE 82

84 MAEKAWA Senpan
(1888–1960)
Aquarium at Mitohama

1954
Annotations: (printed in red on image, bottom right) Maekawa Senpan; (in pencil, lower right margin) Senpan Maekawa; (on reverse) seal of Vergez Collection
Colour woodblock print, 334×265 mm
Provenance: Robert Vergez Collection
1987.3–16.0606

Senpan was already fifty-seven by the end of the Pacific War and the oldest of the established *Sōsaku Hanga* artists. By temperament and age he was disinclined to change his style, expanding gladly instead into the gradually larger formats which were becoming popular among foreign connoisseurs. He is quoted in Statler (1), p. 47, as saying '. . . creative prints were small and amateurish in those days (ie 1927). I was always sure that we had to make them bigger and better'. This scene typifies much of that gritty, simplified, yet colourful manner which the pre-war *Sōsaku Hanga* artists had sought after, but on a larger and more optimistic scale. The print is executed with simple poster colours on *torinoko* paper, which were Senpan's normal materials. Mitohama is a beach on the sea near to the town of Numazu in Shizuoka Prefecture, looking across the bay towards Mount Fuji in the distance. The Aquarium is still a tourist attraction there.

PLATE 85

85 MAEKAWA Senpan
(1888–1960)
Akita Dancer

1954
Annotations: (printed on image, bottom right) Maekawa Senpan; (on reverse) seal of Vergez Collection
Colour woodblock print, 386×289 mm

Provenance: Robert Vergez Collection
1987.3–16.0605

Akita Prefecture, on the north-west coast of Honshu, is isolated and mountainous and hence an area where folk culture has survived well. Its many hot spirngs would have been an additional attraction to the bath-loving Senpan. The artist returned frequently in his career to the subject of rosy-faced peasant women depicted in a style close to that of the cartoons by which he made his living. The colour scheme is apparently simple but balanced with extreme care; the print has a typical clarity derived from the artist's not mixing any paste into the pigments and from the force with which he took his impressions with the *baren*.

PLATE 87

86 YAMAGUCHI Susumu
(1897–1983)
Taishō Pond

1952
Annotations: (in pencil, lower margin) –52 31/50 S. YAMAGUCHI; (on image, bottom left) *Yamaguchi Susumu* (artist's seal); (on reverse in pencil) *Taishō Ike*; (on reverse) seal of Vergez Collection
Colour woodblock print, 31/50, 460×611 mm
Provenance: Robert Vergez Collection
1987.3–16.0454

Taishō Pond is a lake which was formed in the year 1915, early in the Taishō era, when the volcano Yakedake (still active) erupted and formed a natural dam on the Kamikōchi River in the northern Japan Alps in Nagano Prefecture. To this day the skeletons of the trees killed by the inundation stand in the water, making it a haunting scene. According to Statler (1), no. 68, writing in 1956, only twenty copies had been made at that time of an unlimited edition. Demand was presumably lifted, as in the case of many prints in Statler's influential book, resulting in a further limited edition of fifty. Statler states that there were eight blocks of *katsura* with fourteen printing stages on *torinoko* paper (Statler (1), pl. 68, p. 112). The scene gains much of its grandeur from the use of pure ink (*sumi*) as the black pigment, and its atmosphere from the artist's use of very wet pigments and paper.

PLATE 88

87 AZECHI Umetarō (b.1902)
Kazan no Michi ('Volcano Path')

1952
Annotations: (in pencil, lower margin) –52 U. AZECHI 47/50; (on image) U (artist's seal, highly stylised); (on reverse in pencil) *Kazan no michi*; (on reverse) seal of Vergez Collection
Colour woodblock print, 47/50, 324×438 mm
Provenance: Robert Vergez Collection
1987.3–16.0381

The resemblance in subject to Cat. 86 by Yamaguchi Susumu is not surprising. He and Azechi were close friends and both were devoted to the mountains of Japan, and as recorded in 1956 by Statler (1), p. 114, Azechi would visit Yamaguchi in the mountains in Nagano Prefecture. Azechi's stark, barren treatment is far, however, from Yamaguchi's sombre but romantic approach. Statler gives the English title for this print as 'Remains of a Volcano', and identifies the scene as an active volcano crater near the summit of Mount Takachiho in the Kirishima National Park, Kagoshima Prefecture, southern Kyushu. There were six blocks (plywood faced with *shina*) and nine printing stages on *torinoko* paper. The density of the sky and the red crater derive from the use of tube water-colours; the other areas are done in poster colours.

PLATE 89

88 AZECHI Umetarō (b.1902)
Tori o Idaku ('Holding a Bird')

1956 (printed 1972)
Annotations: (in pencil, lower margin) *Tori o idaku* – 56 AP U AZECHI; (in pencil, left margin) *Okuru Chikushin Sama* ('A present for Mr Chikushin' = Gaston Petit); (on image, bottom right) U (artist's seal)
Colour woodblock print, artist's proof, 452×350 mm
Provenance: Gaston Petit Collection
1986.3–21.094

This copy was reproduced in colour in Petit, c. 7, and in the Descriptive List of Plates, pp. 6–7, Petit states 'The print, a personal gift from the artist to the author, was printed in 1972 from the artist's old blocks, one of which had been amended. The artist signed it a.p. and dated it 1956'. The original edition of 1956 was of fifty sheets. Petit also gives the following technical details: '8 blocks of *Shina*-faced plywood, 15 printing stages. Paper: kōzo from Eichizen [*sic*], Fukui Prefecture. Pigment: Turner Artists' Poster Colours.'

PLATE 90

89 AZECHI Umetarō (b.1902)
Kenkoku ni Tatsu Yama-otoko
('Mountain Man Standing in a Circular Valley')

1967
Annotations: (in pencil, lower margin) *Kenkoku ni Tatsu Yama-otoko* 67 AP U.AZECHI; (on image) U (artist's seal)
Colour woodblock print, artist's proof, 444×355 mm
Provenance: Gaston Petit Collection
1986.3–21.095

Petit gives the English title as 'Mountaineer in a Circle' and reproduces a copy of it as no. 23 (in black and white). In the Descriptive List of

Plates, p. 8, he states 'Although the blocks were first cut in 1967, the first attempts of the artist were not convincing and he discarded the print until early 1972. Trying new colours, he printed two a.p. in preparation for an exhibition. The print reproduced here is one of those two' (that is, the copy then in the Hildebrand Collection, London, probably passed on by Petit; the British Museum's copy is presumably the other). The official edition then made was of 150 sheets, using four blocks of *shina*-faced plywood and twelve printing stages on *kōzo* paper from Echizen, Fukui Prefecture; the pigments were Turner Artists' Poster Colours. This is one of Azechi's strongest images of the spiritual intensity experienced by the mountaineer.

PLATE 91

90 ONO Tadashige (1909–90)
Sakura ('Cherry Blossoms')

1957
Annotations: (in pink pigment on image, bottom right) T Ono; (on accompanying label) *Sakura* 1/20 1957 *nen Ono Tadashige* Tadashige Ono; (on printed label with handwriting and typing):

SOSAKU-HANGA *Sosaku-Hanga* ORIGINAL WORKS OF ART SELF CARVED SELF PRINTED
ARTIST Tadashige Ono TITLE Cherry NISHI-GINZA TOKYO JAPAN The Yoseido Gallery;
(on small label) Y.4; (on further printed label)
YOSEIDO GALLERY GINZA TOKYO
Colour woodblock print, 1/2, 310×450mm
Provenance: Gaston Petit Collection
1986.3–21.0557

This is one of the earliest prints by Ono to show a greater optimism after the harrowing events of his earlier personal life, the disasters of the Pacific War and the isolation which his political stance had imposed on him. The change of tone is marked in his art by his using subjects from the natural world and landscape for the first time, and a resulting lightening of his palette. Because of this lightening his technique of laying one pigment over another begins to resemble the effects of stained glass. The simplification of forms, always latently there in his work, also becomes more apparent about this time, and in this example the stylisation of the hills and of the flowering cherries reveals a more traditional Japanese sensibility. Even so Ono still links this ancient Japanese pictorial motif with an urban scene, though this time on the edge of green hills, and for once not overwhelming the natural world but itself softened by it.

As with many of his prints from this period onwards, the work is accompanied by a large hand-inscribed label on fine Japanese paper flecked with the black bark of the paper mulberry (also Cat. 91–2).

PLATE 92

91 ONO Tadashige (1909–90)
Kawa ('River')

1957
Annotations: (in red pigment on image, bottom right) T Ono; (on accompanying label) *Kawa* Tadashige Ono
Woodblock print, 293×446mm
Provenance: Gaston Petit Collection
1986.3–21.0556

Throughout his life Ono reverted again and again to the theme of the urban river, apparently always remembering the industrialised banks of the Sumida River in Tokyo near which he was born. In the same year (1957) as this example he produced an almost monochrome-blue scene of Tokyo docklands entitled *Sumida River*, full of the old political bleakness. In *River*, however, the familiar theme is redeemed by the rosy light of a dawn or sunset, and by the sinister but not entirely soulless figure of a cat. In this print Ono's powers as a colourist are shown at their most effective, using overprinting in blue and rose over a black-dyed paper and white underprinting to produce a twilight texture of extaordinary density and reverberance.

PLATE 86

92 ONO Tadashige (1909–90)
Asa ('Dawn')

1964
Annotations: (in red pigment on image) T Ono; (on label) *Asa* 3/20 1964 *nen Ono Tadashige* Tadashige Ono; (on reverse) seal of Gaston Petit
Woodblock print, 444×357mm
Provenance: Gaston Petit Collection
1986.3–21.0553

The glowing colours of this print show most effectively Ono's special technical achievement of converting an essentially oil-painting style into a graphic medium which is uniquely his own. Although the later influences of Maurice Vlaminck and Bernard Buffet (then becoming very popular in Japan) are very obvious in his pictorial method, the print itself glows with an almost three-dimensional presence and a palette which could not be confused with that of any other artist. As with other prints of his later years, nature and a more rural way of life seem to be gradually pushing out the urban desolation which had dominated the first half of his career. The building is a traditional wooden one in rural style, its morning bleakness lightened by the pecking bird. Like all his later prints, this example has a large label, originally attached to the reverse, inscribed in Ono's own hand on handmade Japanese paper.

PLATE 93

93 SAITŌ Kiyoshi (b.1907)
Solitude, Onrian, Kyoto

1955
Annotations: (in pencil, lower margin) SOLITUDE ONRIAN KYOTO 86/150 1955; (on image, lower right) *Kiyoshi* (square artist's seal); (below seal in pencil) Kiyoshi Saitō; (on reverse) *Kiyoshi* (oblong artist's seal); (on accompanying slip, printed in woodblock) Self-carved self-printed KIYOSHI SAITŌ, with *Kiyoshi* (oblong artist's seal as above)
Colour woodblock print, 86/150, 332×478mm
Provenance: Given by Sir Stanley Unwin, 1958
1958.2–8.02

This print, reproduced in black and white in Smith (1), no.92, is an early example of the very effective simplification which Saitō began to use about this time, and which ushered in the best period of his work. The influence of Mondrian, whom he greatly admired, shows in his successfully simplified forms, while he has retained an austere palette suitable to the muted tones of Kyoto temple architecture and garden scenes. He has also made much use of the wood grains of the blocks. The relatively large edition of 150 shows how popular he had already become, mostly with American buyers.

PLATE 95

94 SAITŌ Kiyoshi (b.1907)
Maiko, Kyoto, H

1961
Annotations: (in pencil, lower margin) MAIKO KYOTO (H) 116/300 1961; (on image, lower left) *Kiyoshi* (square artist's seal); (below seal, written in brush and white pigment) Kiyoshi Saitō; (on accompanying slip, printed in woodblock) self-carved self-printed KIYOSHI SAITŌ with *Kiyoshi* (oblong artist's seal); (on reverse) seal of Vergez Collection
Colour woodblock print, 116/300, 602×452mm
Provenance: Robert Vergez Collection
1987.3–16.0440

Saitō experimented for some years after the Pacific War with human subjects all more or less influenced by Western artists, from Gauguin to Munch to Buffet; but it was only after his discovery of the virtues of that abstract patterning inherent in much Japanese art that he was able to produce a print of a human figure of this strength. Significantly, it is a back view, focusing on the made-up back of the neck which has long been considered most erotically expressive in the Japanese woman. *Maiko* are the young geishas of Kyoto, celebrated for their sweetness of dress and face, and portrayed frequently and realistically by *Nihonga* artists from the city. Saitō's version, by contrast, selects the salient features – the neck, the characteristic hair-style, the floral or decorated

59

hairpin, and above all the great hanging sash, which he prints in two colours from a highly grained block of wood. The popularity of this image is indicated by the high edition number quoted.

PLATE 96

95 SHINAGAWA Takumi
(b.1908)
Haiyū ('Kabuki Actor')

1953
Annotations: (in pencil, lower margin) *Haiyū*
TAKUMI SHINAGAWA 1953; (on reverse) seal of Vergez Collection
Colour woodblock print, 552×357mm
Provenance: Robert Vergez Collection
1987.3-16.0438

Shinagawa, who worked in a number of graphic techniques, became a member of Onchi Kōshirō's Ichimoku-kai (First Thursday Society) which met from 1939 to 1950 as the core of the *Sōsaku Hanga* movement during the Pacific War and Occupation. The influence of Onchi was very much directed to simplification of forms, as in the later works of Azechi Umetarō, Yamaguchi Gen and Yoshida Masaji. This print shows the same tendencies, as well as similar influences from European art seen in Saitō Kiyoshi (Cat.93-4). Like Saitō, Shinagawa uses these models in combination with a very Japanese emphasis on the grain and texture of the woodblocks themselves. The actor in question is not specific but is wearing the blue-striped make-up of villainous parts in the traditional popular Kabuki theatre.

According to Statler (1), no.44, *Kabuki Actor* was an unlimited edition. It was made with five blocks of plywood faced with *shina* and five printing stages on *torinoko* paper. The pigments were German, except for the white which was Japanese *gofun* (shell-white). Powdered mica was also used to heighten the white and black areas.

PLATE 98

96 MAEDA Tōshirō (1904-90)
Yoroidake

1965 (this copy printed 1972)
Annotations: (on image, bottom right) *Mae* (artist's seal); (in pencil, lower margin) '72 3/20; (on reverse) seal of Vergez Collection
Colour linocut print, 3/20, 465×584mm
Provenance: Robert Vergez Collection
1987.3-16.0421

A yellow label, pasted to the back in inscribed brush and ink in the artist's own hand in Japanese, may be translated 'Yoroidake (1965) Exhibited at the Brussels exhibition of modern Japanese prints and the exhibition of the Japanese Print Society; Shunkyōkai Committee Member, Maeda Tōshirō' with the seal *Mae*. Maeda, like many woodblock artists who worked on after 1945, found himself slipping

into a gradual simplification of forms; this was derived both from historic tendencies in Japanese art and the more recent example of Western abstraction, now completely respectable in the post-war era. The influence of Maeda's other favourite technique of linocut is even more apt to produce clear-cut forms. Yoroidake ('Armour Peak') is a prominent mountain in the south of Ōita Prefecture on the east side of Kyushu.

PLATE 99

97 INAGAKI Tomoo (1902-80)
Senobi suru neko ('Stretching Cat')

1963
Annotations: (printed on image, top left) Tomo; (on reverse) seal of Vergez Collection
Colour woodblock print, 16/50,
585×445mm
Provenance: Robert Vergez Collection
1987.3-16.0400

An early *Sōsaku Hanga* artist, Inagaki did not find his favourite subject of cats until after the Pacific War. From the 1950s onwards he did little else, exploring the one subject with a typically Japanese intensity. Here he uses a favourite device of combining various stages of one cat's movement, and dominates the print with brown pigments which were also characteristic of his later work. Like most Japanese artists who have used cats as subject-matter, Inagaki sees them as somewhat sinister and unsympathetic to human beings.

PLATE 97

98 SEKINO Jun'ichirō (1914-88)
Bunraku Puppet

1950s
Annotations: (in pencil on image, bottom right) Jun Sekino; (above signature) *Jun* (artist's seal); (in pencil, lower margin) 108/150; (on reverse) seal of Vergez Collection
Colour woodblock print, 108/150,
462×316mm
Provenance: Robert Vergez Collection
1987.3-16.0250

The date is supplied by the artist's widow. Among Sekino's many subjects for prints the Bunraku puppet theatre, which dates from the seventeenth century, was a favourite. In this work he shows the puppet standing without the two or three black-robed manipulators present in actual performance. So great is the sense of being alive which the operators are able to put into their puppets that this semi-lifeless pose must slightly shock anyone who has seen the Bunraku in action. Sekino also provides a virtually blank background which disguises the fact that puppets are less than one metre high and gives the illusion of a full-sized human being. As with the masks of the Nō drama, Bunraku puppet heads are types rather

than individual characters; however, this example represents Osome, tragic heroine of the play *The Love Suicide at Amijima* by Chikamatsu Monzaemon (1653-1724).

PLATE 94

99 SEKINO Jun'ichirō (1914-88)
Mitsuke, from *Tōkaidō Gojūsan Tsugi* ('Fifty-three Stations of the Tōkaidō Road')

1967 (?1961)
Annotations: (in pencil on image, lower right) Jun. Sekino; (above signature) *Jun* (artist's seal); (on reverse in Roman, top margin) MITSUKE-53 STATIONS ON TOKAIDO (1967); (on reverse) seal of Vergez Collection
Colour woodblock print, 422×550mm
Provenance: Robert Vergez Collection
1987.3-16.0446

Sekino preceded Munakata (Cat.64) in 1960 by starting a modern series based on the old highway between Tokyo and Kyoto, but it took him until 1974 to complete it, in contrast to the dynamic speed with which the older master finished his extended set. Sekino more conventionally produced fifty-five prints (fifty-three posting-stations plus the beginning at Tokyo and the end at Kyoto), as Andō Hiroshige had done in the 1830s. Mitsuke, near to Hamamatsu in Shizuoka Prefecture, is about halfway along the old road and is now in the town of Iwata. Merritt and Yamada (p.259) give the subtitle of this print as *Stone Embankment Along the River* (that is, the Tenryūgawa River) and the date as November 1961. If the note on the reverse of the British Museum's example is correct, then it must be a later reprint by the artist, or by his printers Kobayashi Sōkichi, Yoneda Minoru and Iwase Koichi. *Mitsuke* is a notable example of Sekino's skilful use of wood grain.

PLATE 100

100 YAMAGUCHI Gen (1896-76)
Mou

1962
Annotations: (in pencil on image, bottom right) Gen Yamaguchi; (in pencil, lower margin) 32/50, 1962 MOU
Colour woodblock print, 32/50,
798×616mm
Provenance: Gaston Petit Collection
1986.3-21.0847

In Petit (Descriptive List of Plates, p.53) it is explained that '[Yamaguchi] personally feels titling to be unnecessary, and only does so to satisfy the buyer. His titles do not necessarily reflect the content of the print, but may be simply words that hold some appeal for him'. This print was executed with six plywood blocks, one faced with *hō-no-ki* and five with *shina*. The pigments were poster colours and the paper *torinoko*. This work has much of the austere, grainy grandeur Yamaguchi learned from his association with Onchi.

PLATE 101

101 YAMAGUCHI Gen (1896–76)
Kyorai ('Past and Future')

1965
Annotations: (in pencil, lower margin)
['*Kyorai*'] 1965.v.26. Gen Yamaguchi
Colour woodblock print, 562×413 mm
Provenance: Gaston Petit Collection
1986.3–21.0846

For Yamaguchi's titles see Cat. 100. No edition or other number is quoted on the print, so it is assumed that it was an unofficial pull given to Gaston Petit with whom the artist worked closely. The hot red background of *Kyorai* clearly owes much to Onchi's practice of making each work completely individual from the point of view of its colour.

PLATE 102

102 YAMAGUCHI Gen (1896–76)
The Positive and Negative

March 1970
Annotations: (in pencil, lower margin)
A.P. THE POSITIVE AND NEGATIVE 1970, III
Gen Yamaguchi
Colour woodblock print, 648×477 mm
Provenance: Gaston Petit Collection
1986.3–21.0842

This example was illustrated in black and white in Petit, II, p. 239; for Yamaguchi's titles see Cat. 100. This assured exploration of opposites relies on ancient East Asian philosophical traditions of *yin* and *yang* (negative and positive) for its confident balance. The official edition was of fifty sheets, but this extra sheet was given to Gaston Petit by the artist, who worked in Petit's studio from time to time and was a friend. According to Petit, the artist used eight blocks of plywood faced with *shina*, on *torinoko* paper with poster colours.

PLATE 106

103 YOSHIDA Masaji (1917–71)
Kagirinaku No. 1 ('Without Limit, No. 1')

1958
Annotations: (in pencil on image, bottom right) Masaji Yoshida; (above signature) *Masaji* (artist's seal); (in pencil, lower right margin) 1960 *Kagirinaku* No. 1 9/30
Woodblock print, 9/30, 528×448 mm
Provenance: Gaston Petit Collection
1986.3–21.0903

This monumental piece is related to the *Silence* prints of the same period (one of them, *Shizuka Nagare*, is reproduced in colour in Smith, Harris

and Clark, no. 242) in which the artist found what proved to be a temporary sense of peace. His very individual system of registration (see Introduction) was particularly suited to achieving the serenity of surface found in his works of this period.

PLATE 103

104 YOSHIDA Masaji (1917–71)
Mukashi No. 8 ('Ancient No. 8')

1961
Annotations: (in pencil, lower margin) 1961. *Mukashi* No 8 2/20 Masaji Yoshida; (on image, bottom right) *Masaji* (artist's seal; (on reverse) seal of Vergez Collection
Colour woodblock print, 2/20, 652×627 mm
Provenance: Robert Vergez Collection
1985.10–23.020

This is a particularly effective example of the artist's use of gentle overprinting to produce the sort of subtle shifts and variations of tone found in traditional Japanese architecture and gardens. It also shows how he made use of very damp paper to produce 'blotting' effects at the edges of his shapes in certain prints. In spite of the sureness of this powerfully central design, there is an unease at its heart which characterises Yoshida's last decade of work.

PLATE 105

105 YOSHIDA Masaji (1917–71)
Kūkan No 13 ('Space No. 13')

1962
Annotations: (in pencil, lower margin) 1962 *Kūkan* No 13 1/30 Masaji Yoshida; (on image, bottom right) *Masaji* (artist's seal); (on reverse) seal of Vergez Collection
Colour woodblock print, 1/30, 605×460 mm
Provenance: Robert Vergez Collection
1985.10–15.015

In the early 1960s Yoshida was doing a lot of work of great density and intensity using only one main ink block carved with considerable detail in herringbone patterns and printed over one or two grainy colours. His earlier practice of carving all of his blocks from one surface, like a jigsaw puzzle, had given him a notably unified approach to the production of his prints. Unlike Onchi or any of his other main pupils, whose work was characterised by elegant, lyrical and even detached abstraction, Yoshida's work increasingly displayed a sense of menace, despair or unease.

PLATE 104

106 YOSHIDA Masaji (1917–71)
Geijutsu no Kabe, No 3 ('Wall of Craft, No. 3')

1965
Annotations: (in pencil, lower margin) 1965 *Geijutsu no Kabe* No 3 6/30 Masaji Yoshida;

(on image, bottom right) *Masaji* (artist's seal)
Colour woodblock print, 6/30, 630×945 mm
Provenance: Gaston Petit Collection
1986.3–21.0901

An even more extreme example of the tendencies described in Cat. 105, this grand print is one of Yoshida's most disturbing compositions, contrasting extreme detail, representing the artist's own craft, with an encroaching blackness at its heart. The print is done with only two colours, black and purple.

PLATE 107

107 MAKI Haku (b.1924)
Work 73–50–A (Nothing)

1973
Annotations: (in pencil, lower margin) *Haku Maki* Work 73–50–A (Nothing) 5/60; (on image, in red) *Haku Maki* (artist's seal)
Black and white woodblock print, 5/60, 845×840 mm
Provenance: Gaston Petit Collection
1986.3–21.0420.A

This and Cat. 108 form a grand pair, which might well be mounted in Japan as a twofold screen for display. The 'Nothing' refers to the character *Mu* ('not') which dominates the composiiton and is one of the written characters practised repeatedly by Zen Buddhist monks and adherents as part of their spiritual exercises, an expression of the void, or nothingness, at the heart of existence which has to be grasped intuitively before its converse can be understood. To this idea Maki has added the concept of *yin* and *yang* (Japanese *in* and *on*), the negative and positive essences which are equal and which unite to form the phenomenal universe. This concept, originally derived from Chinese Daoism, came to permeate the thought and culture of East Asia. Calligraphy in black ink on white paper was thought of as a practical expression of the interdependence of *yin* and *yang*, as was its converse in the form of rubbings taken from monumental calligraphy carved in stone, which would come out as white against black. This pair of prints combines all these ideas and traditions.

Each is printed from a single plywood block faced with *shina*. The carved-away areas are then built up again with sand, cement, glue or even small stones to provide an elaborately textured surface which is printed by *gauffrage*. This technique is characteristic of Maki's later work. The black is a simple printing ink. He has used similar technology in many other calligraphic prints and in relief-studies of the chunky, textured teabowls used in *Chanoyū* (the Tea Ceremony).

PLATE 108

108 MAKI Haku (b.1924)
Work 73–50–B (Nothing)

1973
Annotations: (in pencil, lower margin) *Haku Maki* Work 73–50–B (Nothing) 5/60; (on image, in black against red) *Haku Maki* (artist's seal)
Black and white woodblock print, 5/60, 845×840mm
Provenance: Gaston Petit Collection
1986.3–21.0420.B

This is the pair to Cat. 107, with the blacks and whites reversed. The technique and materials are the same.

PLATE 109

109 KITAOKA Fumio (b.1918)
Fuyu no Inabanuma ('Winter at Inabanuma')

1979
Annotations: (in pencil, lower margin) 72/120 *Fuyu no Inabanuma* Fumio Kitaoka 1979
Colour woodblock print, 72/120, 475×627mm
Provenance: Purchased from the Red Lantern Shop, Kyoto, 1980
1980.12–29.01

The scene is a marshland in Chiba Prefecture, west of Narita City, close to Narita International Airport, and no great distance from Tokyo. It is typical of the artist's work since the 1960s, which has appealed equally to foreigners and to Japanese nostalgia for a fast-disappearing picturesque rural scene. These sentiments have also inspired other print artists in the same vein, such as Unno Mitsuhiro (1939–79) and Nishijima Katsuyuki (b.1945), and even to some extent later Sekino (q.v.). Kitaoka's style is essentially that of pre-war *Sōsaku Hanga* landscape expanded to a larger scale and using thicker pigments in a rather more painterly manner, reflecting his early training as an oil-painter. Another print by the artist in the British Museum's collection is reproduced in colour in Smith (1), no. 108.

PLATE 112

110 HAGIWARA Hideo (b.1913)
Ishi no Hana (Ao) ('Stone Flower: Blue')

1960
Annotations: (in pencil, lower margin) Hideo Hagiwara 60 *Ishi no Hana (Ao)* 22/30
Colour woodblock print, 22/30, 664×952mm
Provenance: Gaston Petit Collection
1986.3–21.0216

Hagiwara's work in woodblocks is more varied than that of most of his contemporaries, and has explored different styles and techniques with varying success. His most acclaimed prints have been those of the late 1950s and early 60s when he achieved great density of tone and texture in dark or intense colours. This was seen most notably in his series of *Yoroeru Hito* ('Man in Armour'), but *Stone Flower: Blue* is of the same period and of equal strength. The effect is realised principally through his printing the back of the paper first with one dark dye which is rubbed through to the front of the sheet with great vigour. This provides a rich background for further printing, with an already varied surface with much texture. According to Petit (Descriptive List of Plates, no. 49), there were four blocks of plywood faced with *shina* and eleven printing stages for the surface, but this was for a 'polychrome version' of the print which included poster colour, and not the blue version reproduced here.

PLATE 110

111 HAGIWARA Hideo (b.1913)
Den'en no Matsuri, No 2 ('Village Festival, No. 2')

1968
Annotations: (in pencil, lower margin) Hideo Hagiwara –68 *Den'en no Matsuri* No 2 Village festival No 2 5/50, 1968
Woodblock print, 657×992mm
Provenance: Purchased from the Red Lantern Shop, Kyoto, 1985
1985.12–21.02

This is typical of a more highly coloured stage of Hagiwara's prints which began in the late 1960s, and more noticeably influenced by certain aspects of Western twentieth-century art, a result of his teaching in the USA in 1967. One can see especially the influence of the work of Miró, who was becoming extremely popular in Japan at this period. The Catalan artist's fondness for brilliant, lucid colours clearly appeals to one side of Japanese sensibility. In this group, which includes also the *Circus* series, Hagiwara covers his typically rich-textured background with a mass of freely drawn lines which recall the marks of the crayon in lithography, but which are in fact done by shallow engraving of the ink block. Hagiwara was himself doing some lithography at this period of his career. The Japanese title of the print implies that this is a Japanese country festival, but the atmosphere seems universal.

PLATE 111

112 IWAMI Reika (b.1927)
Hitori dake no Ongakkai, C ('Concert of One, C')

1967
Annotations: (in pencil, lower margin) a.p. *Hitori dake no Ongakkai* C Reika Iwami '67
Monochrome woodblock print with gold foil, artist's proof, 692×514mm
Provenance: Gaston Petit Collection
1986.3–21.0271

Petit (Descriptive List of Plates, no. 79) translates the title as 'Concert for Self C'. He states that the main edition was of twenty sheets and that the printing was executed by laying down the foil first over adhesive and letting it dry, before printing from four blocks (two faced with *shina* and two with *rawan*) on *torinoko* paper. The pigments were *sumi* (carbon ink) and *ganryō* (mineral pigment), both diluted to produce the grey tones. There is a classic simplicty in this print which recalls the native Japanese fondness for ink-painting gently combined with gold wash. The central gold shape, however, already anticipates the artist's use of driftwood found in many of her later works. The physical force of the printing also looks forward to the *gauffrage* which was to become another important characteristic of her work.

PLATE 113

113 FUKITA Fumiaki (b.1926)
Hoshi no Den'etsu ('Legend of the Stars')

1968
Annotations: (in pencil, lower margin) 20/50 *Hoshi no Den'etsu* Fumiaki Fukita *Fumi* (in a circle) 68
Colour woodblock print, 20/50, 960×635mm
Provenance: Gaston Petit Collection
1986.3–21.0155

According to Petit (Descriptive List of Plates, no. 34), this composition was made from four blocks of plywood faced with *rawan* (an imported mahogany) on *torinoko* paper. The colours are a combination of water-based Japanese pigments, which are printed by hand, and oil-based inks, which are printed through a press. Both use the gradation (*bokashi*) found in Japanese woodblock prints of all periods from the mid-eighteenth century onwards. The coloured dots are applied by hand with Neo Colour Bright. The dark vibrancy of the oil-based inks allows Fukita to suggest depth without excessive attention to the actual surface of the blocks and hence to produce large compositions like this one more easily. The artist tended in subsequent works to overuse the motif of cylindrical light rays which are so potent in this early example.

PLATE 114

114 TAKAHASHI Rikio (b.1917)
Niwa ('Garden (End of Summer)')

1984
Annotations: (in pencil, bottom margin) '84 7/50 NIWA (End of Summer) Rikio Takahashi
Colour woodblock print, with embossing, 7/50, 898×617mm
Provenance: Purchased in Tokyo, 1985
1985.4–4.03

Takahashi, like many Japanese artists of the post-war era, found a theme and has kept to it, endlessly exploring and refining over more than forty years his prints inspired largely by the classic gardens of Kyoto. Unlike most, however, his concentration on virtually one theme has led to ever-greater depth and ease, each print very subtly yet unequivocally creating a different little world of colour and mood. These colours reflect not only the quiet tones of the gardens themselves but the almost imperceptible changes in light which the seasons bring. The same atmosphere is found even in his prints which do not refer specifically to gardens. Like every Japanese poet, artist or musician whose work is inspired by nature, Takahashi always has a season in mind; in this example it is the dried-out period of late summer before the storms of early autumn. A fine balance is struck between the heat of the sun and the cool of the garden's rocks and raked sand. The print is executed with the *shina*-faced plywood blocks which the artist invariably uses.

PLATE 115

115 TAKAHASHI Rikio (b.1917)
Full Season

1984
Annotations: (in pencil, bottom margin) '84 8/50 Full Season Rikio Takahashi
Colour woodblock print with embossing, 8/50, 912×627mm
Provenance: Purchased in Tokyo, 1985
1985.4–4.02

From the same series as Cat. 114, this is also a garden scene (viewed from above, if anything so representational can be attributed to the artist), though the title does not say so. 'Full Season' refers to the hottest time in summer, usually dry in Kyoto with grass turned yellow, providing Takahashi with an opportunity to indulge in his favourite tawny colours.

PLATE 116

116 KŌSAKA Gajin (1877–1953)
Kokubunji Village

1948
Annotations: (on image, lower right) *Gajin* (artist's seal); (on reverse) seal of Vergez Collection
Monochrome woodblock print, 390×527mm
Provenance: Robert Vergez Collection
1987.3–16.0411

This example was previously reproduced in Smith, Harris and Clark, no. 241, under the title *Shrine among trees*.

Kōsaka was known to be vague about the subjects of his late prints, and it is not certain if this one (quoted in Jenkins *et al.*) is more correct than any other. If so, then this is a very small subsidiary Buddhist temple building. *Kokubunji* were the temples established in each

province by Imperial decree in the eighth century (cf. no. 24). This is typical of the artist's late work, in which he cut his blocks with ill-defined shallow edges so that the ink would spread outwards, rather in the manner of certain types of ink-painting traditional in East Asia. This effect could be achieved only by using unsized paper and applying extra water during the printing. In their careful balance of black and white his late prints are reminiscent of Hiratsuka's works of the same period (for example, Cat. 23), though Hiratsuka's printing was done relatively dry in a more conventional technique.

PLATE 117

117 SEIMIYA Naobumi (b.1917)
Still Life in Moonlight

Early 1970s
Annotations: (in pencil, lower margin) 9/10 N Seimiya; (on reverse) seal of Vergez Collection
Colour woodblock print, 231×310mm
Provenance: Robert Vergez Collection
1987.3–16.0244

Seimiya's woodblocks are small, apparently simple, and filled with a sense of loneliness and transience which is very close to the ancient Japanese aesthetic concept of *aware*. They are also surprisingly intense in concentration. It is these qualities that have made him much admired in Japan but little collected outside his own country. This example typically links the small and the unobtrusive with hints of the cosmic dimension, in a technique of extreme delicacy and refinement.

PLATE 118

118 MURAI Maçanari (b.1905)
Untitled

1963
Annotations: (in pencil, lower margin) 6/20 MAÇANARI '63
Black and white woodblock print, 6/20, 414×504mm
Provenance: Gaston Petit Collection
1986.3–21.0513

Maçanari, who continues to use this French form of his name, has always taken a rather European view of prints as a method of more widely disseminating his work, which is essentially painting in oils. This and the ever more extreme simplification of form which he has pursued since around 1960 have made him little interested in printing techniques as such, and he has tended to entrust the actual printing to other professionals. In his post-war career he has used woodblock, lithograph and silk screen. Woodblock has been the least used, although he is known to like the varied textures it can provide; but it can certainly be claimed that the leaking of ink on to the white areas in this example add vitality, as they did

consistently in the work of Munakata. The subject of this print, as of almost all of his works, is a human face.

PLATE 119

119 MABUCHI Tōru (b.1920)
Budō to uri ('Grapes and Melons')

1968
Annotations: (in pencil on image, upper left) Tōru Mabuchi; (in pencil, on accompanying label) *Budo to uri* 10/20 1968; (on reverse) seal of Vergez Collection
Colour woodblock print, 10/20, 480×305mm
Provenance: Robert Vergez Collection
1987.3–16.151

The title of this print remains puzzling, since no melons are visible. Mabuchi's allegiance to Pointillisme and to Byzantine art, both acquired in his student days, led him to seek a new sort of technique, which consisted of constructing blocks from numerous tiny pieces of wood cut originally from lunch-boxes (*bentō-bako*) or later from other very thin woods and then glued to a solid base for printing. In this example these 'mosaical' areas are used with others done from more conventional blocks. Mabuchi's unusual technique produces a surface of great richness suitable to still-life subjects, but the result is necessarily expensive because it entails so much labour.

PLATE 120

120 MIZUFUNE Rokushū (1912–81)
Rainbow Music

Undated
Annotations: (in white pigment on image, lower right) Mizufune; (on reverse) seal of Vergez Collection
Colour woodblock print, 274×362mm
Provenance: Robert Vergez Collection
1987.3–16.0170

For Mizufune's methods see Cat. 121. It is difficult to detect here forms of the written characters for 'Rainbow' or 'Music', but judging from the artist's normal practice it may be assumed that they are there. This print seems to be stylistically of much the same date as Cat. 121. Mizufune's use of sea-birds, learned from his childhood by the sea, is one of the most persistent images in his prints.

PLATE 121

121 MIZUFUNE Rokushū (1912–81)
Rainbow Bird

Undated
Annotations: (in white pigment on image, bottom) Mizufune; (on reverse) seal of Vergez Collection

Colour woodblock print, 384×285 mm
Provenance: Robert Vergez Collection
1987.3–16.0171

Mizufune did not date his prints, as he regarded each new impression as a fresh work of art. This example seems to belong to the late 1960s or early 70s, but his stylistic changes are few and difficult to chart. His declared editions were usually of thirty or fifty sheets, but none is recorded on this example. Like most of his print subjects, this is based both on things from the natural world and on highly stylised forms of the originally pictorial Chinese characters used in written Japanese for those things – in this case 'bird'. This system provides a solid structural base to the composition, which harmonises well with the black ground of each print, black, of course, being the colour of the ink used in character calligraphy. Mizufune's main profession as a sculptor is also well harnessed in the sureness and balance of his forms. His characteristic thick palette was achieved by printing the whole sheet first with black (*sumi* ink, according to Merritt), then with repeatedly printed blocks of tube water-colours mixed with *gofun* (shell-white). Petit records (Descriptive List of Plates, nos 145–50) that all of his prints used *torinoko* paper and plywood blocks faced with *shina*. Some were printed nearly ten years later than the blocks were cut.

PLATE 123

122 HOSHI Jōichi (1913–79)
Ginkawa F ('The Milky Way (F)')
1968
Annotations: (in pencil, lower margin) *Ginkawa* (F) 18/30 The Milky Way (F) Joichi Hoshi '68; (in pencil on image, bottom right) Joichi Hoshi; (next to signature on image) *Jōichi* (artist's seal)
Colour woodblock print, 18/30, 663×768 mm
Provenance: Gaston Petit Collection
1986.3–21.0238

As in his tree subjects, so in his star pieces, Hoshi prefers to use just a few carefully patinated colours to create a specific mood. According to Petit (Descriptive List of Plates, no. 64), the pigment is printing ink diluted with turpentine and applied to the block by brush. There were eight blocks of plywood faced with *shina*, printed on to *torinoko* paper. The sense of mystery in this large print, which uncannily balances peace with explosiveness, is enhanced by the few almost unnoticeable dots of yellow and purple which relieve and irradiate the blue of the night. This is one of Hoshi's last and finest star pieces before he discovered his final and conclusive subject of trees.

PLATE 124

123 HOSHI Jōichi (1913–79)
Akai Chiheisen ('Red Horizon')
1972
Annotations: (in pencil, lower margin) *Akai Chiheisen* 50/80 Joichi Hoshi '72; (on reverse in pencil) 11–2
Colour woodblock print, 50/80, 475×737 mm
Provenance: Gaston Petit Collection
1986.3–21.0236

Always entranced by the grandeur of nature, Hoshi spent the last decade of his career on studies of trees. Their increasingly dazzling technique and the superficial ease of their subject-matter made them popular among Western collectors; since his death Hoshi's reputation has risen rapidly within Japan, and the relative smallness of his output has made his work among the most expensive of postwar print artists except Munakata's. The earlier tree subjects, like this one, are sometimes placed in a recognisable spatial context, but later the trees themselves came to be the sole subjects. Petit (Descriptive List of Plates, no. 66) describes this print as using nine blocks. The present example is done in red printing ink diluted with turpentine, and in brown and black pigments, on white *torinoko* paper.

PLATE 122

124 HOSHI Jōichi (1913–79)
Asa no Ki ('Tree at Dawn')
1976
Annotations: (in pencil, lower margin) *Asa no ki Sakka Hozon* ('Kept by the artist') Joichi Hoshi '76; (on image, bottom right) *Jō'ichi* (artist's seal)
Colour woodblock print with silver foil, artist's proof, 680×515 mm
Provenance: Purchased in London, 1980
1980.1–28.027

This copy was reproduced in black and white in Smith (1), no. 97. The dignity of composition survives monochrome reproduction, but the delicacy of atmosphere does not. The official run was ninety-nine sheets. Hoshi used silver foil on the tree itself to suggest a deep frost. This was applied over adhesive printed by woodblock over the brown-black of the bark. Although it might be claimed that Hoshi's small tree prints are emotionally weak, the larger compositions lose that quality and their subjects become almost personalities, which to the artist they were. The combination of a strong overall composition with relentless detail recalls Chinese and Japanese traditions of scholarly ink-painting, especially pine trees.

PLATE 126

125 AMANO Kazumi (b.1927)
Moral (B)
1963
Annotations: (in pencil, lower margin) Moral (B) Kazumi Amano '63 2/30
Colour woodblock print with embossing, 900×610 mm
Provenance: Gaston Petit Collection
1986.3–21.044

The artist trained as a furniture designer, a skill which can be sensed in this neatly interlocking design. In fact, the upper and lower parts are printed from the same blocks mirror-imaging each other and dovetailing together. The lower half relies on pale monochrome tones and embossing, the upper on bright colours. It is virtually an image of woodblock printmaking itself. Petit (Descriptive List of Plates, no. 2) claims that only three blocks were used, made of plywood faced with Japanese birch, on *torinoko* paper. The colours were oil-based pigments and lithographic inks.

PLATE 127

126 AMANO Kunihiro (b.1929)
Enclosure (9)
1965
Annotations: (in pencil, lower margin) Enclosure (9) 17/30 Kunihiro Amano 65.11 (in pencil on image, bottom left) Kunihiro Amano
Colour woodblock print with embossing, 17/30, 925×570 mm
Provenance: Gaston Petit Collection
1986.3–21.053

According to Petit (Descriptive List of Plates, no. 10), four blocks were used for this print, all being of plywood faced with *shina*. One of the blocks was used for the embossing. The rather oily depth of the pigments is not surprising, as they are actually derived from oil paints. These are left on newspaper for 'about eight hours' to draw out the oil. The result is then remixed with petrol, turpentine and poppy oil. The resulting liquid solution leaves no oil stain on the *torinoko* paper when printed. The condensed elegance seen in this print has been well maintained by the artist in his later career, but few of his later works have matched the passionate intensity of *Enclosure (9)*.

PLATE 130

127 TAJIMA Hiyoyuki (1911–84)
Fūshoku D ('Wind Erosion D')
1968
Annotations: (in pencil, lower margin) Wind Erosion D. *Fūshoku D* 50–1 Hiroyuki Tajima '68
Colour woodblock print, ?1/50, 635×450 mm
Provenance: Purchased in Kyoto, 1985
1985.12–21.02(a)

This and Cat. 128, though they have different titles, in fact form a pair, linked by the theme of wind. From Tajima's best period, they have a glowing ardour of colour which is unique to this artist and make him when at his best arguably Japan's greatest exponent of abstract Expressionism, even though his work is restricted to the woodblock medium. To achieve his effects of light glowing incandescently through or out of his prints he developed a technique of using both oil pigments and water-based ones. The water-based colours are applied sparingly on those parts of the paper which have been left without oil and are repelled (in the manner of lithography) by the oily areas. The latter are printed from relief areas built up on the block with a variety of materials, such as shells, torn paper or sand, giving surfaces of great interest and movement. This pair was bought directly from Tajima's main dealer, the Red Lantern Shop, Kyoto. It is not clear if this was a trial proof or the first of the edition.

PLATE 129

128 TAJIMA Hiroyuki (1911–84)
Fūbaika B ('Anemophilous Flower B')

1968
Annotations: (in pencil, lower margin) Anemophilous flower B 50–1 Hiroyuki Tajima '68
Colour woodblock print, ?1/50, 635×450 mm
Provenance: Purchased in Kyoto, 1985
1985.12–21.02 (b)

This forms the left of a pair with Cat. 127, where Tajima's printing method is described. 'Anemophilous' is the scientific name for 'wind-pollinated'.

PLATE 125

129 KUSAKA Kenji (b.1936)
Sakuhin 1 ('Work No. 1')

1964
Annotations: (in pencil, lower margin) 1964 20/20 *Sakuhin* 1 KEN KUSAKA
Colour woodblock print, 20/20, 874×636 mm
Provenance: Purchased in London, 1984
1984.10–23.03

An earlier state of this print from the Petit Collection is also now in the British Museum, lacking a few of the details which the artist later added. Petit (Descriptive List of Plates, no. 41) describes that as printed from four *shina*-faced plywood blocks, cut on both sides as is the artist's custom. The pigments were oil paints, which were dried of their oil on newspaper. They were then remixed with poppy oil and turpentine, which could be applied to the blocks by brush but left no oil stain on the *torinoko* paper. Much of Kusaka's later work has been of large-scale, dynamic abstraction, but this, his first in his officially numbered

series, plays with the idea of zip-fasteners in a manner obviously influenced by the Pop Art movement.

PLATE 128

130 FUNASAKA Yoshisuke
(b.1939)
Work At 26

1969
Annotations: (in pencil, lower margin) 3/27 Y. Funasaka 1969; (on printed label on reverse, filled out in ink) No 188 Year 1969 Title – WORK At 26–1969 Name YOSHISUKE FUNASAKA with seal; (on reverse) seal of Vergez Collection
Colour woodblock print, with perforations, 3/27, 410×301 mm
Provenance: Robert Vergez Collection
1987.3–16.042

Funasaka's work has developed through many technical stages over his career but has always been notable for its cool elegance of form. Few of his prints are pure woodblock and hence eligible for this catalogue, but this delicate example qualifies in spite of using the perforations which he first discovered accidentally by leaving a cigarette to burn on a print. The paper itself is deliberately flecked with very small, pale brown spots, but it is not clear if this has been applied by the artist (by screen) or by the paper-maker. Almost all the artist's prints have no title but a serial number. A work with very similar borders by Funasaka is described technically in Petit and Arboleda, pp. 127–31, with reproductions of stage proofs, pp. 38–9.

PLATE 132

131 KUROSAKI Akira (b.1937)
Fūkei Yami w–115 ('Landscape – Night')

1971
Annotations: (in pencil, lower margin) 43/50 Landscape – Night *Fukei Yami* w–115 A. Kurosaki ?71; (on reverse) seal of Petit Collection
Colour woodblock print, 43/50, 560×405 mm
Provenance: Gaston Petit Collection
1986.3–21.0387

Petit does not describe this print, but others of this period by Kurosaki are listed by him as printed from *shina*-faced plywood on *torinoko* paper, with a variety of mineral pigments, oil paints and inks. Like most of the works of his early maturity it is an enclosed, dream-like landscape making much use of shadow (skilfully gradated on the blocks by his assistant), with perspective handled in the manner of Surrealism and prominent sexual imagery. Surprisingly, the black wave-like motif on the yellow/gold ground is very close to traditional Japanese stylisations of waves. This is no. 115 in Kurosaki's continuing numbered series.

PLATE 131

132 KUROSAKI Akira (b.1937)
Kurai Yokan ('Premonition B')

1972
Annotations: (in pencil, lower margin) 24/45 Premonition B *Kurai Yokan* w–117 A. Kurosaki '72
Colour woodblock print, 24/45, 585×784 mm
Provenance: Gaston Petit Collection
1986.3–21.0380

The Japanese title translates as 'Dark Premonition'. Kurosaki in his early work experimented with unusual shapes, which added to their Surrealistic and dream-like atmosphere. The effect here is of looking through a window into a nightmare interior, including his obsessive motifs of this period of breasts and of stairs leading nowhere. According to Petit (Descriptive List of Plates, no. 115), describing a different copy, this was printed from nine blocks of *shina*-faced plywood on *torinoko* paper. The colours were a combination of mineral pigments (*ganryō*), black carbon ink (*sumi*) and oil paints. The *bokashi* (shading on the block) of the *sumi* on the central red column is particularly accomplished.

PLATE 133

133 MOROZUMI Osamu (b.1948)
No. 8

1971
Annotations: (in pencil, lower margin) 18/30 No 8 *Morozumi*; (on reverse) seal of Vergez Collection
Black and white woodblock print, 10/30, 540×677 mm
Provenance: Robert Vergez Collection
1987.3–16.0429

Morozumi's very individual technique has been well described in Petit and Arboleda. He has, since graduating from his art university, used a complex system of punching and gouging holes into a single block which produces a highly varied surface very well suited to reproducing the sculptured forms he favours. The printing is relatively simple and is done through a press to ensure the ink is forced into the very large number of holes. It might be viewed as a form of Pointillisme, which exerted a strong influence on many younger post-war Japanese artists. A few of Morozumi's compositions have simple titles, but most have only a serial number, as in this example.

PLATE 134

134 MATSUMOTO Akira
(b.1936)
Tenkai (w5 In'yō) ('Revolve –
(W5 – Negative/Positive)')
1985
Annotations: (in pencil, lower margin) 4/20
A. Matsumoto '85; (on reverse in pencil)
Tenkai (W5 – In'yō) Revolve (w5 – Nega-Posi)
A. MATSUMOTO *Matsumoto Akira*
Colour woodblock print, 4/20, 685×695 mm
Provenance: College Women's Association of
Japan touring exhibition *Symbols of A Society
in Transition*, 1985 (given by the artist)
1986.10–29.034

This copy was also reproduced in colour in
Smith (2), no. 34.

The prints in the College Women's Association of Japan touring exhibition were chosen by a jury in Tokyo in 1985 and were subsequently all donated to the British Museum's collection. Matsumoto's skill in expressing a highly complex abstract pattern in the woodblock medium reflects his early training as a woodblock printer in the artisan tradition. Five colour blocks are superimposed on each other to produce this kaleidoscopic effect. The reverse of the print shows vigorous use of the *baren* and also supplies the 'Negative' pole of his equation, which corresponds to the dark or negative pole of the *yin-yang* concept. Matsumoto has also explored the principles of colour dots in many silk-screen prints, which, however, lack the texture of this example.

PLATES 135–8

135–8 KAWACHI Seikō (b.1948)
The Flying: Ki ('Introduction')
The Flying: Jō ('Development')
The Flying: Ten ('Turn')
The Flying: Ketsu ('Conclusion')
1985
Annotations: (in pencil, lower margin of each print) '4/8 1985 flying (with appropriate Japanese title as above in brackets)
S Kawachi'
Set of four colour woodblock prints, 4/8, each
1655×915 mm
Provenance: Purchased in Tokyo, 1985
1985.12–23.01–04

The artist describes these prints (Kawachi, p.101) as follows: '. . . anastatic and intaglio printing in woodcut, 7 plates, 10 colours', the paper as '*Fukui Kizuki Hōsho*' and the edition as eight, plus two artist's proofs, one trial proof and two ex-edition proofs. He has preferred to use the word 'anastatic' for conventional relief printing in woodblock as contrasted with 'in-

taglio', where the block is engraved. '*Kizuki Hōsho*' is proper handmade *hōsho* paper (the sort used in the past for *Ukiyo-e* prints) from Fukui Prefecture and must have been specially ordered by the artist.

Woodblock prints of this size are most unusual: the clamping together of large enough blocks is extremely complex, and it is more normal for sheets of paper beyond a certain size to be spliced together rather than left as complete single sheets like these. On top of this the registration of the actual printing becomes extremely arduous when the prints are taken by an artist working alone. The small edition is therefore not surprising. In a Japanese context Kawachi would have had in mind a fourfold screen or a pair of twofold screens as a way of mounting and displaying these very noticeable prints.

Kawachi first used the image of chickens trapped in crumbling and collapsing telephone boxes and shops against a grim black background in 1977. The theme of the tumbling collapse of man-made structures and materials had emerged in the same year. His first somewhat smaller prints in a long series called 'The Flying' were published in 1982 and continued to get bigger until culminating in this decisive series. They represent to the artist the helplessness of living creatures trapped in a decadent and brutalised urban world, one of Kawachi's persistent themes. In spite of the monumental quality of this continuous composition there is a remarkable sense of surface movement, created not only by the direction of flying birds and falling timbers but also by the tensions between the carefully used wood-grain effects and the nervous ink strokes scratched into the blocks. These latter recall more than anything the East Asian traditions of Expressionsitic ink-painting.

PLATE 140

139 TSURUYA Kōkei (b.1946)
*The Actor Bandō Tamasaburō V as
Agemaki in Sukeroku, from Ōkubie*
('Bust Portraits'), Series III
1983
Annotations: (on image, bottom left)
Sanjūroku-hin ('Edition of 36'); (inscribed over it in ink in seal form) *Nijū-nana* ('27'); (below it) *Kōkei no in* ('Kōkei's seal')
Colour woodblock print with powdered mica, 27/36, 397×272 mm
Provenance: Purchased in London, 1986
1986.7–7.08

This is printed on Hodomura paper from Tochigi Prefecture, made from *ganpi* fibres, and the mica is applied over a pinkish-purple ground. In spite of the small edition Kōkei, as

always, defaced his blocks at the end of it so that the prints could not be revived. *Sukeroku* is one of the eighteen plays in the canon of *Aragoto* ('Rough Stuff') dramas compiled by Ichikawa Danjūro VII (1791–1859) and is still performed today. The character shown here is the courtesan Agemaki (easily identified by her elaborate hair-style bristling with combs) who is rescued from a brutal old client by the chivalrous Sukeroku. Agemaki spends much of the action under the influence of saké which she uses to forget her unhappy lot. The whole action of the play is related in detail in Halford. The actor Bandō Tamasaburō was born in 1950 and in his prime for playing young women at the time of this print.

PLATE 139

140 TSURUYA Kōkei (b.1946)
*The Actor Nakamura Utaemon VI as
Tonase in Kanadehon Chūshingura,
from Ōkubie* ('Bust Portraits'),
Series IV
1984
Annotations: (on image, bottom left) *Yonjūgo-hin* ('Edition of 45'); (inscribed over it in ink in seal form) *Jūyon* ('14'); (below it) *Tsuruya Kōkei* (artist's seal)
Colour woodblock print with powdered mica background, 14/15, 395×250 mm
Provenance: Purchased in London, 1984
1984.10–24.05

Kōkei's actor prints, unlike most contemporary woodblock prints, are done on translucently thin paper, in this case *ganpi* paper from Kōchi Prefecture. This has a silky feel which seems almost insubstantial and creates considerable tension against the forceful lines of the images themselves. This is all the more noticeable where a character as forcible as Tonase is represented. She is from the best known of all Kabuki dramas, *Kanadehon Chūshingura*, a story of loyalty and revenge usually translated as 'The Loyal League' and acted every year (at least in part) in the Kabuki-za Theatre in Tokyo. Tonase is the heroic mother of the tragic heroine of the main sub-plot. She accompanies her daughter Konami to Kyoto to ensure her honourable marriage, and in her husband's unavoidable absence wears his two swords as symbols of his soul and authority as a samurai. In this print she is shown with the hilt of one of the swords prominently visible. The extremely complex sub-plot (mainly in Acts 8 and 9) is related in detail in Halford. The actor Nakamura Utaemon was born in 1917 and hence just the right age to play this formidable but not ancient lady in 1983.

Glossary

aware Aesthetic and emotional Japanese concept meaning the sense of sadness and transience in life.

baren A hand-held pad, covered with bamboo bark, used in Japan since at least the seventeenth century to take impressions of woodblock prints.

bentō-bako Lunch-box taken to work, traditionally made of very thin, cheap wood and disposable after use.

bijin 'Beautiful woman', the subject of much Japanese art.

bokashi Technique of loading a woodblock with pigment so that the impression moves from dark to light, almost like shading.

Bunraku The national puppet theatre which has flourished since the seventeenth century.

Chanoyū 'Hot water for tea', the usual term in Japanese for what is called the 'Tea Ceremony' in English.

chitsu Folding card wrapper used to protect books, often covered with a textile.

fukuro-tōji The pre-modern way of constructing a book, with deliberately uncut folded sheets facing outwards, sewn up at the spine with thread; always made of *washi* (q.v.).

ganpi One of the three principal plant fibres used in Japanese handmade paper.

ganryō General word for mineral pigments used in native-style painting and occasionally in prints.

geisha 'Skilled person', a professional hostess (or host) and conversationalist, usually with skills in traditional dancing and music.

haiku Seventeen-syllable poetic form popular since the seventeenth century.

hanmoto Old-style print publisher who co-ordinated and financed a team consisting of artist, cutter and printer.

Hōgan 'Eye of the Law', a title conferred by Buddhist temples on persons of religious, intellectual or artistic distinction.

hō-no-ki The silver magnolia, a wood sometimes used for woodblock printing instead of *sakura* (q.v.).

hōsho A paper made from *kōzo* fibres, traditionally used in *Ukiyo-e* prints.

intaglio (Italian) General term used for metal-plate printing (etching, engraving, aquatint, mezzotint, etc.). Called *toppan* in Japanese.

Kabuki The popular Japanese theatre which developed in the seventeenth century, a subject for print artists at all periods from the seventeenth century to the present.

katsura A prestigious Japanese timber much used in the twentieth century for woodblocks, especially by later *Sōsaku Hanga* artists.

kentō The old method of registering the different blocks for a print by cutting matching angles and raised ridges in each of a set; it has continued to be used by recent artists.

komasuki A round-ended chisel used for removing large areas of wood from woodblocks. Since the later nineteenth century the preferred carving tool of the *Sōsaku Hanga* movement.

koto Horizontal stringed instrument played with plectra, originating in China.

kōzo The paper-mulberry, the commonest fibre for *washi* (q.v.) since at least as early as the eighth century AD.

kuchi-e 'Opening pictures', woodblock-printed frontispieces, usually folded, inserted in Western-style novels, especially in the period 1890–1915.

maiko A young *geisha* in Kyoto, supplying the commonly held ideal of the Japanese woman much favoured by Westerners.

Maruyama-Shijō An extensive school of painting originating in the work of Maruyama Ōkyo (1733–95) and dominant in Japan for much of the nineteenth century.

Mingei Undō 'Folk Art Movement', founded by Yanagi Sōetsu (1839–1961) and a group of potters in 1926.

mitsumata One of the three principal plant fibres used in making *washi*.

momigami A type of thick paper deliberately crumpled by hand, used by some stencil printers.

Nanga 'Southern painting', a school of art emulating the scholar-painters of China, which flourished in Japan from the early eighteenth century and still exists.

Nara ehon 'Picture-books from Nara', romances simply illustrated by hand, produced in the seventeenth century for bourgeois clients.

Nihonga 'Japanese painting', the national school of painting which developed in the late nineteenth century as a response to *Yōga* ('Western painting'), dominant in Japan since *c*.1915.

nisōshi A thick, very absorbent *kōzo* (q.v.) paper used by some recent printmakers.

rawan A mahogany imported from the Philippines and used as a veneer for woodblocks since the 1950s.

sakura Cherry-wood, the commonest material for woodblocks of the *Ukiyo-e* school.

sashi-e Book illustrations.

shibugami The thick paper coated with persimmon juice (*shiba*) used to make stencils for printing paper or textiles.

shina The Japanese lime, widely used since 1945 as a veneer for woodblocks for printing.

Shin Hanga A movement beginning early this century to revive the styles and techniques of *Ukiyo-e* prints.

Sōsaku Hanga 'Creative Prints', a movement of printmakers beginning in the early twentieth century who sought to avoid the control of traditional publishers.

sumi The normal Japanese word for the ink used with a brush for writing.

tanrokubon 'Red and green books', a type of popular printed book with hand-colouring, flourishing in the mid-seventeenth century.

torinoko A type of handmade paper, using fibres of *ganpi* (q.v.) and *mitsumata* (q.v.), much used by post-war woodblock artists, though often including a proportion of pulp.

Ukiyo-e 'Pictures of the Floating World', the best-known school of Japanese art, recording the life of pleasure and fashion of the great cities, broadly speaking from *c*.1660 to *c*.1910.

urushi-e 'Lacquer pictures', woodblock prints imitating the lustrous effects of lacquer by mixing a glue with the black pigment.

waka Traditional thirty-one-syllable poetic form.

washi General word for Japanese handmade papers, almost invariably used for woodblock prints.

Yōga 'Western painting', a term used in contrast to *Nihonga* (q.v.).

yūgen Aesthetic and philosophical concept of the mystery inherent in all of life.

Bibliography

Literature in English on the subject of this catalogue has greatly increased since 1984: most of the important books and articles are included here. Literature in Japanese is now extensive: a selection of the most useful books and articles has been made. Where an author or editor of an exhibition catalogue is clearly identifiable, it is entered under that name; otherwise it is entered under the exhibition venue. Collected works of artists published in Japanese often give the artist as the author of the book. In such cases the title is simply quoted (for example *Murai Masanari Sakuhin-shū*).

The Abbey Gallery (ed.)
An Exhibition of the Colour Woodcuts by Y. Urushibara, London, 1928

Abrams, Leslie E.
The History and Practice of Japanese Printmaking. A selectively annotated bibliography of English language materials, Greenwood Press, Westpoint and London, 1984

Aichi Prefectural Art Museum
Fauvism and Modern Painting, exh. cat., 1992

Amano, Kunihiro
'Jigusō ga: Gyōshaku suru Watashi Jishin' ('A Jigsaw: Condensing Myself'), *Hanga Geijutsu*, 11, autumn 1975, pp. 79–85

Asano, Takeji
Asano Takeji Jisen Mokuhanga-shū, Kyoto Shoin, Kyoto, 1981

Austin, James B.
'Notes on the Early Days of Sōsaku Hanga', *Newsletter on Contemporary Japanese Prints*, vol. 3, no. 2, Los Angeles, 1973, pp. 3–17

Azechi, Umetarō
Japanese Woodblock Prints. Their technique and appreciation, Tuttle, Rutland, Vermont, 1963

Azechi Umetarō Zen Hanga-shū Kōdansha, Tokyo, 1979

Baba, Kyōko
'Kitano Tsunetomi: Nakamura Daisaburō', *Bijinga Zenshū*, III, Shūeisha, Tokyo, 1979

Baskett, Mary W.
'Kazumi Amano: The New York Connection', *Newsletter on Contemporary Japanese Prints*, vol. v, no. I, Los Angeles, 1977, pp. 3–14

Blair, Dorothy (1)
A Special Exhibition of Modern Japanese Prints, Toledo Museum of Art, 1930

Blair, Dorothy (2)
Modern Japanese Prints: Woodblock Prints by Ten Artists: The work of the past five years, Toledo Museum of Art, 1936

Blakemore, Frances
Who's Who in Modern Japanese Prints, Weatherhill, New York and Tokyo, 1975

Brannen, N., and Elliot, V. (trans)
Festive Wine, Weatherhill, New York and Tokyo, 1969

Carey, Frances (ed.)
Collecting the 20th Century, British Museum Press, London, 1991

Centre Georges Pompidou, Paris
Japon des Avant Gardes, 1910–1970, exh. cat., 1986

Clark, John (ed. Tim Clark)
Japanese Nineteenth Century Copperplate Prints, British Museum Occasional Papers, no. 84, London, 1994

Clark Timothy
Demon of Painting: The Art of Kawanabe Kyōsai 1831–89, British Museum Press, London, 1993

Committee for the Editing of the Genshoku Ukiyo-e Daihyakka Jiten (ed.)
Genshoku Ukiyo-e Daihyakka Jiten ('Encyclopedic Dictionary of Ukiyo-e Illustrated'), 11 vols, Taishūkan Shoten, Tokyo, 1980–2

Eliot, Charles
Japanese Buddhism, Edward Arnold, London, 1935 (4th impression by Routledge and Kegan Paul, London, 1969)

Fujii, Hisae
Onchi Koshirō to Tsukuhae (*Kindai no Bijutsu*, 35), Shibundō, Tokyo, 1976

Fujikake, Shizuya
Japanese Woodblock Prints: (1) Tourist Library 10, Japan Travel Bureau, Tokyo, enlarged and rev. edn, 1949; (2) further rev. edn, 1957

Fukita, Fumiaki
'Watashi no Teknikku. Hyōgen to Gijutsu no Orijinarite o motomete' ('My technique: in search of originality in expression and skill'), *Hanga Geijutsu*, 21, Tokyo, spring 1978, pp. 124–31

Fukunaga, Shigeki
Kindai Nihon Hanga (*Kindai no Bijutsu*, 40), Shibundō, Tokyo, 1977

Gendai Hanga ('Contemporary Japanese Prints: Artists, Technique and Collection') ed. Kōdansha, Tokyo, 1979

Gendai Meikō Shokunin Jinmei Jiten Nichigai Associates Company, Tokyo, 1990

Goldman, Paul
Looking at Prints, Drawings and Watercolours: A Guide to Technical Terms, British Museum Press, London, 1988

Griffiths, Antony
Prints and Printmaking, British Museum Publications, London, 1980

Hagiwara, Hideo
Hagiwara Hideo Hanga-shū, Kōdansha, Tokyo, 1982

Halford, Aubrey and Giovanna
The Kabuki Handbook, Tuttle, Rutland, Vermont, and Tokyo, 1956 (11th edn, 1979)

Hamada, Taiji, and Hosono, Masanobu
Itō Shinsui Zenshū, 6 vols, Shūeisha, Tokyo, 1981–2

Hanga Geijutsu, 12 Special feature on Saitō Kiyoshi, pp. 61–72, Abe Publishing Co., Tokyo, 1976

Hanga Geijutsu, 19 Special feature on Natori Shunsen, pp. 186–95, Abe Publishing Co., Tokyo, 1977

Hanga Geijutsu, 37 Special feature on Fujimori Shizuo, pp. 138–47, Abe Publishing Co., Tokyo, 1982

Hanga Geijutsu, 39 Special edition on Japanese woodblock prints (*Nihon Mokuhanga Taikei*), Abe Publishing Co., Tokyo, 1982

Hanga Geijutsu, 76 Special feature 'Mokuhanga Hyakunen', pp. 79–160, Abe Publishing Co., Tokyo, 1993

Hasegawa, Kimiyuki (ed.)
Gendai Hanga Zukan, Keisuisha, Tokyo, 1977

Hashiguchi, Goyō
'Nihon no Mokuhanga' ('Japanese Woodblock Prints'), *Shin Shōsetsu*, September 1915

Hashiguchi, Masae
'Goyō no Imada Happyō Shokan to Shaseijō', *Hanga Geijutsu*, 9, Tokyo, spring 1975, pp. 126–8

Hashimoto, Okiie
Nihon no Shiro: Zen Hanga-shū, Tokyo, 1978

Hayward Gallery, London
The Woodblock and the Artist: The Life and Work of Shiko Munakata, exh. cat., Kōdansha *et al.*, 1991

Higuchi, Ryōichi (ed.)
Hangaka Meiran (Meiji-matsu, Taishō, Shōwa), Yamada Shoten Han Garō, Tokyo, 1984

Hillier, Jack
The Art of the Japanese Book, 2 vols, Sotheby's Publications, London, 1987

Hiratsuka, Un'ichi (1)
Hanga no Gihō, Ars, Tokyo, 1927

Hiratsuka, Un'ichi (2)
Hiratsuka Un'ichi Meisaku Hanga-shū, Nihon Geijutsu Shuppansha, Tokyo, 1951

Hisamatsu, Sen'ichi
Biographical Dictionary of Japanese Literature, Kōdansha, Tokyo, 1976

Hoshi, Jōichi
'Ki' *Mokuhanga Zen Sakuhin-shū*, Katō Gallery, Tokyo, 1988

Hosono, Masanobu
Itō Shinsui (Gendai Nihon Bijinga Zenshū, 5), Shūeidō, Tokyo, 1979

Hōsun
Facsimile reproduction of the complete run, 1907–11, Sansaisha, Tokyo, 1972

Igami, Bonkotsu
'Mokuhanga no Shinka' ('The True Value of Woodblock Prints'), *Waseda Bungaku*, 7, May 1907

Iino, Masahiro, Kōno, Minoru, and Hirasawa, Kanzō
Itō Shinsui Zen Mokuhanga, Yamanashi Prefectural Museum, 1992

Ishii, Hakutei
Hakutei Ishii, Bijutsu Shuppansha, Tokyo, 1952 (bilingual)

Itabashi Bijutsukan, Tokyo
Taishō-ki no Hanga-ten, exh. cat., February–March 1988

Jenkins, Donald, *et al.*
Images of a Changing World: Japanese Prints of the Twentieth Century, exh. cat., Portland Art Museum, Oregon, 1983

Johnson, Margaret D., and Hilton, Dale E.
Japanese Prints Today: Tradition with Innovation, Shufunotomo, Tokyo, 1980

Johnson, Scott
'Sketch-tour books and prints of the early twentieth century', *Andon*, 37, 1990, pp. 3–33

Kabuki Jiten
eds Hattori, Yukio; Tomita, Tetsunosuke; and Hiro, Sueyasu, Heibonsha, Tokyo, 1983

Kabuki-za (Theatre), Tokyo (ed.)
Tsuruyu Kokei: Kabuki Actor Prints, Shochiku Co., Tokyo, 1988

Kaempfer, H. M.
Ukiyo-e Studies and Pleasures. A Collection of Essays on the Art of Japanese Prints, Society for Japanese Arts and Crafts, The Hague, 1978

Kamon, Yasuo, Tozaka, Kōji, and Asahi, Akira
Shin Tōkyō Hyakkei, Heibonsha, Tokyo, 1978

Kanagawa Prefectural Museum of Modern Art (1)
Senkyūhaku-nendai No Hangakatachi (Taninaka Yasuo to Fujimaki Yoshio O Chūshin to Shite), exh. cat., 1987

Kanagawa Prefectural Museum of Modern Art (2)
Kindai Nihon no Mokuhanga-ten, exh. cat., 1990

Katō, Junzō (ed.)
Kindai Nihon Hanga Taikei, 3 vols, Mainichi Shinbun, Tokyo, 1975

Kawachi, Seikō (1)
Seikō Kawachi: The Graphic Work, 1968–1987, Abe Publishing Co., Tokyo, 1987

Kawachi, Seikō (2)
Seikō Kawachi – Graphic Works, 1988–91, Art Mu Inc., Tokyo, 1991

Kawai Bijutsu Kenkyūjō
Takehisa Yumeji-ten, exhibition at Espace Printemps, Tokyo, 1986

Kawai, Shizuo (ed.)
Gendai Hanga ('Contemporary Japanese Prints (Artist, Technique and Collection)'), Kōdansha, Tokyo, 1979

Kawakami, Sumio
Hanga, Tōhō Shoin, Tokyo, 1958

Kawakami Sumio Zenshū
Chūō Kōronsha, Tokyo, 1979

Kawakita, Michiaki (1)
Contemporary Japanese Prints, Kōdansha International, Tokyo, 1967 (English version of *Gendai Hanga*, 11 (*Nihon Hanga Bijutsu Zenshū*, 8), Kōdansha, Tokyo, 1961)

Kawakita, Michiaki (2)
Modern Currents in Japanese Art, Heibonsha Survey of Japanese Art, 24, Heibonsha, Tokyo, 1974

Kawakita, Michiaki (ed.) (3)
Kindai Nihon Bijutsu Jiten, Kōdansha, Tokyo, 1989

Kawakita, Michiaki (ed.) (4)
Hiratsuka Un-ichi Hanga-shū, Kōdansha, Tokyo, 1978

Kawakita, Michiaki, and Kobayashi, S.
Kiyokata Kaburagi (Gendai Nihon Bijinga Zenshū ('Complete Collection of Contemporary Japanese Pictures of Beautiful Women'), 2), Shūeisha, Tokyo, 1979

Keene, Donald
Bunraku, Tokyo, 1965

Keith, Elizabeth
Eastern Windows, An Artist's Notes of Travel in Japan, Hokkaido, Korea, China and the Philippines, Houghton Mifflin, Boston and New York, 1928

Keyes, Roger
The Theatrical World of Osaka Prints, Philadelphia Museum of Art, 1973

Kida, Yasuhiko
Nippon Matsuri, Kōdansha, Tokyo, 1985

Kitaoka Fumio (1)
Kitaoka Fumio Mokuhanga Sakuhin-shū, Bijutsu Shuppansha, Tokyo, 1986

Kitaoka, Fumio (2)
Hanga no Naka no Fūkei, Bijutsu Shuppansha, Tokyo, 1983

Kitaoka, Fumio (3)
Mokuhanga no Gihō, Yūzankaku, Tokyo, 1976

Koizumi, Kishio
Mokuhanga no Horikata to Surikata, Tokyo, 1924

Kozaki, Gunji
Yamamoto Kanae, Ueda City Yamamoto Kanae Municipal Museum, Ueda City, 1981

Kubo, Sadajirō (ed.)
Ono Tadashige Hanga-shū, Keishōsha, Tokyo, 1977

Kurita, Isamu
Takehisa Yumeji Shashinkan, Shinchōsha, Tokyo, 1983

Kurosaki, Akira
Wood Cut (*Art Technique*, 15), Kawade Shobō, Tokyo, 1971

Kusaka, Kenji
Kusaka Kenji Mokuhanga Sakuhin-shū, Seinensha, Tokyo, 1983

Kuwabara, Sumio
'Sekino Jun'ichirō no Shikon', *Hanga Geijutsu*, 8, Tokyo, winter 1975, pp. 55–8 (with photographs of his working methods)

Kuwayama, George
Contemporary Japanese Prints, exh. cat., Los Angeles County Museum of Art, 1972

Kyoto Bunka Hakubutsukan
Miyako no Bijinga-ten, exh. cat., Kyoto, 1993

Kyoto Municipal Museum of Fine Arts
Kyoto no Kindai Hanga, exh. cat., Kyoto, 1986

Lowe, Adam (ed.)
Shiko Munakata, Redstone Press, London, 1991

Machida Municipal Museum of International Graphic Art (1)
Taishō Jojō-Shin Hanga no Biten: Watanabe Shōzaburō to Shin Hanga Udō, exh. cat., Machida City, 1989

Machida Municipal Museum of International Graphic Art (2)
Azechi Umetarō Zen Hanga-shū, Tokyo, 1991 (includes bibliography and extensive biography)

Machida Municipal Museum of International Graphic Art (3)
Ono Tadashige Mokuhanga-ten, exh. cat., Machida City, 1993

Maeda, Tōshirō
Hanga-shū Maeda Tōshirō, Kyoto Shoin, Kyoto, 1978

Maria Shobō (ed.)
Nihonga no Isan, Maria Shobō, Tokyo, 1987

Maruei Department Store, Nagoya
Serizawa Keisuke-ten, exh. cat., Nagoya, 1984

Matsubara, Naoko
Kyoto Woodcuts, Kōdansha International, Tokyo and New York, 1978

Matsumoto, Akira
Matsumoto Akira Sakuhin-shū, Gallery Natsuhiko, Tokyo, 1991

Matsumoto, Ryūnosuke
Meiji Taishō Bungaku Bijutsu Jinmei Jisho ('Dictionary of Figures of the Meiji- and Taishō-period literature and art'), Kokusho Kankōkai, Tokyo, 1926 (repr. 1980)

Matsuya Department Store, Ginza, Tokyo
Tsuruya Kōkei Mokuhanga-shū, Matsuya, Tokyo, 1922

Meech, Julia, and Weisberg, Gabriel
Japonisme Comes to America: The Japanese Impact on the Graphic Arts 1876–1925, Abrams, New York 1990

Meech-Pekarik, Julia
The World of the Meiji Print, Weatherhill, New York and Tokyo, 1986

Menzies, Jacqueline
Contemporary Japanese Prints. The Urban Bonsai, exh. cat., Art Gallery of New South Wales, 1992

Merritt, Helen
Modern Japanese Woodblock Prints: The Early Years, University of Hawaii Press, Honolulu, 1990

Merritt, Helen, and Yamada Nanako
Guide to Modern Japanese Woodblock Prints 1900–1975, University of Hawaii Press, Honolulu, 1992

Michener, James A.
The Modern Japanese Print. An Appreciation, popular edn, Tuttle, Rutland, Vermont, and Tokyo, 1962

Mitchell, C. H.
'Hanshin Meisho Zue: A Little-Known Early Shin Hanga Series', *Essays on Japanese Art Presented to Jack Hillier*, Robert G. Sawers, London, 1982, pp. 118–24

Miyagawa, Torao
Modern Japanese Painting, Kōdansha International, Tokyo, 1967

Mizuo, Hiroshi (ed.)
Munakata Shikō (Kindai Nihon no Bijutsu, 54), Shibundō, Tokyo, 1979

Mori Yoshitoshi Kappa-ban
Catalogue of an exhibition at
Matsuzakaya, Ginza and The
National Museum of Ethnology,
Leiden, Leiden, 1985

Morobushi, Tetsurō (1)
'Mujūryoku no Kyokō Fukei'
(atelier interview with Kanamori
Yoshio), *Hanga Geijutsu*, 8, Tokyo,
winter 1975, pp. 63–6, with colour
plates pp. 67–72

Morobushi, Tetsuro (2)
'Hana to Mito' (atelier interview
with Hashimoto Okiie), *Hanga
Geijutsu*, 21, spring 1978, pp. 106–
13 (with reproductions of prints)

Morse, Peter (ed.)
'Tokuno's Description of Japanese
Printmaking', *Essays on Japanese
Art Presented to Jack Hillier*, Robert
G. Sawers, London, 1982,
pp. 125–34

Munakata Shikō Hanga Zenshū
12 vols, Kōdansha, Tokyo, 1978–9

Murai Masanari Sakuhin-shū
Bijutsu Shuppansha, Tokyo, 1974

Musée des Arts Décoratifs, Paris
*L'Estampe Japonaise Moderne et ses
Origines*, exh. cat., Paris, 1934

Nakamura, Ōsaburō (ed.)
Bijinga Zenshū, III, Shūeisha,
Tokyo, 1979

Nara Kenritsu Bijutsukan
Zōhin Zuroku, II, Nara, 1979

Narazaki, Muneshige (ed.) (1)
Kawase Hasui Mokuhanga-shū,
Mainichi Shinbun, Tokyo, 1979

Narazaki, Muneshige (ed.) (2)
*Hizō Ukiyo-e Taikan: Mura
Korekushon* ('Comprehensive View
of Ukiyo-e Treasures: the Muller
Collection') Kōdansha, Tokyo,
1990

Newland, Amy, and Uhlenbeck,
Chris (eds)
Ukiyo-e to Shin Hanga, Mallard
Press, New York, 1990

Nihon Ukiyo-e Kyōkai (ed.) (1)
'Tokushū Taishō ki Hanga'
('Special edition: Prints of the
Taishō Period'), *Ukiyo-e Geijutsu*, 4,
Tokyo, 1963

Nihon Ukiyo-e Kyōkai (ed.) (2)
'Hashiguchi Goyō Gojūnen Kinen-
ten: Goyō no Onna Tokushū'
('Special edition: Goyō's Women'),
Ukiyo-e Geijutsu, 23, 1969

Nishinoi, Masayoshi
Nenjū Gyōji Jiten, Tokyōdō
Shuppan, Tokyo, 1958 (17th
printing 1970)

Oda, Saburō
Sashie no Egakikata, Tokyo, 1934

Ogura, Tadao (ed.) (1)
Hanga (*Genshoku Gendai Nihon no
Bijutsu*, 11), Shogakkan, Tokyo,
1978

Ogura, Tadao (2)
Takehisa Yumeji (*Kindai no Bijutsu*,
23), Shibundō, Tokyo, 1974

Ogura, Tadao, *et al.*
Yoshida Hiroshi Zen Mokuhanga Shū,
Abe Publishing Co., Tokyo, 1987

Oka, Isaburō
'An Introduction to the Prints of
the Taisho Era (1912–1926)',
trans. U. Osamu and C. H. Mitchell
in *Ukiyo-e Geijutsu*, 4, 1963,
pp. 3–15

Onchi, Kōshirō (1)
Onchi Kōshirō Hanga-shū,
Keishōsha, Tokyo, 1975

Onchi, Kōshirō (2)
'The Modern Japanese Print: An
Internal History of the Sōsaku
Hanga Movement', trans. U. Osamu
and C. H. Mitchell in *Ukiyo-e
Geijutsu*, 11, 1965, pp. 3–34

Onchi, Kōshirō (3)
*Chūshō no byōjō – Onchi Kōshirō
Hanga Geijutsu Ronshū* ('The
Expression of Abstraction –
Collection of Discussions of the Art
of Woodblock Prints of Onchi
Kōshirō'), Abe Publishing Co.,
Tokyo, 1992

Onchi, Kōshirō (4)
Nihon no Gendai Hanga, Sōgensha,
Tokyo, 1953

Onchi, Kōshirō (5)
Onchi, Kunio (ed.)
Sōhon no Shimei, Abe Publishing
Co., Tokyo, 1991

Onchi, Kunio
Onchi Kōshirō Hanga-ten, exh. cat.,
Tokyo, 1987

Ono, Tadashige (1)
Kindai Nihon no Hanga, Sansaisha,
Tokyo, 1971

Ono, Tadashige (ed.) (2)
Yamamoto Kanae Hanga-shū, Ueda
City Yamamoto Kanae Municipal
Museum, Ueda City, 1970

Ono, Tadashige (ed.) (3)
Hanga no Seishun, Keishōsha,
Tokyo, 1978

Ono, Tadashige (4)
'Goyō Hanga no Haikei', *Hanga
Geijutsu*, 9, Tokyo, spring 1975,
pp. 118–21

Ono, Tadashige (5)
Gendai Hanga (1) Meiji-Shōwa
(*Nihon Hanga Bitjutsu Zenshū*, 7),
Kōdansha, Tokyo, 1962

Ōta District Local Museum of Art
(ed.)
*Ryōjō Shijin Taishō-Shōwa no Fūkei;
Hangaka Kawase Hasui*, exh. cat.,
1990

Ōtani Kinen Bijutsukan
Itō Shinsui-ten, exh. cat.,
Nishinomiya, 1978

Paechter, Irwin J.
*Kawase Hasui and his
Contemporaries*, exh. cat., Everson
Museum of Art, Syracuse, New
York, 1986

Petit, Gaston
44 Modern Japanese Print Artists,
2 vols, Kōdansha International,
Tokyo, 1973

Petit, Gaston, and Arboleda,
Amadio
*Evolving Techniques in Japanese
Woodblock Prints*, Kōdansha,
Tokyo, New York and San
Francisco, 1977

Pinckard, W. H., Jr.
*Post-Meiji Japanese Woodblock Prints
1912–1962*, Oakland, California,
1983

Riccar Art Museum, Tokyo (1)
Hiroshi Yoshida Mokuhanga-shū,
exh. cat., 1976

Riccar Art Museum, Tokyo (2)
Maekawa Senpan Meisaku-ten, exh.
cat., 1977

Riccar Art Museum, Tokyo (3)
*Taishō no Onna: Hashiguchi Goyō-
ten*, exh. cat., 1976

Riccar Art Museum, Tokyo (4)
Ichimoku-kai-ten ('Exhibition of
Prints by Ichimoku-kai: Koshiro
Onchi and his Circle'), exh. cat.,
1979

Roberts, Laurence P.
A Dictionary of Japanese Artists,
Weatherhill, Tokyo and New York,
1976

Robertson, Ronald G.
Contemporary Printing in Japan,
Crown, New York, 1965

Rubin, Jay
*Injurious to Public Morals: Writers
and the Meiji State*, University of
Washington Press, Seattle and
London, 1984

Saitō, Kiyoshi (1)
Nengajō, Sanko Shobō, Osaka,
1974

Saitō, Kiyoshi (2)
Saitō Kiyoshi Hanga-shū
Kōdansha, Tokyo, 1978

Sakamoto, Akihiko (ed.)
Sakamoto Hanjirō Zen Hanga-shū,
Zōsha, Tokyo, 1980

*Sakamoto Yoshinobu Hanga-shū
(Tosa Sanjūezu)*, Kōchi Art Gallery,
Kōchi, 1979

Salaman, M. C.
'Mr Urushibara's Woodblock
Colour-Prints' *Studio*, 86, 1923,
pp. 258–61

Sasajima, Kihei
Sasajima Kihei Gabunshū. Ittchin,
Bijutsu Shuppansha, Tokyo, 1967

Seibu Art Forum
Kida Yasuhiko-ten, exh. cat., Tokyo
1987

Sekigawa, Sakio
'Komura Settai Hanga Josetsu',
Hanga Geijutsu, 21, spring 1978,
pp. 155–65

Sekino, Jun'ichirō (1)
Waga Hangashi-tachi, Kōdansha,
Tokyo, 1983

Sekino, Jun'ichirō (2)
Hanga o kizuita hitobito, Bijutsu
Shuppansha, Tokyo, 1976

Sekino, Jun'ichirō (3)
'"Watashi ga Hangaka
Meimeiroku", XI – Maeda Masao',
Hanga Geijutsu, 21, spring 1978,
pp. 197–201

Sekino, Jun'ichirō (4)
'"Watashi ga Hangaka
Meimeiroku", I – Taninaka
Yasunori', *Hanga Geijutsu*, 11,
autumn 1975, pp. 97–101

Seo, Audrey Yoshiko
'Kamisaka Sekka: Master of
Japanese Design', *Orientations*,
December 1993, pp. 38–44

Serizawa Keisuke Zenshū
31 vols, Chūō Kōronsha, Tokyo,
1983 (with extensive bibliography
in vol. 31 but no chronology)

Shashin Munakata Shikō
(photographs of Munakata Shikō),
Kōdansha, Tokyo, 1972

Shirota Gallery, Tokyo
*Akira Kurosaki: Woodblock Prints
1965–1983*, Tokyo, 1984

Shirota, Sadao (ed.)
Kurosaki Akira: Zen Mokuhanga,
Shirota Gallery, Tokyo 1984

Smith, Henry D., II
Kiyochika: Artist of Meiji Japan,
Santa Barbara Museum of Art,
California, 1988

Smith, Lawrence (1)
*The Japanese Print Since 1900: Old
Dreams and New Visions*, British
Museum Publications, London,
1983

Smith, Lawrence (2)
*Contemporary Japanese Prints:
Symbols of a Society in Transition*,
British Museum Publications,
London, 1985

Smith, Lawrence (ed.) (3)
Images of Unknown Japan, British Museum Publications, London, 1988

Smith, Lawrence (4)
Nihonga: Traditional Japanese Painting 1900–1940, British Museum Press, London, 1991

Smith, Lawrence, Harris, Victor, and Clark, Timothy
Japanese Art: Masterpieces in the British Museum, British Museum Press, London, 1990

Stanley-Baker, Joan
Mokuhan: The Woodcuts of Munakata and Matsubara, exh. cat., Art Gallery of Greater Victoria, British Columbia, 1976

Statler, Oliver (1)
Modern Japanese Prints: An Art Reborn, Tuttle, Rutland, Vermont, and Tokyo, 1956

Statler, Oliver (ed.) (2)
Japan's Modern Prints – Sōsaku Hanga, exh. cat., Art Institute of Chicago, January–March 1960

Statler, Oliver (3)
'Rokushū Mizufune', *Newsletter of Contemporary Japanese Prints*, vol. 2, Los Angeles, 1972

Stephens, Amy Reigle (ed.)
The New Wave: 20th Century Japanese Prints from the Robert V. Muller Collection, London and Leiden, 1993

Swinton, Elizabeth de Sabato
The Graphic Art of Onchi Kōshirō, Garland Publishing, New York and London, 1986

Takashimaya Department Store, Tokyo
Kaburagi Kiyokata-ten, exh. cat., 1993

Takehisa Yumeji Ikaho Kinenkan
Takehisa Yumeji, Ikaho, 1982

Tazawa, Yutaka
Biographical Dictionary of Japanese Art, Kōdansha International, Tokyo, New York and San Francisco, 1981

Tobari, Kōgan
Mokuhanga no Horikata to Surikata, Tokyo, 1924

Tōbu Department Store, Tokyo
Sekino Jun'ichirō Hanga-ten, exh. cat., 1989

Tokuriki, Tomikichirō (trans. Arimatsu, Teruko)
Woodblock Printing, Arimatsu Color Book Series no. 14, 8th English edn, Hoikusha, Osaka, 1977

Tokyo National Museum of Modern Art (1)
Onchi Kōshirō to Tsukuhae, exh. cat., 1976

Tokyo National Museum of Modern Art (2)
Shiko Munakata, exh. cat., 1985

Tsuruta, Heihachirō
Suian to Hyakusui (*Kindai no Bijutsu*, 51), Shibundō, Tokyo, 1979

Ueda-shi Yamamoto Kanae Kinenkan
Yamamoto Kanae Tanjō Hyakunen-ten, exh. cat., Ueda City, 1982

Vergez, Robert (1)
'Kuchi-e by Kaburagi Kiyokata', *Ukiyo-e Geijutsu*, 100, Tokyo, 1991, pp. 89–92

Vergez, Robert (2)
'Illustrated Books and Magazines by Onchi Kōshirō', *Andon*, 5, 1985, pp. 23–9

Vergez, Robert (3)
'Book Designs by Onchi, the Graphic Master', *Andon*, 9/3, 1989, pp. 84–9

Volker, T.
Ukiyo-e Quartet, Brill, Leiden, 1949

Wakayama Kenritsu Kindai Bijutsukan (1)
Yoshida Masaji Isaku-ten, 1974, exh. cat., Wakayama, 1977

Wakayama Kenritsu Kindai Bijutsukan (2)
Tanaka Kyōkichi no Geijutsu, exh. cat., Wakayama, 1977

Watanabe, Shōzaburō (1)
Catalogue of Wood-cut Color Prints of S. Watanabe, Watanabe Hangaten, Tokyo, 1936 (original Japanese version as *Mokuhanga Mokuroku*, 1935)

Watanabe, Shōzaburō (2)
Catalogue of Wood-Cut Colour Prints by Contemporary Japanese Artists, Tokyo, 1951

Watanabe, Tadashi (ed.)
Watanabe Shōzaburō, Watanabe Mokuhan Bijutsu Gahō, Tokyo, 1974

Webber, Lucille R.
Japanese Woodblock Prints: The Reciprocal Influence between East and West, Brigham Young University Press, ?1979

Yamaguchi Gen Hanga-shū
Keishōsha, Tokyo, 1979

Yamaguchi Gen Kenshōkai
Yamaguchi Gen Hanga-shū, Numazu, 1983

Yamanashi Prefectural Museum of Art (1)
Natori Shunsen, exh. cat., 1981

Yamanashi Prefectural Museum of Art (ed.) (2)
Jojō no shi Taishō Shōwa no Fūkei; Hangaka Kawase Hasui, exh. cat., 1990

Yanagi, Sōetsu (ed.) (1)
Shikō Munakata Woodblock Prints: Chronologically arranged (1935–1958), Chikuma Shobō, Tokyo, 1958

Yanagi, Sōetsu (2) (adapted by Bernard Leach)
The Unknown Craftsman, Kōdansha International, Tokyo, New York and San Francisco, 1972

Yomiuri Shinbun and Nihon Ukiyo-e Kyōkai (ed.)
Torii-ha Sanbyakunen to Kyūdaime Kiyomitsu ten, exh. cat., Tokyo, 1990

Yoshida, Hiroshi (1)
The Complete Woodblock Prints of Yoshida Hiroshi, Abe Publishing Co., Tokyo, 1987 (includes good bibliography in Japanese and English)

Yoshida, Hiroshi (2)
Japanese Woodblock Printing, Sanseido, Tokyo and Osaka, 1939

Yoshida, Kōgorō
Tanrokubon. Rare Books of Seventeenth Century Japan, Kōdansha, Tokyo, New York and San Francisco, 1984

Yoshida, Susugu
'Hashiguchi Goyō no Bijinga', *Hanga Geijutsu*, 9, Tokyo, spring 1975, pp. 122–5, and colour plates pp. 129–36

Yoshida, Tōshi, and Yuki, Rei
Japanese Print Making: A Handbook of Traditional and Modern Techniques, Tuttle, Rutland, Vermont, and Tokyo, 1966

Plate 1 YAMAMOTO, Kanae (1882–1946): *French Pastoral in Spring, c.* 1913(?). 262 × 355 mm (Cat. 1)

Plate 2 YAMAMOTO, Kanae (1882–1946): *Bathing*, 1918. 348 × 260 mm (Cat.2)

Plate 3 (*right*) NODA, Kyūho (1879–1971): *Ōwada*, 1916.
345 × 245 mm (Cat.4)

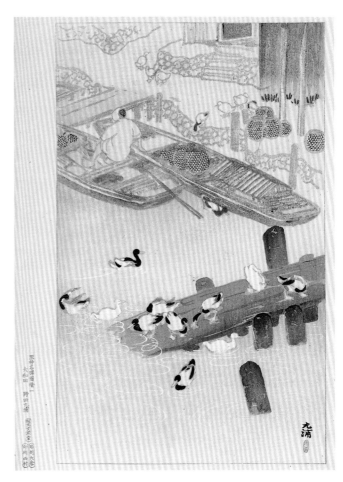

Plate 4 (*left*) ISHII, Hakutei (1882–1958): *Nihonbashi*, 1916.
381 × 252 mm (Cat. 3)

Plate 5 HIRAFUKU, Hyakusui (1877-1933): *Naruko*, 1917. 188 × 252 mm (Cat.5)

Plate 6 SAKAMOTO, Hanjirō (1882-1956): *The Chikugo River*, 1918. 182 × 250 mm (Cat.6)

Plate 7 HENMI, Takashi (1895–1944): *Rain at Yotsuya Mitsuke*, 1930. 210 × 263 mm (Cat.8)

Plate 8 HIRATSUKA, Un'ichi (b. 1895): *The Spa at Izu Yugano*, undated. 295 × 265 mm (Cat.7)

Plate 9 SUWA, Kanenori (1897–1932): *Asakusa Rokku*, 1930.
265 × 210 mm (Cat.9)

Plate 10 ONO, Tadashige
(1909–90): *Komagata Bridge*,
1933. 245 × 305 mm (Cat.11)

Plate 11 FUJIMORI, Shizuo (1891–1943): *Anemones in July*, 1934. 319 × 245 mm (Cat.10)

Plate 12 KOIZUMI, Kishio (1893–1945): *Ueno View*, 1937. 302 × 392 mm (Cat.13)

Plate 13 SAKAMOTO, Yoshinobu (b. 1895): *Harimaya-chō, c.* 1935. 260 × 375 mm (Cat.12)

Plate 14 ASADA, Benji (1899–1984): *Lake Biwa*, 1939. 352 × 327 mm (Cat.15)

Plate 15 MAEKAWA, Senpan (1888–1960): *River Pool at Dorohatchō, Kishū*, 1938. 249 × 326 mm (Cat.14)

Plate 16 FUKAZAWA, Sakuichi (1896–1947): *The Back of Fuji*, 1939. 250 × 331 mm (Cat.16)

Plate 17 KURIYAMA, Shigeru (b. 1912): *Early Autumn at Lake Hakone*, April 1940. 252 × 336 mm (Cat.17)

Plate 18 MAEDA, Tōshirō (1904–90): *'Round Moon Island' at Shirahama*, 1940. 255 × 318 mm (Cat.18)

Plate 19 TANINAKA, Yasunori (1897–1946): *Ōkawabata*, 1940. 259 × 331 mm (Cat.19)

Plate 20 KAWANISHI, Hide (1894–1965): *Girl on the Verandah*, 1944. 240 × 167 mm (Cat.21)

Plate 21 KAWANISHI, Hide (1894–1965): *Kobe Port*, February 1940. 252 × 330 mm (Cat.20)

Plate 22 MAEDA, Masao (1904–74): *Black Cat*, 1940. 409 × 490 mm (Cat.22)

Plate 23 HIRATSUKA, Un'ichi (b. 1895): *Hida Kokubunji*, 1942. 384 × 319 mm (Cat.24)

Plate 24 HIRATSUKA, Un'ichi (b. 1895): *The Innermost Temple of Kōyasan*, 1941. 428 × 511 mm (Cat.23)

Plate 25 HASHIMOTO, Okiie (1899–1933): *Nagoya Castle*, from *Castles of Japan*, 1944. 289 × 380 mm (Cat.25)

Plate 26 AKAMATSU, Rinsaku (1878–1953): '*Dōtonbori, theater street*', 1947. 245 × 361 mm (Cat.26)

Plate 27 ONCHI, Kōshirō (1891–1955): *The Sea*, 1937 (left sheet). 496 × 479 mm (Cat.28)

Plate 28 ONCHI, Kōshirō (1891–1955): *The Sea*, 1937 (right sheet). 491 × 459 mm (Cat.29)

Plate 29 ONCHI, Kōshirō (1891–1955): *Mannequin in the Studio*, 1936. 540 × 416 mm (Cat.27)

Plate 30 ONCHI, Kōshirō (1891–1955): *Portrait of the Poet Hagiwara Sakutarō*, 1943. 541 × 403 mm (Cat. 30)

Plate 31 HASHIGUCHI, Goyō (1880–1921): *Woman Making Up,* 1918. 550 × 390 mm (Cat. 31)

Plate 32 HASHIGUCHI, Goyō (1880–1921): *Nakatani Tsuru Dressing,* 1920. 452 × 296 mm (Cat. 32)

Plate 33 (right) ITŌ, Shinsui (1898–1972): *Snowy Night*, July 1923. 434 × 258 mm (Cat. 36)

Plate 34 (left) ITŌ, Shinsui (1898–1972): *Summer Kimono*, 1922. 440 × 266 mm (Cat. 35)

Plate 35 ITŌ, Shinsui (1898–1972): *The Ukimidō at Katata*, May 1918. 322 × 219 mm (Cat.34)

Plate 36 ITŌ, Shinsui (1898–1972): *Gifu Lantern*, 1930. 425 × 280 mm (Cat. 37)

Plate 37 ITŌ, Shinsui (1898–1972): *Awazu*, 1917. 224 × 315 mm (Cat.33)

Plate 38 KAWASE, Hasui (1883–1957): *Ba'nyū River*, 1931. 265 × 395 mm (Cat.39)

Plate 39 MIKI, Suizan (1887–1957): *Visiting Kiyomizu Temple*, 1924. 420 × 278 mm (Cat.40)

Plate 40 (*right*) TORII, Kotondo (1900–76): *Rain*, 1929.
383 × 264 mm (Cat.41)

Plate 41 (*left*) KAWASE, Hasui (1883–1957): *Rain at Uchi Yamashita, Okayama*, 1923. 300 × 225 mm (Cat.38)

Plate 42 (*right*) NATORI, Shunsen (1886–1960): *The Actor Ichikawa Ennosuke*, 1927. 390 × 272 mm (Cat.43)

Plate 43 (*left*) YOSHIKAWA, Kanpō (1894–1979): *The Actor Kataoka Gadō*, 1924. 401 × 275 mm (Cat.42)

Plate 44 (*left*) UEHARA, Konen (1878–1940): *Dōtonbori*, 1928.
362 × 240 mm (Cat.44)

Plate 45 (*right*) ISHIWATA, Kōitsu (1897–1987): *Barber's shop,
Koyasuhama*, 1931. 386 × 260 mm (Cat.45)

Plate 46 KAWASE, Hasui (1883–1957): *Shiobara*, 1946.
402 × 269 mm (Cat.49)

Plate 47 TOKURIKI, Tomikichirō
(b. 1902): *Rain at Yoshida-guchi*,
?1947. 289 × 415 mm (Cat.50)

Plate 48 KASAMATSU, Shirō (b. 1898): *Morning at the Spa: Nozawa*, 1933. 387 × 262 mm (Cat.46)

Plate 49 YOSHIDA, Hiroshi (1876–1950): *Ōmuro*, 1940. 267 × 395 mm (Cat.47)

Plate 50 YOSHIDA, Hiroshi (1876–1950): *Spring at a Spa*, 1940. 277 × 415 mm (Cat.48)

Plate 51 YOSHIDA, Tōshi (b. 1911): *Mendocino, Sunrise*, 1982. 1210 × 850 mm (Cat. 51)

Plate 52 (*left*) TAKEHISA, Yumeji (1884–1934): Illustration from *Samisen Gusa*, 1915 (edition of 1919). 170 × 112 mm (Cat.52)

Plate 53 (*right*) TAKEHISA, Yumeji (1884–1934): *Tanabata Festival (Dinner Menu)*, 1929. 370 × 240 mm (Cat.53)

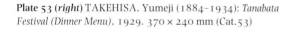

Plate 54 (*left*) TAKEHISA, Yumeji (1884–1934): *To the Morning Light*, printed 1938. 432 × 305 mm (Cat.54)

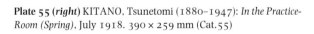

Plate 55 (*right*) KITANO, Tsunetomi (1880–1947): *In the Practice-Room (Spring)*, July 1918. 390 × 259 mm (Cat.55)

Plate 56 (*left*) ISHIKAWA, Toraji (1875–1964): *In the Bathroom*, 1934. 480 × 372 mm (Cat.56)

Plate 57 (*right*) DOMOTO, Inshō (1891–1975): *New Year Toilette*, 1935. 507 × 375 mm (Cat.57)

Plate 58 MUNAKATA, Shikō (1903–75): *Goddess*, 1937. 530 × 725 mm (Cat.59)

Plate 59 MUNAKATA, Shikō (1903–75): *Ashura-Ō*, 1937. 530 × 725 mm (Cat.60)

Plate 60 MUNAKATA, Shikō (1903–75): *The Disciple Subodai*,
1939 (printed in or after January 1962). 1023 × 396 mm (Cat.61)

Plate 61 SERIZAWA, Keisuke (1895–1984): *Don Quixote knows no fear*, from *Ehon Don Kihōte*, 1936. Stencil print, 285 × 370 mm (Cat.58)

Plate 62 MUNAKATA, Shikō (1903–75): Dust-jacket for *Hankei*, 1944. 245 × 390 mm (Cat.62)

Plate 63 MUNAKATA, Shikō (1903–75): *Stars of the Whole Sky*, 1967. 347 × 307 mm (Cat.65)

Plate 64 MUNAKATA, Shikō (1903–75): *Shells*, 1945 (printed 1956). 550 × 390 mm (Cat.63)

Plate 65 MUNAKATA, Shikō (1903–75): *Kanaya.* 1964. 630 × 480 mm (Cat.64)

Plate 66 SASAJIMA, Kihei (1906–93): *Wind God B*, 1963. 386 × 524 mm (Cat.66)

Plate 67 KANAMORI, Yoshio (b. 1922): *Lake 38-4*, 1963. 250 × 326 mm (Cat.67)

Plate 68 MORI, Yoshitoshi (1898–1992): *Sanskrit Fudo Myō-ō*, 1968. Stencil print, 894 × 578 mm (Cat.69)

Plate 69 MORI, Yoshitoshi (1898–1992): *'Posturize'*, 1967. Stencil print, 696 × 852 mm (Cat.68)

Plate 70 (*right*) MORI, Yoshitoshi (1898–1992): *Kagura Dancers*, 1978. Stencil print, 690 × 515 mm (Cat.71)

Plate 71 (*left*) MORI, Yoshitoshi (1898–1992): *Geisha*, 1970. Stencil print, 447 × 304 mm (Cat.70)

Plate 72 WATANABE, Sadao (b. 1913): *The Flight into Egypt*, 1974. Stencil print, 630 × 531 mm (Cat.73)

Plate 73 KIDA, Yasuhiko (b. 1944): *Yakushiji Flower Ceremony*, 1985. 370 × 359 mm (Cat.75)

Plate 74 WATANABE, Sadao (b. 1913): *The Three Wise Men*, 1972. 303 × 398 mm (Cat.72)

Plate 75 MATSUBARA, Naoko (b. 1937): *Walden Pond* (portfolio cover for *Solitude*), 1971. 420 × 805 mm (Cat.74)

Plate 76 ONCHI, Kōshirō (1891–1955): *Dusk in Ginza*, from *Fujisawa Calendar*, 1948. 360 × 245 mm (Cat.76)

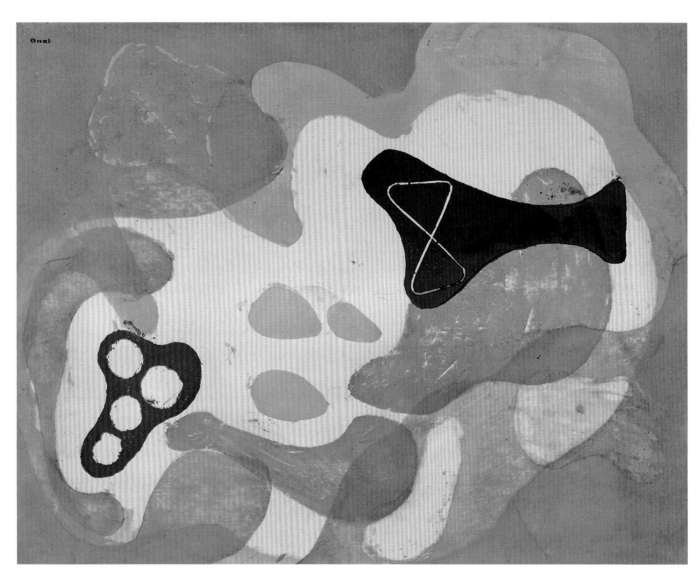

Plate 77 ONCHI, Kōshirō (1891–1955): *Poème No.7: Landscape of May*, 1948. 385 × 487 mm (Cat.77)

Plate 78 ONCHI, Kōshirō (1891–1955): *Form No.3: Uprise of Blue*, 1948. 557 × 456 mm (Cat.78)

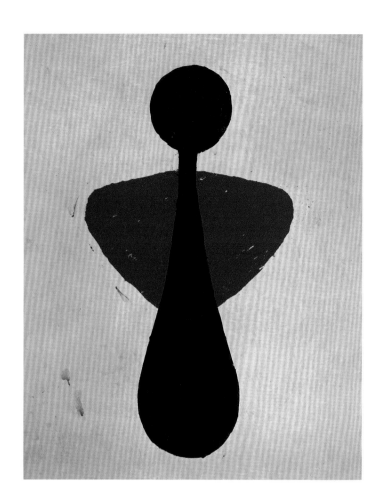

Plate 79 ONCHI, Kōshirō (1891–1955): *Image No.7: Black Cat (a)*, 1952. Colour paperblock print, 499 × 361 mm (Cat.80)

Plate 80 ONCHI, Kōshirō (1891–1955): *Poème No.7: Nihil*, 1949. 605 × 511 mm (Cat.79)

Plate 81 MAEKAWA, Senpan (1888–1960): *Woman in Hot Spring Bathroom*, 1949. 503 × 432 mm (Cat.83)

Plate 82 MAEKAWA, Senpan (1888–1960): *Aquarium at Mitohama*, 1954. 334 × 265 mm (Cat.84)

Plate 83 HIRATSUKA, Un'ichi (b. 1895): *View of Pines in Matsue Tsuda*, 1947. 400 × 325 mm (Cat.81)

Plate 84 HIRATSUKA, Un'ichi (b. 1895): *Steps to the Jakkōin, Kyoto,* 1960. 479 × 322 mm (Cat.82)

Plate 85 MAEKAWA, Senpan (1888–1960): *Akita Dancer*, 1954.
386 × 289 mm (Cat.85)

Plate 86 ONO, Tadashige (1909–90): *Dawn*, 1964. 444 × 357 mm
(Cat.92)

Plate 87 YAMAGUCHI, Susumu (1897–1983): *Taishō Pond*, 1952. 460 × 611 mm (Cat.86)

Plate 88 AZECHI, Umetarō (b. 1902): *Volcano Path*, 1952. 324 × 438 mm (Cat.87)

Plate 89 AZECHI, Umetarō (b. 1902): *Holding a Bird*, 1956.
452 × 350 mm (Cat.88)

Plate 90 AZECHI, Umetarō (b. 1902): *Mountain Man Standing in a Circular Valley*, 1967. 444 × 355 mm (Cat.89)

Plate 91 ONO, Tadashige (1909–90): *Cherry Blossoms*, 1957. 310 × 450 mm (Cat.90)

Plate 92 ONO, Tadashige (1909–90): *River*, 1957. 293 × 446 mm (Cat.91)

Plate 93 SAITŌ, Kiyoshi (b. 1907): *Solitude, Onrian, Kyoto*, 1955. 332 × 478 mm (Cat.93)

Plate 94 SEKINO, Jun'ichirō (1914–88): *Mitsuke*, 1967 (?1961). 422 × 550 mm (Cat.99)

Plate 95 SAITŌ, Kiyoshi (b. 1907): *Maiko, Kyoto, H*, 1961.
602 × 452 mm (Cat.94)

Plate 96 SHINAGAWA, Takumi (b. 1908): *Kabuki Actor*, 1953.
552 × 357 mm (Cat.95)

Plate 97 SEKINO, Jun'ichirō (1914–88): *Bunraku Puppet*, 1950s. 462 × 316 mm (Cat.98)

Plate 98 MAEDA, Tōshirō (1904–90): *Yoroidake*, 1965 (printed 1972). Colour linocut, 465 × 584 mm (Cat.96)

Plate 99 INAGAKI, Tomoo (1902–80): *Stretching Cat*, 1963. 585 × 445 mm (Cat.97)

Plate 100 YAMAGUCHI, Gen (1896–1976): *Mou*, 1962. 798 × 616 mm (Cat.100)

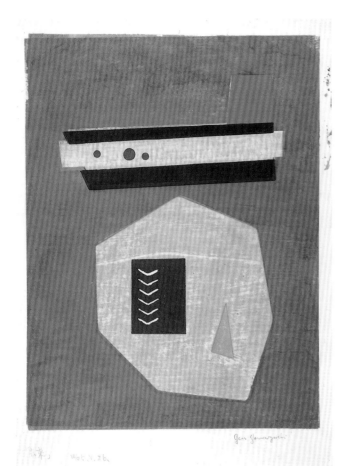

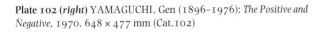

Plate 101 (*left*) YAMAGUCHI, Gen (1896–1976): *Past and Future*, 1965. 562 × 413 mm (Cat.101)

Plate 102 (*right*) YAMAGUCHI, Gen (1896–1976): *The Positive and Negative*, 1970. 648 × 477 mm (Cat.102)

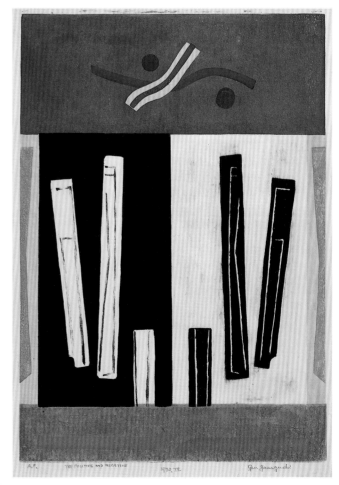

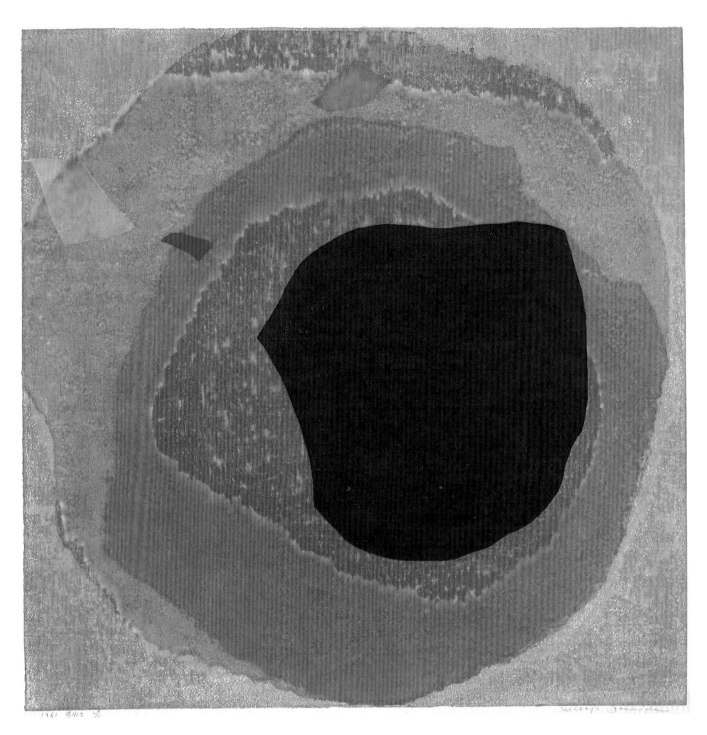

Plate 103 YOSHIDA, Masaji (1917–71): *Ancient No.8*, 1961. 652 × 627 mm (Cat.104)

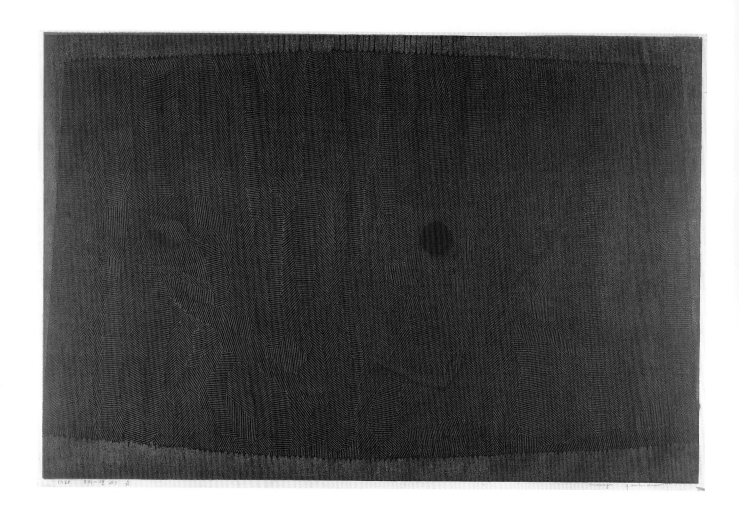

Plate 104 (*above*) YOSHIDA, Masaji (1917–71):
Wall of Craft, No. 3, 1965. 630 × 945 mm (Cat. 106)

Plate 105 YOSHIDA, Masaji (1917–71): *Space No. 13,*
1962. 605 × 460 mm (Cat. 105)

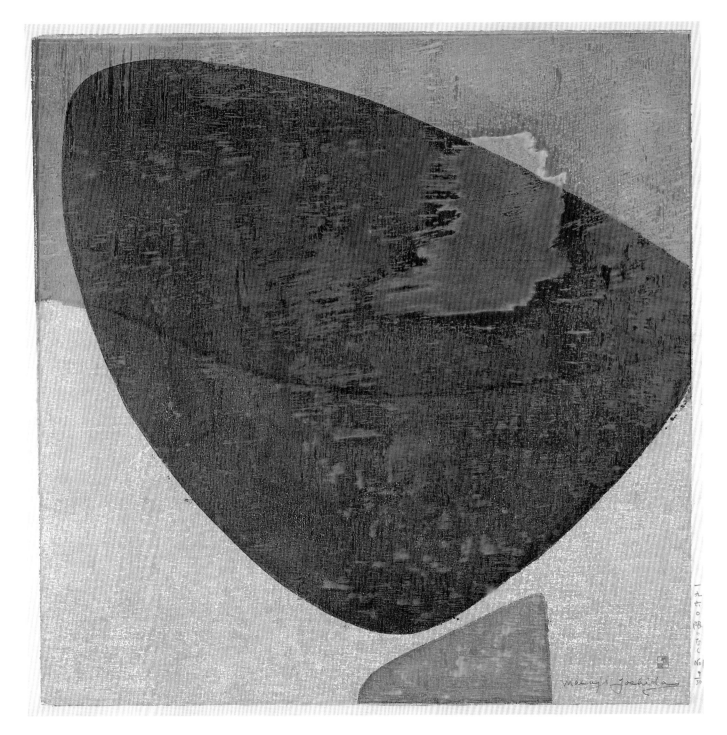

Plate 106 YOSHIDA, Masaji (1917–71): *Without Limit No.1*, 1958. 528 × 448 mm (Cat.103)

Plate 107 MAKI, Haku (b. 1924): *Work 73-50-A (Nothing)*, 1973. 845 × 840 mm (Cat.107)

Plate 108 MAKI, Haku (b. 1924): *Work 73-50-B (Nothing)*, 1973. 845 × 840 mm (Cat.108)

Plate 109 KITAOKA, Fumio (b. 1918): *Winter at Inbanuma*, 1979. 475 × 627 mm (Cat.109)

Plate 110 HAGIWARA, Hideo (b. 1913): *Village Festival No.2*, 1968. 657 × 992 mm (Cat.111)

Plate 111 IWAMI, Reika (b. 1927): *Concert of One, C,* 1967. 692 × 514 mm (Cat.112)

Plate 112 HAGIWARA, Hideo (b. 1913): *Stone Flower: Blue*, 1964. 664 × 952 mm (Cat. 110)

Plate 113 FUKITA, Fumiaki (b. 1926): *Legend of the Stars*, 1968. 960 × 635 mm (Cat.113)

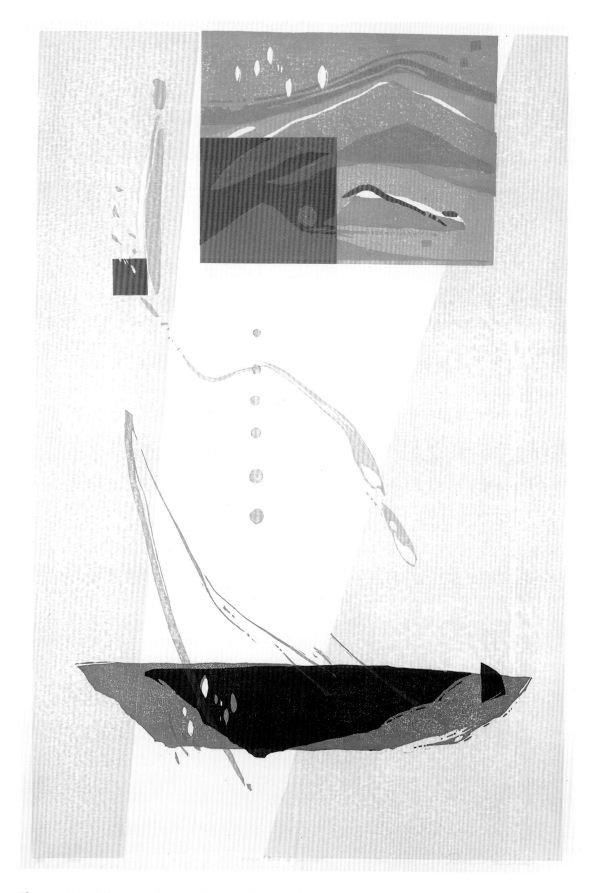

Plate 114 TAKAHASHI, Rikio (b. 1917): *Garden (End of Summer)*, 1984. 898 × 617 mm (Cat. 114)

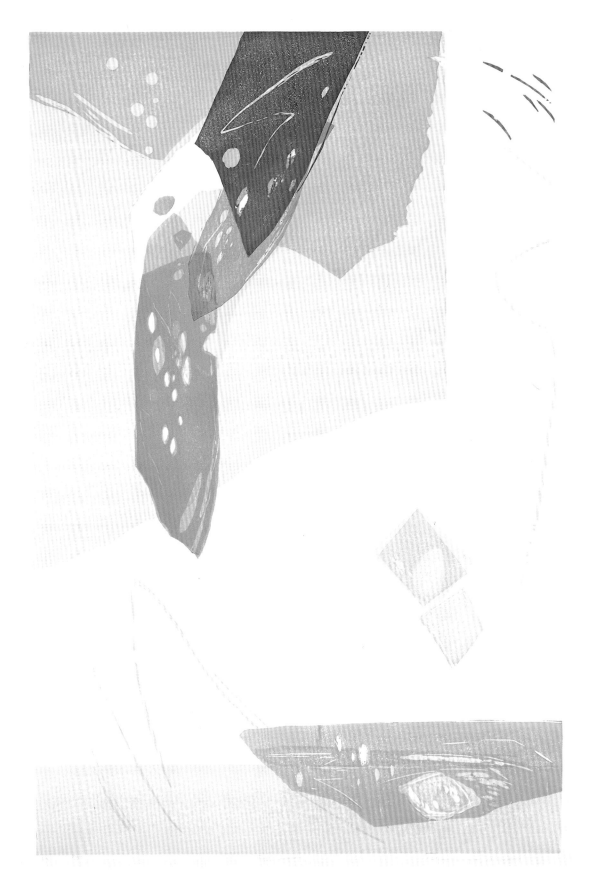

Plate 115 TAKAHASHI, Rikio (b. 1917): *Full Season*, 1984, 912 × 627 mm (Cat. 115)

Plate 116 KŌSAKA, Gajin (1877–1953): *Kokubunji Village*, 1948. 390 × 527 mm (Cat.116)

Plate 117 SEIMIYA, Naobumi (b. 1917): *Still Life in Moonlight*, early 1970s. 231 × 310 mm (Cat.117)

6 / 20   MAÇANARI '63

Plate 118 MURAI, Maçanari (b. 1905): Untitled, 1963. 414 × 504 mm (Cat. 118)

Plate 119 MABUCHI, Tōru (b. 1920): *Grapes and Melons*, 1968. 480 × 305 mm (Cat. 119)

Plate 120 (*right*) MIZUFUNE,
Rokushū (1912–80): *Rainbow
Music*, undated. 274 × 362 mm
(Cat.120)

Plate 121 MIZUFUNE, Rokushū (1912–81): *Rainbow Bird*,
undated. 384 × 285 mm (Cat.121)

朝の木　　　作家摺　　　　　　　　　　　　　　jōichi hoshi 76

Plate 122 HOSHI, Jōichi (1913-79): *Tree at Dawn*, 1976. 680 × 515 mm (Cat.124)

Plate 123 HOSHI, Jōichi (1913–79): *The Milky Way (F)*, 1968. 663 × 768 mm (Cat.122)

Plate 124 HOSHI, Jōichi (1913–79): *Red Horizon*, 1972. 475 × 737 mm (Cat.123)

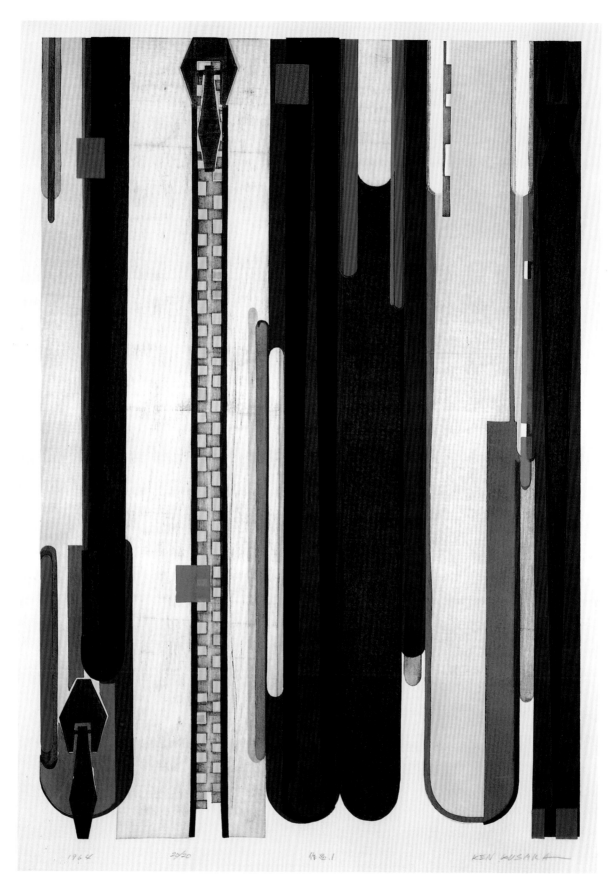

Plate 125 KUSAKA, Kenji (b. 1936): *Work No. 1*, 1964. 874 × 636 mm (Cat. 129)

Plate 126 AMANO, Kazumi (b. 1927): *Moral (B)*, 1963. 900 × 610 mm (Cat.125)

Enclosure (9) I/50   Kunihiro Amano   —65·11—

Plate 127 AMANO, Kunihiro (b. 1929): *Enclosure (9)*, 1965. 925 × 570 mm (Cat.126)

3/27.   y. Funasaka. 1969.

Plate 128 FUNASAKA, Yoshisuke (b. 1939): *Work At* 26, 1969. 410 × 301 mm (Cat.130)

Plate 129 TAJIMA, Hiroyuki (1911–84): *Anemophilous Flower B*, 1968. 635 × 450 mm (Cat.128)

Plate 130 TAJIMA, Hiroyuki (1911–84): *Wind Erosion D*, 1968. 635 × 450 mm (Cat.127)

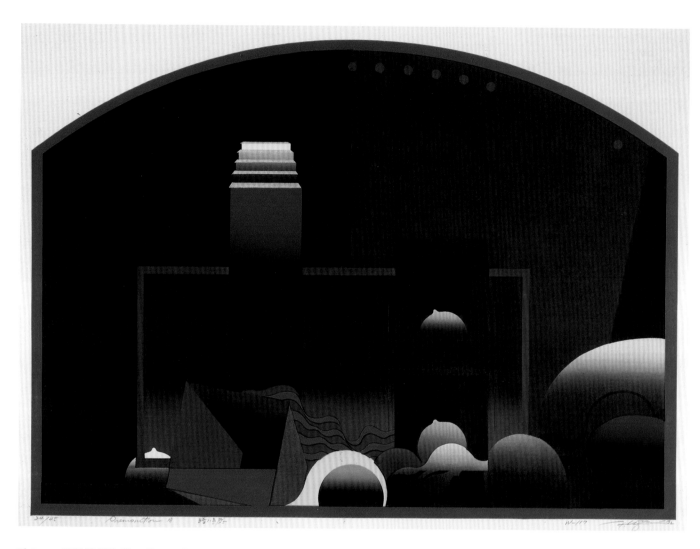

Plate 131 KUROSAKI, Akira (b. 1937): *Premonition B*, 1972. 585 × 784 mm (Cat. 132)

43/50　Landscape—Night　風景・闇　W.115　Akira '71

Plate 132 KUROSAKI, Akira (b. 1937): *Landscape – Night.* 1971. 560 × 405 mm (Cat.131)

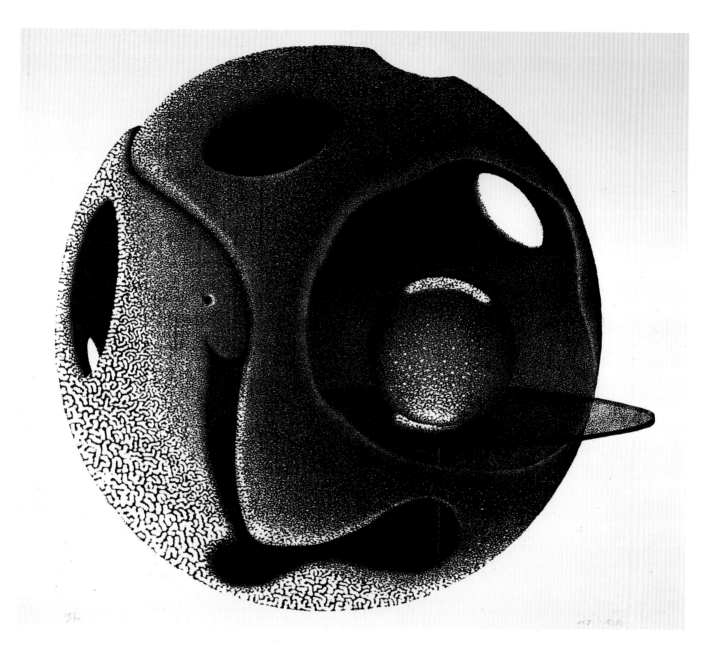

Plate 133 MOROZUMI, Osamu (b. 1948): *No.8*, 1971. 540 × 677 mm (Cat. 133)

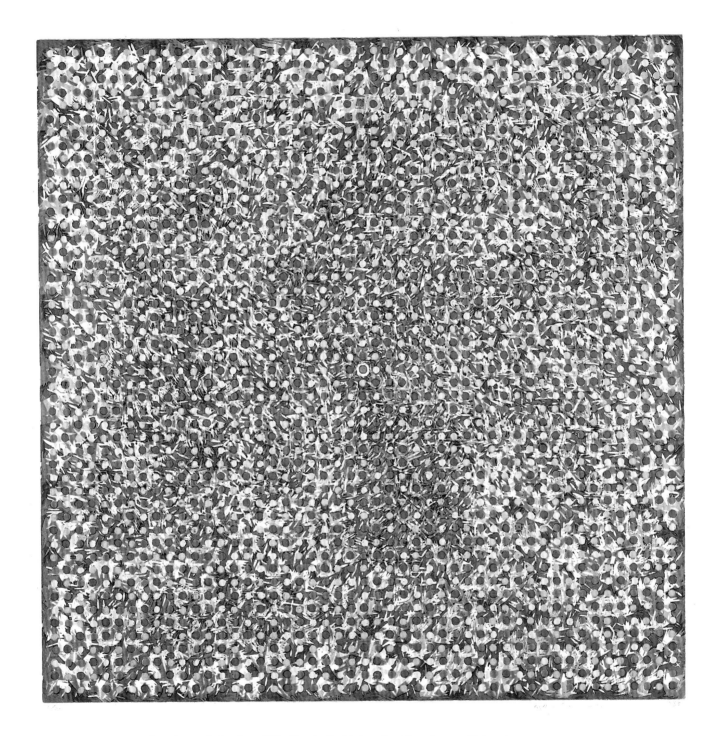

Plate 134 MATSUMOTO, Akira (b. 1936): *Revolve – (W5 – Negative/Positive)*, 1985. 685 × 695 mm (Cat.134)

Plate 135 KAWACHI, Seikō (b. 1948): *The Flying (Conclusion)*, 1985. 1655 × 915 mm (Cat.138)

Plate 136 KAWACHI, Seikō (b. 1948): *The Flying (Turn)*, 1985. 1655 × 915 mm (Cat.137)

Plate 137 KAWACHI, Seikō (b. 1948): *The Flying (Development)*, 1985. 1655 × 915 mm (Cat. 136)

Plate 138 KAWACHI, Seikō (b. 1948): *The Flying (Introduction)*, 1985. 1655 × 915 mm (Cat. 135)

Plate 139 (*right*) TSURUYA, Kōkei (b. 1946): *The Actor Nakamura Utaemon VI*, 1984. 395 × 250 mm (Cat.140)

Plate 140 (*left*) TSURUYA, Kōkei (b. 1946): *The Actor Bandō Tamasaburō V*, 1983. 397 × 272 mm (Cat.139)